THE WORLD BOOK OF

Science
Power

THE WORLD BOOK OF

Science
Power

Volume 1

● Chemistry

● Physics

● Life Sciences

1996 printing

© 1994 World Book, Inc. All rights reserved. This volume may not
be reproduced in whole or in part in any form without prior written
permission from the publisher.

World Book, Inc.
525 W. Monroe
Chicago, IL 60661

ISBN 0-7166-2294-7
Library of Congress Catalog Card No. 93-61591
Printed in the United States of America

4 5 6 7 8 9 10 99 98 97 96

Contents

Staff

What is science?

From the beginning of history, people have been fascinated by the world around them. A distinguishing characteristic of humans is the passion to understand their world. That passion has created science. Without science, we wouldn't understand why night follows day. A solar eclipse would be a terrifying event. Our own bodies would be mysteries to us. Much of the world would scare and confuse us.

Although many of us share a curiosity about the universe, some are destined to be at the forefront of discovery and others are happy just to read about it. It is those men and women at the forefront whom we call scientists. Scientists are people who devote their lives to exploring the unknown.

To practice science is to ask questions, propose answers, and test those answers against available evidence. Science is a search—a search for knowledge, for unity in diversity, for patterns in events that seem unrelated.

Scientific study typically is divided into four major branches: (1) mathematics and logic; (2) the physical sciences; (3) the life sciences; and (4) the social sciences.

Stemming from these branches are groups of closely related specialties. For example, anthropology, psychology, and sociology are behavioral sciences included in the social sciences. Geology, meteorology, physical geography, and physical oceanography are grouped together as the Earth sciences within the branch of the physical sciences.

Mathematics and logic

While mathematics and logic are not based on experimental testing, they are vital to science. Logic provides the basis for all scientific reasoning. Scientists use two kinds of logic: deductive logic and inductive logic.

In using *deductive logic*, a scientist relies on scientific principles to draw a conclusion. For example, in the 1920's astronomer Edwin Hubble knew that objects moving away from an observer emit waves of light that fall toward the red end of the spectrum. When astronomical observations showed that many galaxies in the universe emitted red light rays, he used logic to conclude that these galaxies were moving away from the Milky Way, and therefore that the universe is expanding.

In using *inductive logic*, a scientist makes repeated observations of something, then uses those observations to draw a conclusion. For example, one group of people suffering from a disease might be treated with a new drug immediately after being diagnosed. A second group might receive the drug only after their symptoms become painful. If scientists find that the disease progresses at the same rate in both groups, they could conclude that early treatment has no benefits.

Without mathematics, scientists would be unable to prove or communicate their findings and theories. Other scientists would be unable to use those findings to do further research. Mathematics enables scientists to state their findings and theories and make predictions.

Here are some main fields of mathematics:

Sometimes called "the science of numbers,"

Chemical researchers use specialized equipment to study natural and artificial substances.

arithmetic is the study of numbers and calculation methods. Arithmetic supplies the basis for many other fields of mathematics.

Scientists use a*lgebra* to solve problems with equations (mathematical sentences that say two expressions are equal) in which letters, such as *x* and *y*, stand for unknown quantities.

Calculus provides a way of developing theories and solving problems that involve motion or changing quantities. It is widely used in engineering, physics, and other sciences. For example, the laws of aerodynamics are expressed in terms of calculus.

Concerned with the mathematical relationships of points, lines, angles, surfaces, and solids in space, *geometry* helps scientists better understand and appreciate the universe, which is filled with geometric shapes. Geometry has many practical purposes in everyday life. For example, architects and carpenters must understand the properties of geometric objects to construct safe and attractive buildings.

How likely is it that a certain event will take place? Scientists use *probability* to help them determine the chances. For example, people can use probability to calculate their chances of winning a raffle.

Statistics, which relies heavily on probability, is concerned with the collection and analysis of large amounts of data to identify trends and overall patterns. For example, doctors use statistical methods to see if certain medicines are effective. Engineers use statistics to set standards for product safety.

The physical sciences

The physical sciences deal with the nature of the universe. They study the structure and characteristics of nonliving things, from tiny atoms to vast galaxies. Here are just a few of the sciences that make up the physical sciences:

One of the oldest sciences, *astronomy* is concerned with the study of stars, planets, and other celestial objects. Astronomers map the locations of heavenly bodies and investigate the physical and chemical processes that occur within them. They also search for answers to such questions as "What are planets made of?" and "How do stars create light?"

To study *chemistry* is to study the structure and characteristics of natural and artificial substances. Chemists examine the changes that occur when substances combine and form other substances. They create many useful substances that do not occur in nature. Products such as drugs, fertilizers, and plastics have been developed by chemical researchers.

Geologists study the Earth to try to explain how it was formed and how it changes. They study rocks, soil, mountains, rivers, oceans, and other features of the Earth. There are two main fields of geology. *Physical geology* is the study of the materials that make up the Earth and the forces that shape it. *Historical geology* is concerned with the history of the Earth.

Meteorology is the study of the Earth's atmosphere and the conditions that produce weather. Meteorologists attempt to predict the weather by analyzing data about the atmosphere.

Physicists study such matter as the superconducting material shown in this computer image.

Physics is concerned with matter and energy. Physicists try to understand what matter is and why it behaves as it does. They seek to learn how energy is produced, how it travels from place to place, and how it can be controlled. Knowledge obtained from the study of physics is important in other sciences, including astronomy, biology, chemistry, and geology. Physics plays an important role in new developments in engineering, medicine, and technology. For example, engineers design automobiles and airplanes according to the principles of physics.

Earth science combines many related specialties, including geology, meteorology, oceanography, and physical geography. Earth scientists study the Earth and its origin and development.

The life sciences

The life sciences, as the name implies, study living organisms. They also are known as the *biological sciences* or *biology*. The life sciences are divided into two main fields. *Botany* deals with plants. *Zoology* deals with animals. Botany and zoology are further divided into various specialties, each of which are subdivided even further. Many of the branches, such as anatomy and physiology, overlap with and contribute to the study of medicine.

Anatomy examines the structure of living things. Anatomists investigate the parts of organisms and how the parts work together and are related. Because the bodies of human beings and animals are so complex, anatomy is divided into many subspecialties.

Physiology deals with the normal functions of living things and their parts. It examines the characteristics and systems of living things, such as how organisms absorb and use food.

Other branches of the life sciences include *bacteriology*, the study of bacteria; *genetics*, which investigates how organisms pass on characteristics to their offspring; and *molecular biology*, which focuses on the structure and function of molecules essential to life.

The social sciences

The social sciences deal with the individuals, groups, and institutions that make up human society. Social scientists focus on human relationships and the interactions between individ-

Botany, the study of plants, is an important field of the life sciences.

uals and their families, religious or ethnic communities, cities, governments, and other social groups. Social scientists attempt to develop general "laws" of human behavior. But this is no easy task. It is hard to design controlled experiments involving human beings. Human behavior is hard to control or predict, and studying it raises ethical issues. Therefore, social scientists must rely on careful observation and the systematic collection of data to arrive at their conclusions. The use of statistics and mathematics is important in analyzing information and developing theories in the social sciences.

Some of the specialties within the social sciences include the following:

Anthropology studies the origin and development of human cultures and physical characteristics. Anthropologists examine the strategies for living that are learned and shared by people as members of social groups. Much of their research is based on observing various groups of people to determine their similarities and differences. Anthropologists can contribute to international harmony by providing an understanding of various cultures.

Geologists study the Earth's structure and try to explain how it was formed.

The field of *economics* focuses on how the things people need and want are made and brought to them. It also studies how people and nations choose purchases from the many things that are available. Economists examine how people produce goods and services, how they distribute them among themselves, and how they use them.

Forms of government, political parties, lobby groups, elections, and other aspects of politics are the concern of *political science*. Political scientists ask such questions as "Whose interests

are served by government?" and "How much power should government have?" Political science deals with such fundamental ideas as equality, freedom, justice, and power. This social science is closely related to economics, history, law, philosophy, and sociology.

Psychology investigates mental processes and behavior. Psychologists observe and record how people and other animals relate to one another and their environments. They look for patterns that will help them understand and predict behavior, and use scientific methods to test their ideas. Through such studies, psychologists have learned much that can help people fulfill their potential as human beings and increase understanding between individuals, groups, nations, and cultures. Psychology is closely related to other sciences, such as biology, anthropology, and sociology.

Individuals, groups, and institutions that make up human society as a whole are examined by the science of *sociology*. Sociologists observe and record how people relate to one another and to their environments. Sociology is closely related to the other social sciences.

Overlapping sciences

As scientific knowledge has grown and become increasingly complicated, hundreds of fields of scientific study have emerged. At the same time, the boundaries between scientific fields have become muddled. Many areas of science overlap. For instance, both chemistry and physics deal with the structure of atoms.

In some cases, sciences overlap so much that *interdisciplinary* fields have emerged. For example, mathematics is a part of all sciences. *Biochemistry* combines areas of biology and chemistry in studying the chemical processes that occur in living creatures. *Economic geology* draws upon economics and geology in investigating the distribution of natural resources such as gold, silver, and petroleum.

Pure and applied science

Why do people study science? To quench their thirst for knowledge? Or to use that knowledge for some other purpose? The answer to both these questions is "yes."

Every scientist has his or her own reason for

wanting to study some aspect of the universe. Some want to know why the wind blows or how plants grow just because they want to know about these things. *Pure science* seeks knowledge for its own sake. In other words, its chief goal is to satisfy curiosity.

Applied science seeks knowledge for a purpose. The term *applied science* sometimes refers to scientific research that focuses on the development of technology. *Technology* is the use of scientific knowledge for everyday purposes. While science attempts to explain how and why things happen, technology is concerned with making things happen. The applied scientist wants to know why the wind blows in order to control it for some purpose. The applied scientist wants to know how plants develop so that perhaps he or she can learn how to make plants grow faster, stronger, or bigger.

The theories formed through science suggest possibilities not only for understanding nature, but also for doing something with that knowledge. For example, Sir Isaac Newton's findings about force and motion make it possible for scientists to predict the behavior of machines as well as planets. The concept that atoms can combine to form molecules enables chemists to understand the countless substances of Earth as combinations of the natural elements. At the same time, this concept reveals the possibility—first realized by scientists in the 1800's—that new substances can be created by humans.

Scientists at work

In their quest for knowledge, where and how do scientists begin? What helps them move from an idea to a theory? What is the source of their confidence and persistence? The answers lie in the scientist's special style of research. This approach, known as the scientific method, is at the heart of all that scientists do.

The scientific method

Scientists use a number of techniques while developing theories. These techniques include making observations, classifying data, forming hypotheses, conducting experiments, proposing explanations, and communicating their findings mathematically. These techniques are used to carry out the scientific method, which consists of the following steps: (1) observing and defining a problem, (2) gathering and classifying data, (3) forming a hypothesis (proposed explanation) based on the data, (4) testing the hypothesis, and (5) drawing a conclusion about the hypothesis to share with others. Here's a closer look at each of the five steps of the scientific method.

DEFINE THE PROBLEM. Science does not begin with facts; it begins with the perception of a problem. Astronomers of long ago did not begin by gathering data on the motion of the sun, moon, and stars. Rather, they began with the belief that such motions existed and that it would be helpful to know more about those motions.

A critical step in any creative thinking is to understand the problem. This is essential to stating it clearly and correctly. Once a problem is stated so that it may be reasonably solved, a scientist is well on the way to solving it.

Some examples of science problems include the following:

- An ecologist wants to research how to protect an endangered species.
- A chemist wants to discover a substance that will fight a deadly disease.
- An anthropologist wants to find out why an ancient civilization died off.

GATHER AND CLASSIFY DATA. The most careful scrutiny of existing facts is vital to the practice of the scientific method. In order to form or prove a theory, scientists must gather facts.

Scientists collect data through research of existing information and through observation. They may begin researching existing information by reading several books, reports, and journals related to the problem. Such writings contain the experience of others, one of the most valuable resources available to scientists. All scientific discovery moves ahead through small steps taken by many scientists over many years.

The art of observation is critical to all scientists. Being able to observe something means that a scientist can learn about it by using all

Astronomy, the study of celestial objects, is one of the oldest sciences.

five senses: sight, sound, touch, taste, and smell. Observation is one of the oldest scientific techniques. For example, many ancient peoples, including the Egyptians and Babylonians, learned to predict the changing of the seasons by studying the movements of heavenly bodies.

Without research and observation, scientists have nothing with which to put together their new thought, also known as their hypothesis.

FORM A HYPOTHESIS. A hypothesis is an educated guess, a proposed explanation or solution to a problem. It is a provable or nonprovable statement about events or phenomena that have occurred or that will occur. Scientists use the data they gather and classify to form a hypothesis, which should in turn explain, unify, or organize that data.

The discovery of the planet Neptune in the mid-1800's resulted from the formation of a hypothesis. Astronomers noticed that Uranus,

which they thought was the most distant planet, was not always in the position predicted by the laws of gravitation and motion. Some astronomers concluded that the laws did not apply at such great distances from the sun. But others hypothesized that the variations in the orbit of Uranus might be caused by the force of gravity from an unknown planet. By calculating where such a planet would be located, astronomers eventually discovered Neptune.

Here are some hypotheses related to the problems previously stated:

- If the polluting of rivers used by this animal were to cease, then this animal would again begin to flourish.
- If substance X helps fight this disease in laboratory animals, then it may help fight the disease in humans.
- The spread of a disease carried by wild animals was a great contributor to the decline of this civilization.

TEST THE HYPOTHESIS. Proving that a hypothesis is correct or incorrect involves collecting evidence. Experiments often are the method of choice in developing and testing scientific theories. Galileo was one of the first scientists to recognize that systematic experimentation could help reveal the laws of nature. In the late 1500's, he began performing carefully designed experiments to study the basic properties of matter in motion. By rolling balls of different weights down inclined planes, he discovered that all objects fall to the ground with the same acceleration, or rate of increase in speed, unless air resistance or some other force slows them down.

In sciences that deal with the behavior of individuals or groups of people, surveys and field observations often are used to collect evidence.

DRAW AND SHARE A CONCLUSION. Is the hypothesis correct? Drawing a conclusion about a hypothesis usually requires logic, statistics, or both to analyze the results of experiments, surveys, or field observations. Computers often aid in the analysis of large amounts of information.

When drawing conclusions, scientists depend on both deductive logic and inductive logic. In using deductive logic, a scientist reasons from known scientific principles or rules to draw a conclusion relating to a specific problem. Inductive logic requires a scientist to make repeated observations of an experiment or an event. From the many observations, the scientist can form a general conclusion.

Most scientists finally must express their findings mathematically so that others can understand and use their results for further study. This is why the science of mathematics is so crucial to every other science.

The scientist's essential tool

Socrates, an ancient Greek philosopher, was a creative thinker who left behind a record of his method. He taught his students that creative thinking can begin only when the thinker recognizes a problem and decides to do something about it. The scientific method is really not a "method" in the true sense of the word. It is not a strict, formal procedure. Nor is it a detailed map for exploring the unknown. It gives scientists no assurances that their theories are correct or will lead to a discovery. Rather, the scientific method is an attitude. It is a way of thinking and

of conducting the business of science. It offers guidance so that scientists can attempt to prove their theories. The scientific method allows scientists to distinguish between ideas that have meaning and usefulness and those that are empty and misleading.

Every kind of scientist—from chemists to microbiologists to sociologists to economists—uses the scientific method. But while it is an essential tool, the scientific method is not flawless. It cannot replace inspiration, creativity, or hard work. And it cannot produce good fortune like that experienced by Sir Alexander Fleming in 1828. Fleming, a British bacteriologist, discovered penicillin accidentally when he noticed that a bit of mold had contaminated a laboratory dish containing bacteria. Examining the dish, Fleming saw that the bacteria around the mold—now known as penicillin—had died. While Fleming may have been following the scientific method, nothing in the method caused the mold to contaminate his dish.

In short, the scientific method cannot create science any more than a paint brush can create a beautiful painting or a word processor can create a short story. The scientific method is a tool, a tool that is only as good as the scientist who uses it.

Science in the schools

Science class has come a long way in the late 1900's. For a long time, the methods for teaching it were pretty dull. Most students, after about third grade, started to dread science, with its endless vocabulary lists to memorize and its long, boring chapters of textbooks to read. Students were rarely given the chance to experience science. Happily, things have changed. Today, teachers, principals, and other educators are making an effort to design science classes so that they are interesting, exciting, and fun. Educators now know that to learn science, students have to do science. Teachers try to involve students in the scientific process, so that they develop a knowledge base and variety of attitudes and ways of thinking that help ensure success in the real world. For example, students studying gene splicing are likely to discuss the medical use of

gene splicing, the social effects of such therapy, and moral issues raised by its use. They may even have a chance to splice genes themselves.

Today's science class

Today's students aren't just reading about science, they are living it. They are learning that science is important not just for its own sake, but because science is a part of everyday life. This new approach reflects the skills science programs try to foster in students.

SCIENTIFIC LITERACY. Scientifically literate people understand the concepts, skills, attitudes, and values of science. They know the impact science has on society and recognize the role scientific thinking plays in solving all kinds of problems. Students acquire such literacy by discussing scientific topics, making predictions, reading science books and articles, doing database searches, and working on projects.

PROBLEM SOLVING. Students learn to solve problems by thinking critically and creatively. Science programs are taking advantage of children's inquisitive nature and encouraging students to look for the causes and effects of events around them. For example, students might use computers to simulate a certain environment, such as a fishing village, and decide such questions as how much fishing could be done without depleting fish stocks.

ENVRONMENTAL AWARENESS. Our environment is faced with a number of complex problems—air and water pollution, disposal of solid wastes, and depletion of natural resources. School science programs, therefore, are focusing on getting today's students—who are the hope of the future—to learn both the nature of environmental problems and the ways in which they can be controlled. For example, students might study methods of measuring water or air pollution, and then use such methods to test their own water and air.

ABILITY TO CONNECT DISCIPLINES. Science, technology, and society influence one another. Students need to master scientific concepts and skills. They also need to develop an awareness of the social and economic aspects of science and technology, and the values that they offer. For example, students working on a project about waterways might visit waterways, collect water samples, and analyze the contents of the water. But they also might discuss literature in which the action is set on a waterway, the effect waterways have had on a region's history, and their social effects today.

FLEXIBLITY. Scientific knowledge is always changing, and so is society. Students are learning how to cope with these changes so that they can help solve the problems that can go hand in hand with these changes.

INDIVIDUAL LEARNING. Because each student learns differently, science programs now are of-

fering a wide range of learning activities. Instead of just reading and memorizing facts, students are doing hands-on—and minds-on—investigations. They are discussing their thoughts in small groups, expressing their findings through writing, reflecting on what they read, playing games, completing picture and word puzzles, and getting outside the classroom to explore their own communities.

Through the experience of variety in their activities, students are becoming familiar with a number of skills that are critical to success in science—and in life. Students are learning how to observe, communicate, measure, compare and contrast, organize, classify, analyze, infer, hypothesize, and predict.

Integrating the sciences

School science programs are no longer isolating each branch of science. Instead they are integrating them. Students are learning how the different branches—the life sciences, the social sciences, mathematics and logic, and the physical sciences—all relate to one another. They are learning that scientists in these different branches rely on one another to help each other discover new things about the universe.

Students are spending more time learning science, too. Science classes extend over a longer period of time. Taking the lead from countries such as Russia, China, Japan, and Korea—whose students excel in the sciences—many schools in the United States now are requiring that students take more years of science class. Instead of having science class every day for one year, students are taking one or two hours of science each week over four or five years. This approach takes advantage of people's ability to learn better those subjects that they study and use over a long period of time.

Science is for everyone

The kind of science now being taught in schools is a welcome change for all students. But it's especially beneficial for those who don't speak English very well, those from other ethnic and cultural backgrounds, and those who don't learn as well from reading as they do from doing.

Discovery shares a universal language. When students can see a chemical reaction, touch a plant, or see the effects of pollution on their community, words are not always necessary. Students who have not yet mastered the English language can learn about science with their hands and eyes. That's why a hands-on approach to science makes sense for them.

Today's science programs also demonstrate that science is a human effort that has been advanced by the contributions of many cultures and ethnic groups. Therefore, it boosts students' self-confidence and builds personal expectations of success. Also, students learn that scientists—and people interested in science—are normal people. They are not just poorly socialized misfits who wear lab coats and hang out in a laboratory all day. Scientists are people who have families, cherish particular values, and belong to different ethnic groups. They are a diverse group of people who have learned to look at things in a certain way.

Crossing the boundaries

Learning science often calls for skills from other subject areas. When students look up information, they are reading. When they measure and graph changes in a growing plant, they are using mathematics. They are using language skills when they report the results of experiments and observations.

Science often includes activities that cross the boundaries into other areas of study. In this way, students are able to see the impact that science has on these other areas. For example, students learning about the process of aging may be assigned the following activities:

- Read well-known stories about older people, their effects on society, and their thoughts about getting older. (Literature)
- Study and comment on artwork that reflects the effects of aging on people, animals, plants, and so on. (Art)
- Visit a nursing home to talk with older people and see how aging affects different people differently. Calculate the average age of the residents. Compare this to the average life expectancy. Talk about the impact of aging on our society. (Social studies and mathematics)

Ancient Greek philosophers and scientists discuss their theories in this painting by the Italian artist Raphael.

The ultimate goal of today's science programs is not to teach students to be electricians or chemists. Science tries to help people understand the world around them, and decide what reality is by looking at the cause and effect of events. Science provides a picture of a universe that is always changing—not only under a microscope or in outer space, but in the way we live. So, science examines not only changes in biology, chemistry, and physics, but how those changes occur and how they affect people. Today, a goal of science teachers is to give students a selection of scientific processes—creating hypotheses, gathering evidence, and weighing it—so that students become contributing members of society.

Chenistry

1

- **Elementary Particles**

- **Compounds: The Marriage of Elements**

- **The Practice of Chemistry**

1

Elementary Particles

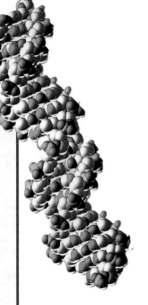

DNA molecule

Chemistry is the scientific study of the substances that make up the universe. Chemists investigate the properties of substances and how different conditions affect the way substances behave. All things—from rock to skin to air—consist of different combinations of chemical elements, the most basic of substances. Elements are made up of units called atoms, which are so tiny that billions of them make up the smallest speck. When atoms combine, they usually form units called molecules, which are the building blocks of most chemical compounds. An understanding of elementary particles—atoms and molecules—forms the basis of chemistry.

A*toms*

All things are made up of basic units of matter called atoms. Atoms vary greatly in weight, but they are all about the same size—more than a million times smaller than the thickness of a human hair. Yet tiny as they are, atoms consist of even more minute subatomic particles. The three basic types of these particles are called protons, neutrons, and electrons. *Protons* and *neutrons* form the *nucleus,* or center, of the atom. Nuclei is the term for more than one nucleus. *Electrons* whirl around the nucleus.

Atoms are the building blocks of the chemical elements, the simplest substances. Hydrogen and lead are examples of well-known elements. Each element has a unique type of atom: Atoms of different elements vary according to their number of protons. A hydrogen atom, for example, has 1 proton, while an atom of lead has 82.

Electricity binds the parts of an atom together. Protons in the nucleus carry a positive electric charge, and electrons rotating around the nucleus carry a negative charge. Neutrons have no charge, and so do not affect the electricity of the atom. Ordinarily, atoms have the same number of protons and electrons. As a result, there is a balance in each atom that makes it electrically neutral. But because opposite charges attract, the atom could collapse in on itself. Additional energy in the electrons keeps them spinning around, which prevents the atom from collapsing. And a force called *strong nuclear force* keeps the protons and neutrons contained within the nucleus.

Structure of an atom

Atoms behave as if they were solid. Electrons spin around the nucleus at such amazing speed that they create the effect of a rigid exterior. But most of an atom is actually made up of empty space. The nucleus fills only the tiniest portion of that space, and the nucleus is proportionately very distant from the orbiting electrons. For example, if a hydrogen atom were about 4 miles (6.4 kilometers) in diameter, its nucleus would be no bigger than a tennis ball.

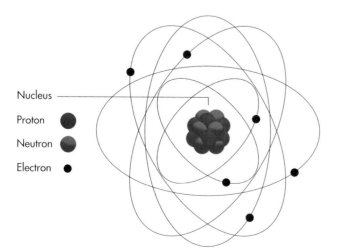

Nucleus

Proton

Neutron

Electron

A carbon atom has six of each of the basic atomic particles—protons, neutrons, and electrons. Protons and neutrons are clustered in the nucleus, and electrons whirl through the empty space outside the nucleus.

The structure of an atom is often compared with that of the solar system, suggesting that electrons orbit the nucleus just as planets orbit the sun. But this is not a completely accurate comparison, because atoms are not nearly as orderly as the solar system. Electrons do not follow regular paths, and protons and neutrons move about constantly within the nucleus. The subatomic particles do, however, show certain patterns of behavior.

● **mass:** *an object's quantity of matter.*

THE NUCLEUS, in spite of its small size, makes up nearly all the mass of an atom. Protons and neutrons compose the nucleus of all atoms except the most common form of hydrogen, which has only a proton at its center. Protons are just slightly smaller than neutrons, and both particles are about 100,000 times smaller than an entire atom.

Every atom of a particular element has the same number of protons. The number of neutrons, however, may vary. Atoms that have the same number of protons but different numbers of neutrons are called *isotopes.* The number of neutrons does not usually affect how an atom behaves in reactions.

Protons and neutrons can be broken down into even tinier particles called *quarks.* Each proton and neutron consists of three quarks. (See "Forces in the nucleus" in Chapter 5.)

ELECTRONS are the vital components of every chemical reaction. Chemistry, therefore, is particularly concerned with the behavior of electrons, particularly in relation to electrons of other atoms.

Electrons are much smaller than protons or neutrons. They have very little mass and do not seem to be made up of smaller parts. However, electrons occupy almost the entire volume of an atom, traveling through the space around the nucleus, and completing billions of trips each millionth of a second.

Electrons move along wavy paths, called *orbitals,* which may appear as any one of a variety of rounded shapes. Each electron carries a certain amount of energy. Those with greater energy are located farther from the nucleus. Electrons are arranged according to their energy level in shells, which are at different average distances from the nucleus.

Each electron shell is designated by a number—the shell closest to the nucleus is called shell 1, and the others are called 2, 3, 4, 5, 6, and 7, in order of their increasing distance from the nucleus. Shells can only hold a limited number of electrons. For example, shell 1 can hold no more than two electrons. The number of shells that atoms have varies, depending on the kind of atom and the energy level of the electrons.

Electrons in the outer shells control the chemical behavior of an atom. This is because these electrons can react with other atoms.

Properties of atoms

The behavior of substances is determined by the behavior of the atoms that make up those substances. Scientists judge the behavior of atoms by identifying the characteristics and properties of different atoms.

THE ATOMIC NUMBER refers to the number of protons an atom has. Since all atoms of the same element have the same number of protons, they share the same atomic number. Helium atoms, for example, have two protons, and so the atomic number for helium is 2. Natural elements have atomic numbers that range successively up to 92, which is the atomic number for uranium. Plutonium, which also occurs in nature, has an atomic number of 94. Elements that have higher atomic numbers must be created in a laboratory.

THE MASS NUMBER is the sum of the protons and neutrons in an atom. Isotopes of the same element have different mass numbers, depending on the number of neutrons each isotope contains. For example, the nucleus of protium, the most common hydrogen isotope, consists of a single proton and so has the mass number of 1. Deuterium, another hydrogen isotope, has a mass number of 2, because its nucleus consists of a proton and a neutron.

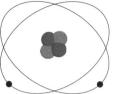

A helium atom has two protons, two neutrons, and two electrons. Helium has a smaller mass than all other elements except hydrogen.

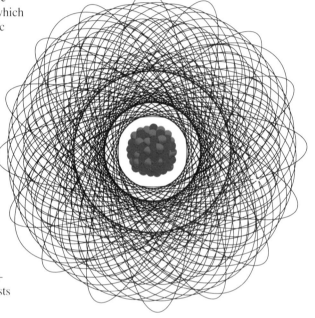

Plutonium has an atomic number of 94.

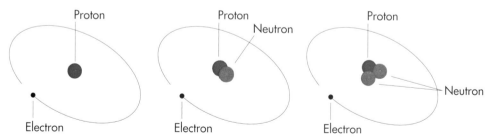

Proton

Proton
Neutron

Proton

Electron

Electron

Electron

Neutron

ATOMIC MASS is the mass of an atom expressed in atomic mass units (amu). Atomic mass units are extremely small—one amu equals 1/12 the mass of an atom of the element carbon 12. The mass of most atoms in amu is almost identical to the mass number. Electrons do not affect an atom's atomic mass because they have virtually no mass.

ELECTRIC CHARGE. Atoms are normally electrically neutral. But they can lose or gain electrons through chemical reactions or in a collision with an

Hydrogen isotopes have different numbers of neutrons. Protium, the most common hydrogen isotope, does not have any neutrons, *left*. Deuterium, *center*, has one neutron, and tritium, *right*, has two neutrons.

electron or another atom. This gain or loss of electrons produces an electrically charged atom called an *ion.* An atom that loses electrons becomes a *positive ion;* one that gains electrons is called a *negative ion.* The gain or loss of electrons is called *ionization.*

VALENCE is the capacity of an atom to combine with another atom, forming a molecule. Atoms combine through the exchange of electrons—they either lose, gain, or share electrons with another atom. Valence refers to the number of electrons involved when atoms combine. If an atom tends to lose electrons to other atoms, it has a positive valence. If an atom tends to gain electrons, its valence is negative. Chlorine, for example, tends to gain one electron from another atom and so has a valence of –1.

E*lements*

Chemical elements, the most basic of substances, can be defined in either of two ways. An element is (1) a substance that cannot be broken down chemically into a simpler substance, or (2) a substance that contains only one kind of atom.

All chemical substances are either elements or compounds, which are combinations of elements. For example, hydrogen and oxygen are elements, and water is a compound of hydrogen and oxygen. A few elements occur naturally in their pure form. They include carbon, sulfur, and certain metals, such as gold and silver. But nearly all other elements—apart from the gases in the atmosphere—occur in combination as compounds.

There are currently 103 officially named and recognized elements. Some elements do not occur naturally and must be created in a laboratory. Since 1964, several groups of scientists claim to have created six new elements, but none of the claims has yet been accepted officially.

Neon signs glow as electric current passes through neon gas in a glass tube. Pure neon in a clear tube gives off bright reddish-orange light. Other colors result from colored tubes and from mixtures of neon and other gases.

Names and symbols of elements

The names of elements come from different sources. Some of these names come from Greek or Latin words. Bromine, for example, gets its name from the Greek word for *stench.* Many artificially created elements are named in honor of a place or individual. Einsteinium, an element created in a laboratory, was named in honor of the physicist Albert Einstein.

Each element has a symbol that consists of one or two letters. Chemists use these symbols as abbreviations for elements. The symbols are universally recognized, and so provide an international language for chemists.

In some cases, the first letter of an element's name is used as its symbol. For example, C is the symbol for carbon. If the names of two or more elements begin with the same letter, two letters of a name are used for all but one of the elements. The second letter is written in lower case. The symbol for calcium is Ca, and the symbol for helium is He. Some symbols come from an old word for the element. Sodium, for example, has the symbol Na, which comes from the Latin word for sodium, *natrium.*

Chemists use the symbols for elements to write formulas for compounds. The formulas tell which elements and how many atoms of each are in a compound. Chemical reactions can be illustrated by placing the formulas in a particular series.

The periodic table of elements

During the 1700's and 1800's, scientists concentrated on gathering information about the characteristics of the elements known at that time. They soon found that there were similarities between some elements, both in their properties and in the way that they form compounds. This information enabled scientists to predict chemical behavior more accurately. Eventually, scientists developed the periodic table of elements, which arranges elements according to their properties and provides a quick reference for essential chemical information.

The periodic table organizes elements in specific vertical and horizontal rows. Elements run horizontally across the table in order of increasing atomic number. Each element has one more proton in its nucleus than the element on its left, but one less than the element on its right. These horizontal rows are called *periods.*

Each vertical column of the periodic table includes elements that are chemically related. These groups of elements tend to show similar properties, particularly in forming compounds. In most cases, the elements in a group have atoms with the same number of electrons in their outer shells. However, atoms of elements in the same group vary greatly in total number of electrons. A complete periodic table provides the following basic information about each element:
- name
- chemical symbol
- atomic number
- atomic mass or mass number
- number of electrons in each shell of its atom
- chemical group to which it belongs

The Periodic Table of Elements

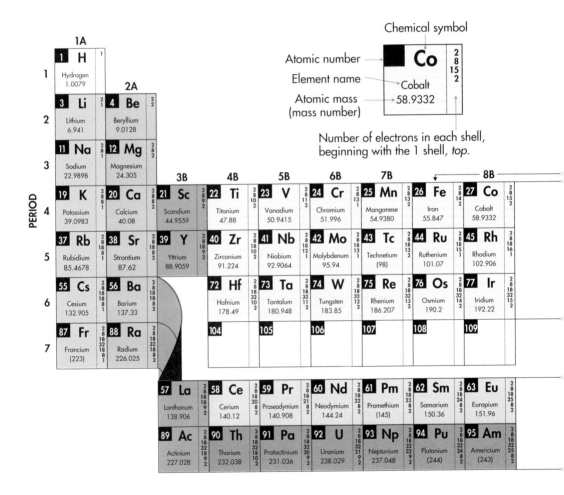

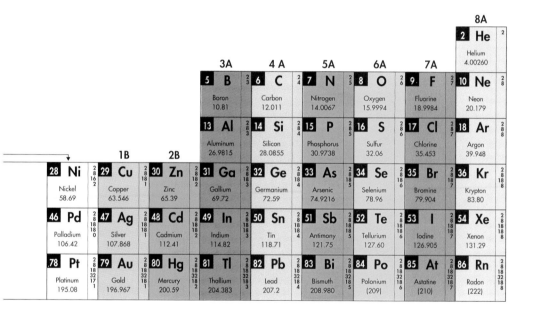

The Discovery of Elements

The German chemist Hennig Brand believed in the concept of a "philosopher's stone," a magical substance that could turn metals into gold and cure all wounds and diseases. He decided to look for such a substance in human urine. In 1669, Brand distilled some urine, then heated the solids that remained. From the vapors of these solids, Brand collected a white, waxy substance that—to his amazement—glowed in the dark. He called the substance phosphorus, after the Greek words for light bringing.

Brand did not know it at the time, but by producing phosphorus, he had become one of the first people to actually isolate a chemical element. Moreover, scientists of Brand's day did not yet understand what the chemical elements truly were. Brand's odd experiment was simply one step toward today's understanding of the elements.

The ancient Greeks

Ancient Greek philosophers were the first to propose the idea that all things are made up

The alchemist's workshop was the forerunner of the modern chemical laboratory.

of elements or combinations of elements. But they were not speaking of the same elements we recognize today. For example, the Greek philosopher Thales, who lived during the 600's B.C., believed that all substances were composed of a single element, which he claimed was water.

The single-element theory persisted until about the mid-400's B.C., when the Greek philosopher Empedocles proposed that the world was made up of four basic elements— earth, air, fire, and water. The great Greek scholar Aristotle endorsed this theory, but added a fifth element called *ether,* which he claimed made up the heavens. Aristotle also maintained that any earthly substance could be turned into another earthly substance by changing the balance of the four elements in the original substance. This process is called *transmutation.*

The alchemists

During the first 300 years after the birth of Christ, scholars and craftworkers in Egypt developed a chemical practice that came to be called alchemy. The alchemists tried to change lead and other metals into gold, basing their craft on Aristotle's theory of transmutation. Alchemy remained popular until about 1700, and despite centuries of experimentation, the alchemists failed in their attempts to produce gold. However, centuries of preparing and studying chemical substances fueled the development of chemistry, resulting in the discovery of arsenic, antimony, and bismuth.

Modern chemistry

During the 1600's, an Irish scientist named Robert Boyle conducted a series of experi-

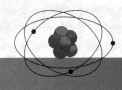

ments that disproved the theory that air, earth, fire, and water were the basic elements of matter. Boyle's work changed the course of chemistry because scientists began to recognize that certain familiar substances could not be broken down into simpler substances—therefore, they must be elements.

Some of the first substances to be accurately identified as elements were gases. English chemist and physicist Henry Cavendish identified hydrogen as an element in 1766. In the 1770's, the Swedish chemist Carl Scheele and the English chemist Joseph Priestley were looking for an explanation of why things burn when they independently discovered oxygen.

During the late 1700's and 1800's, scientists made great strides toward identifying and classifying the chemical elements. The French chemist Antoine Lavoisier worked out the present-day system of chemical names. In 1803, an English chemist named John Dalton developed an atomic theory based on the idea that each chemical element has its own kind of atom. Dalton's theory helped scientists find differences between elements and eventually led to the system of atomic mass.

But chemists continued to have difficulty categorizing the elements until 1869, when the Russian chemist Dmitri Mendeleev and the German chemist Julius Lothar Meyer created the periodic table, which arranged the elements according to a system of classification. This system even enabled chemists to predict the existence of elements that had not yet been discovered. Both scientists left gaps in their table, and Mendeleev predicted that unknown elements would be found to fill them.

Over time, the gaps in the original periodic table were filled by newly discovered elements. Scientists also began to add to it. A new column was added when the Scottish chemist William Ramsay discovered elements in the rare gas group during the 1890's. These elements include argon,

Antoine Lavoisier wrote the first modern textbook on chemistry. His studies revolutionized chemistry during the late 1700's. This painting shows Lavoisier in his laboratory with his wife, who acted as her husband's assistant, recording the results of his experiments and translating English works on chemistry into French.

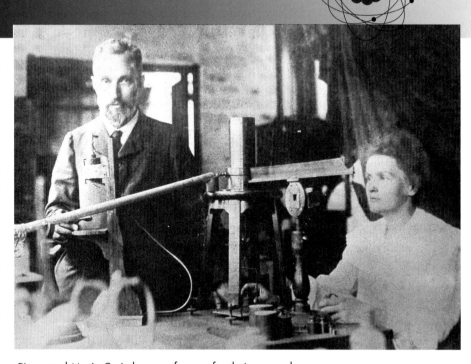

Pierre and Marie Curie became famous for their research on radioactivity. They discovered the radioactive elements radium and polonium in 1898.

helium, neon, krypton, and xenon. The structure of the periodic table remained sound even including these new discoveries, but scientists began to wonder just how far the table could extend—in other words, how many elements could there be?

Radioactive and artificial elements

In 1896, the French physicist Antoine Henri Becquerel put a photographic plate in a drawer that also contained uranium salts. He later found that the plate was darkened, deduced that the uranium must have given off some sort of energy, and thus discovered natural radiation. This discovery set off a surge of interest in radioactive elements. In 1898, French physicists Marie Curie and Pierre Curie discovered two new radioactive elements, polonium and radium.

The work of the Curies and other scien-tists eventually led to the creation of artificial elements. Scientists found that they could create a new element by bombarding atoms of a known element with neutrons or other subatomic particles. The Italian scientists Carlo Perrier and Emilio Segrè created the first artificial element, which they christened technetium, in 1937. Since then, scientists have created about 20 additional artificial elements. Six of these—elements 104 through 109—are not officially recognized. Scientists have observed only a few atoms of these elements.

Today, scientists continue to search for new elements. This search has become increasingly more difficult because some new elements last only for a fraction of a second. But in theory, scientists could continue to create many more new elements. (See "Radioactive elements" in this chapter.)

Major groups of elements

Chemists have divided the elements into groups, based on their chemical behavior. Chemical behavior is determined by the number of electrons in the outer shell of an element's atom. In the periodic table of elements, each vertical column includes elements whose atoms have the same number of outer electrons. Each column, therefore, comprises a group of elements that share certain patterns of chemical behavior. In some cases, chemists consider two or more adjoining columns as forming a group of elements, because the elements in these columns display certain chemical similarities.

The columns of the periodic table are divided into two categories, A and B, based on the electronic structure of the elements included. Certain groups of elements are known by specific names, while others are identified by the column in which they are found. For example, the elements helium, neon, argon, krypton, xenon, and radon form a group called the rare gases. But because they lie in column 8A of the periodic table, they may also be referred to as group 8A. Scientists have discovered that the rare gases are found as gases at ordinary temperatures and pressures and that they do not combine easily with other elements to form compounds. In this way, they show similar chemical behavior.

In the sections that follow, the elements are divided into small family groups. Some of these groups consist of one vertical column of the periodic table, while others consist of several adjoining columns.

HYDROGEN, the first element of the periodic table, is not grouped with any other elements. Its chemical symbol is H. Under normal conditions, hydrogen exists as a gas. It is the most common element in the universe.

Hydrogen forms many compounds and has many uses. Industrial uses of hydrogen include the manufacture of fertilizers and fuels.

Hydrogen gas, which is highly flammable, provided the lift for the Hindenburg and other early airships. The deadly explosion of the Hindenburg in 1937, *below*, resulted when the hydrogen it contained somehow ignited.

ALKALI METALS make up group 1A of the periodic table. The six elements in this group are lithium (chemical symbol Li), sodium (Na), potassium (K), rubidium (Rb), cesium (Cs), and francium (Fr). Most of the elements in this group react violently with water, and some burn in air.

Compounds of alkali metals are among the most common and most useful of all chemicals. Industries use millions of tons of alkali metal salts each year. Alkali metal compounds are used in making glass, paper, soap, and textiles; in refining petroleum; and in preparing leather. Sodium oxide (NaO) is the most abundant sodium compound in the Earth's crust. The best-known sodium compound is sodium chloride (NaCl)—common table salt.

Gold has been used for thousands of years to create jewelry and other ornamental objects, *right.* Mollusk shells consist largely of a compound called calcium carbonate, *below.*

COPPER, SILVER, AND GOLD make up group 1B of the periodic table. These metals are the best conductors of heat and electricity. Copper (Cu), Silver (Ag), and Gold (Au) can be hammered into extremely thin sheets or drawn into very fine wire without cracking. None of these metals rust, and they resist other chemical reactions that cause many metals to decay. Copper, silver, and gold are sometimes called the *coinage metals* because they have been used widely in making coins.

ALKALINE-EARTH METALS, the six elements that make up group 2A, include beryllium (Be), magnesium (Mg), calcium (Ca), strontium (Sr), barium (Ba), and radium (Ra). They are called the alkaline-earth metals because they combine with oxygen to form compounds that are alkaline. Alkaline substances neutralize acids and form salts with them.

Alkaline-earth metals react with water and, except for radium, have many industrial uses. Magnesium, for example, can be combined with other metals to form very light materials used in automobiles and aircraft. Calcium compounds are used to make cement and plaster. Alkaline-earth metals are never found in nature in their pure form. They have to be separated from the minerals that contain them.

ZINC, CADMIUM, AND MERCURY make up group 2B of the periodic table. Physically, these metals are not alike, but they have similar chemical properties. All three react with oxygen to form various compounds.

Zinc (Zn) is an important ingredient in many useful alloys. Cadmium (Cd), which is very poisonous, is mainly used as a protective plating on steel and other metals. Mercury (Hg) is the only metal that is a liquid at ordinary temperatures. Mercury is best known as the liquid in thermometers, but it has many other industrial uses.

THE BORON GROUP, group 3A, includes the elements boron (B), aluminum (Al), gallium (Ga), indium (In), and thallium (Tl). Boron is the only element in this group that is not a metal. Aluminum and boron are the most widely used of these elements.

Borax, an important compound of boron, has been used for hundreds of years as a detergent. Many glazes and enamels are also made of boron. Aluminum is a lightweight metal that has a tremendous number of uses. It is often combined with other metals to make such products as cookware, power lines, and parts of automobiles and airplanes. Gallium is used in semiconductors.

GROUP 4A includes carbon (C), silicon (Si), germanium (Ge), tin (Sn), and lead (Pb). Carbon is unique among the chemical elements in the number and variety of the compounds it can form. Without carbon, life would be impossible. Certain compounds of carbon make up the living tissue of all animals and plants.

Silicon resembles carbon in many respects. Like carbon, it forms many compounds. Silicon is one of the most abundant elements on Earth. Silicon and germanium are used in semiconductors. The metals tin and lead have been used for thousands of years as ingredients in important alloys.

THE TRANSITION METALS make up a group that includes columns 4B, 5B, 6B, 7B, and 8B in the periodic table. There are 21 elements in this group. The transition metals have several chemical similarities. For example, they tend to

● **alloy:** *a combination of metals.*

● **semiconductor:** *a mineral substance that conducts electricity in a predictable manner.*

Carbon exists in a variety of forms. Two of the best-known forms are diamond (shown here both cut, *top left,* and rough, *center*) and graphite, *top right.* Both minerals consist of pure carbon, but they differ in the arrangement of their atoms.

● **catalyst:** *a substance that increases the speed of a chemical reaction.*

act as catalysts. Commonly known transition metals include titanium (Ti), chromium (Cr), iron (Fe), nickel (Ni), tungsten (W), and platinum (Pt). Iron, the most widely used metal, is combined with carbon to produce steel.

GROUP 5A includes nitrogen (N), phosphorus (P), arsenic (As), antimony (Sb), and bismuth (Bi). Nitrogen is the most abundant gaseous element on Earth, making up more than three-quarters of the volume of the atmosphere. All organisms must have nitrogen to live. Scientists have learned to make nitrogen artificially, and it is often used to make fertilizers. Phosphorus is a highly reactive element that is used in matches. When it is exposed to air, phosphorus produces a faint green light.

GROUP 6A consists of oxygen (O), sulfur (S), selenium (Se), tellurium

Oxygen gas compressed in a metal tank enables a scuba diver to breathe underwater for many minutes.

Steel, an alloy of iron and carbon, has many uses. The Spanish artist Pablo Picasso designed this five-story steel sculpture for the city of Chicago.

(Te), and polonium (Po). Oxygen is one of the most plentiful elements on Earth. Nearly all organisms require oxygen to stay alive. It combines with other chemicals in the cells of plants and animals to produce energy. Oxygen is also needed to make most fuels burn.

Under normal conditions, oxygen occurs as a gas. The remaining elements in this group occur as solids. Sulfur, a solid yellow substance, is a particularly important industrial chemical. It is usually combined with oxygen and hydrogen to create sulfuric acid, a compound used in fertilizers, dyes, paints, automobile batteries, textiles, and other valuable products.

THE HALOGENS form column 7A of the periodic table. Fluorine (F), chlorine (Cl), bromine (Br), iodine (I), and astatine (At) make up this group. These elements have a strong, unpleasant odor, and they must be handled with care because they burn skin easily. The halogens combine with metals to form many of the salts in the sea. Halogen means salt-producer. Chlorine, for example, combines with sodium to form sodium chloride, or common table salt.

THE NOBLE GASES are helium (He), neon (Ne), argon (Ar), krypton (Kr), xenon (Xe), and radon (Rn). They make up column 8A of the periodic table. They are also known as the *rare gases.* The elements in this group are all gases found in the atmosphere.

The rare gases do not react easily with other elements to form compounds. This quality makes some of the rare gases useful for particular purposes. Helium, which is best known as the gas in balloons and airships, is also used to prevent chemicals from reacting with other elements during storage and transportation. Neon, argon, krypton, and xenon are used in a variety of light sources, such as incandescent light bulbs, and fluorescent light fixtures.

● **incandescent:**
glowing with heat.

THE SCANDIUM GROUP includes the elements in column 3B of the periodic table. They are scandium (Sc), yttrium (Y), lanthanum (La), and actinium (Ac). However, lanthanum and actinium have their own series of related elements, known as the lanthanides and actinides. These groups appear as separate horizontal bars at the bottom of the periodic table.

Lanthanides, also known as rare earth elements, are used to produce phosphors, which glow when struck by an electron beam to produce a television picture. A color TV screen is coated with dots of red, blue, and green phosphors.

The lanthanides include elements with atomic numbers that range consecutively from 57 to 71, or lanthanum to lutetium (Lu). They are also known as the *rare earth elements* because they were originally considered very rare. By modern standards, however, they are not rare.

The lanthanides always occur in combination with other elements. When they are separated, they have many scientific and industrial uses. Lanthanides are used in lamps, lasers, magnets, and X-ray intensifying screens.

The actinides include elements with atomic numbers that range consecutively from 89 to 103, or actinium to lawrencium (Lr). All of the actinides are radioactive elements.

Radioactive elements

An element is radioactive if its atoms emit *radiation,* or atomic particles and rays of high energy from the nucleus. All elements with atomic numbers of 89 or higher are radioactive.

A radioactive atom has an unstable nucleus. In a stable, or nonradioactive, atom, the protons are electrically balanced by the neutrons in the nucleus. In a radioactive atom, the neutrons are unable to counteract the electric forces between the protons. As a result, the nucleus of a radioactive atom throws out excess protons and neutrons, trying to reach a stable condition. When atoms emit these particles, they change into atoms of another element. Scientists call this change *transformation* or *transmutation.*

Radioactive elements make it possible to measure the age of ancient substances. Scientists determine the age of volcanic rock by measuring the decay of potassium 40 to argon 40, *above.* The common method of dating fossils, such as ancient human bones, *right,* is carbon 14 dating.

When an atom changes into the atom of another element, it is said to *decay*. Sometimes radioactive atoms change into atoms of another radioactive element. In such a case, the new radioactive element also decays to form another element. The process continues until the particular atom achieves stability. For example, U^{238}, one of the isotopes of uranium, goes through 14 different elemental changes before becoming a stable isotope of lead.

All radioactive elements are continually decaying at different rates, producing different isotopes with different half-lives. A *half-life* is the length of time it takes for half the atoms of a radioactive substance to break down or decay. A half-life may range from fractions of a second to billions of years. Elements with higher atomic numbers have shorter half-lives, and so their radioactive decay is more rapid.

Scientists can produce radioactive isotopes, or *radioisotopes,* of different elements by bombarding nuclei with neutrons and other nuclear particles in nuclear reactors. In this way, some scientists have created what they claim to be new elements. These new elements have greater atomic numbers than 103, the atomic number of lawrencium. Each is very short-lived and highly radioactive. Only a few atoms of each new element have been observed. In theory, the number of elements could extend indefinitely. As a result, scientists continue to search for new elements.

The radioisotopes of radioactive elements have many uses. They can be used to determine the thickness of materials, to measure the age of ancient substances, and to study the functions of various body organs. In these uses, and many others, scientists must have a great understanding of the way in which radioisotopes emit energy and how that energy affects other substances.

Molecules

Although they are made up of atoms, molecules are still considered one of the basic units of matter. That is because a molecule is the smallest particle into which a substance can be divided and still have the chemical identity of the original substance. If the substance were divided further, only atoms of chemical elements would remain. For example, a drop of water contains billions of water molecules. If one water molecule were separated from the rest, it would still behave like water. But if that water molecule were divided, only atoms of the elements hydrogen and oxygen would remain.

The structure of molecules

Molecules are made up of atoms held together in certain arrangements. The forces that hold the atoms of a molecule together are called *chemical bonds*. Atoms bond by sharing electrons—some atoms give up electrons, some take on electrons, and in some bonds the electrons orbit the nucleus of two atoms.

Each atom in a molecule consists of a positively charged nucleus surrounded by negatively charged electrons. When atoms bond, these charges balance each other, forming an electrically neutral molecule. In some molecules, positive and negative charges are spread evenly throughout it. In *polar molecules,* however, more positive charge collects at one place in

A polymer is a large molecule formed by the linking of many small units. Polyethylene, one of the simplest polymers, consists of long chains of carbon atoms, each carrying two hydrogen atoms.

A water molecule consists of two hydrogen atoms and one oxygen atom, *above*. Water is the most common substance on Earth, and more than 97 percent of the world's water is in the ocean, *right*.

the molecule and more negative charge collects at another place. Some polar molecules are magnetic because of the way the electrons are unevenly distributed within the molecule.

Scientists show the composition of molecules by using the symbols for elements in chemical formulas. For example, a water molecule consists of two hydrogen atoms and one oxygen atom. Therefore, the chemical formula for water is written as H_2O.

Molecules are measured by their *molecular mass,* which equals all the atomic masses of the atoms in a molecule. The molecular mass of carbon dioxide (CO_2) can be found by adding the atomic mass of one atom of carbon, which is 12, and the masses of the two oxygen atoms, which are about 16 each. The molecular mass of carbon dioxide, therefore, is about 44.

The variety of molecules

Molecules occur in an incredible number of shapes and sizes. This variety plays an important role in the chemical properties that different substances show. Liquids freeze and gases condense at certain temperatures, partly because of the makeup of their molecules.

A molecule's size depends on the size and number of its atoms. Molecules consist of as few as one or as many as millions of atoms. Specific names are given to molecules with particular numbers of atoms. A molecule consisting of two atoms of the same element, like oxygen (O_2), is a *diatomic molecule*. A molecule made up of three atoms, like ozone (O_3), is a *triatomic molecule*.

Forces within a molecule determine its shape. Molecules take the shape that forms the strongest bonds and provides the least amount of strain among its atoms. Some molecular shapes are simple. An ammonia molecule, for example, takes the shape of a tetrahedron. It consists of three hydrogen atoms attached to a nitrogen atom. Other shapes are more complicated. Many protein molecules form long helixes. A benzene molecule has six carbon atoms arranged in a ring with six hydrogen atoms attached.

● **tetrahedron:** *a pyramidlike figure.*

● **helix:** *a figure with a coiled form.*

Molecules in combination

Molecules are held together by forces called *van der Waals forces,* which are usually weaker than those that hold the atoms of a molecule together. The force between molecules depends on the distance between them. Molecules attract each other when they are widely separated; they repel when close together.

In a solid, the forces that attract and repel are balanced. The molecules in a solid vibrate but do not move about to different parts of the solid. But if the solid's temperature is raised, the molecules vibrate more rapidly. Eventually, the energy of these vibrations becomes greater than the van der Waals forces that hold the molecules in place. The solid then melts and becomes a liquid—a change of *phase*.

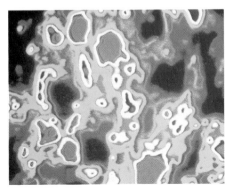

Electron microscopes can make individual atoms visible. This computer image shows platinum and palladium atoms magnified about 3 million times. The individual atoms appear as yellow dots. The yellow areas with red or purple centers are clusters of atoms.

In a liquid, molecules move about easily, but they still have some force that attracts them to one another called *surface tension*. Surface tension pulls the molecules on the surface toward the molecules in the body of the liquid and prevents the liquid from flying apart. The liquid acts as if it has a thin skin on it.

The molecules in a gas move about rapidly, and the attractive forces have little effect on them. Gas molecules move freely through the available space. When they collide, repelling forces send them apart again, so gases will always fill a container completely.

Sometimes, when two kinds of molecules come near enough to each other they react to form one or more new molecules. Two molecules of the same kind may also combine to form a larger molecule. The process by which

Grains of table salt are cube-shaped crystals.

many small molecules combine to form one large molecule is called *polymerization.* (See page 41 for a picture of a polymer molecule.) Certain conditions, such as the presence of ultraviolet light or nuclear radiation, can cause large molecules to break down into several smaller ones.

Ions: alternate units

Almost all gases, most common liquids, and many solids are made up of molecules. However, some substances, called *ionic substances,* consist of units called ions. An *ion* is an atom or a group of atoms with a positive or negative electric charge. In this way, ions differ from molecules, which are electrically neutral. Atoms and molecules become ions if they lose or gain electrons. An atom that loses electrons becomes a *positive ion;* one that gains electrons is called a *negative ion.*

Positive and negative ions tend to attract each other. Ionic substances are made up of both positive and negative ions. Most ionic substances are electrically neutral, because the total charge of all their positive ions equals the total charge of all their negative ions. Ionic substances occur as gases, liquids, and solids.

Ions make up many common substances. Table salt consists of equal numbers of positive sodium ions and negative chloride ions. Other salts, such as those in the sea, are also ionic substances. The ions in salts form regular, repeating, three-dimensional arrangements called crystals. Metals are made up of positive ions, combined with electrons that move about freely through the metal. The Earth's atmosphere also contains many ions, which are concentrated in the ionosphere.

Compounds
The Marriage of Elements

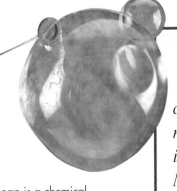

2

Soap is a chemical compound.

Although all matter consists of chemical elements, very little of the matter on Earth is made up of elements in their pure, or uncombined, form. Most matter is made up of compounds, which are combinations of elements. There are millions of different compounds, and they are as unique and varied as the elements. They occur as solids, liquids, and gases, in just about every color and odor. Some readily undergo chemical reactions, while others have little tendency to react. By studying the chemical properties of compounds, chemists are able to create new and useful substances and to understand the chemical processes that take place in nature every day.

A single drop of water contains hydrogen and oxygen atoms in exactly the same proportion as a whole beaker of water.

A *compound's identity*

A compound is a substance that is made up of at least two different elements and, therefore, two different kinds of atoms. Compounds are distinctive in that they always have the same composition by weight. No matter what part or how much of a compound you isolate, it will always have the same ratio between elements that the original compound has. Water, for example, is a compound that consists of molecules that have one atom of oxygen and two atoms of hydrogen. Therefore, in any sample of water, there will always be twice as many hydrogen atoms as oxygen atoms.

Every compound can be described by a particular *chemical formula,* which shows the ratio between the elements that make up the compound. Chemists write formulas using the symbols for chemical elements. Chemical formulas show the makeup of one unit of a compound; these units generally occur as molecules or ions.

The composition of simple molecules can be shown in a formula by combining the symbols for the elements that the compound contains. Hydrogen fluoride, for instance, is made up of molecules that contain one atom of hydrogen and one atom of fluorine. Its formula can be written as HF.

Many molecules have more than one atom of the same element. Formulas for these molecules include numbers written just below the symbols as subscripts. The subscripts indicate the number of atoms included in a molecule. For example, carbon dioxide is a compound that contains one carbon (C) atom and two oxygen (O) atoms. The formula for carbon dioxide is written CO_2.

Formulas for compounds that consist of ions show the symbols of elements whose atoms exist as ions in the compound. The compound sodium chloride, or common table salt, has equal amounts of sodium (Na) and chlorine (Cl) atoms that occur as ions. The formula for sodium chloride is written NaCl.

How compounds are formed

A compound is formed when atoms of one element bond with atoms of another element. Atoms tend to bond as a means of becoming more stable. A stable atom is one that has the maximum amount of electrons in its outer shell. Therefore, atoms bond through the exchange of electrons, which are either transferred from one atom to another or shared by more than one atom.

The capacity of an atom to combine with another atom is referred to as its *valence.* Atoms of an element are assigned a valence number, which generally equals the number of electrons that an atom needs to fill or release from its outermost shell. Atoms that tend to lose electrons have a positive valence, and those that tend to gain electrons have a negative valence. However, an atom of a certain element may combine in a number of different ways with different elements. Thus, an atom may be assigned more than one valence number, depending on the number of different bonds it tends to form.

Water is an example of a common compound. It is made up of hydrogen and oxygen atoms. The outer shell of an oxygen atom requires two additional atoms to become stable. Hydrogen atoms have one electron, but need another to fill the outer shell. So when two hydrogen atoms combine with one oxygen atom, all the vacancies are filled, forming a molecule of water.

There are two types of chemical bonds that produce compounds: ionic bonds and covalent bonds.

Atoms join together to form compounds by means of chemical bonds. An ionic bond, *top,* forms when one atom gives up an electron to another atom. When atoms share electrons, a covalent bond forms, *bottom.*

IONIC BONDS are created by the transfer of electrons from one atom to one or more other atoms. The atom that loses electrons becomes a positive ion. The atoms that gain electrons become negative ions. The force that holds ionic compounds together is called an ionic bond.

Table salt, properly called sodium chloride (NaCl), is an ionic compound. Salt is formed when a sodium atom gives up an electron to a chlorine atom. The sodium atom, which loses the negative electric charge that the electron carries, becomes a positive ion. The chlorine atom gains the negative charge, and becomes a negative ion. Opposite charges attract, and so the two atoms are joined in an ionic bond.

IONIC BONDING

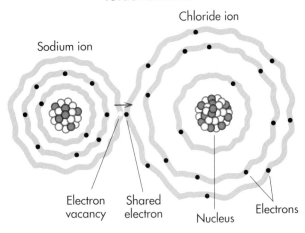

Chloride ion

Sodium ion

Electron vacancy

Shared electron

Nucleus

Electrons

Sodium chloride molecule

COVALENT BONDS are formed when two or more atoms share pairs of electrons. A shared pair consists of one electron from each of two atoms. These electrons revolve around the nucleus of both atoms. Covalent bonds form molecules, which ordinarily have no electrical charge. Compounds that consist of molecules can be called covalent compounds. Water is an example of a covalent compound.

Nearly all elements in their natural states are joined by covalent bonds. Hydrogen, for example, normally consists of covalently bonded molecules. An ordinary hydrogen molecule (H_2) has two atoms that share electrons, so that two electrons revolve around each nucleus. Covalent compounds are often joined by bonds that are much more complicated. Some individual molecules are held together by many different covalent bonds.

COVALENT BONDING

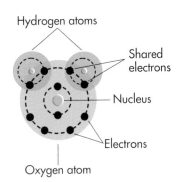

Hydrogen atoms

Shared electrons

Nucleus

Electrons

Oxygen atom

Rust (Fe$_2$O$_3$) is the product of a chemical reaction involving iron and oxygen. If left outside long enough, these iron railroad ties would eventually rust away completely.

Chemical reactions

Chemical reactions are constantly carried out in our lives. The digestion of food, the burning of fuel—even the development of photographic film—all involve chemical reactions. Understanding and predicting chemical reactions is an important way in which scientists apply the concepts of chemistry to everyday life.

A chemical reaction is a process in which one substance is chemically converted into a different substance. In all chemical reactions, bonds between atoms are broken and new ones are formed. Thus, the molecular or ionic structure of the substance a chemical reaction creates is always different from the structure of the original substance.

All the changes we witness, however, are not chemical reactions. There are also physical changes and nuclear reactions. In a *physical change,* the substance undergoing change has the same chemical formula as the resulting substance. The melting of ice, for example, is a physical change, because the structure of the water molecules remains the same. In a *nuclear reaction,* an atom is transformed into another type of atom as a result of changes in the composition of its nucleus.

Components and conditions

The number of substances involved in a chemical reaction varies. In the simplest reactions, a single substance changes chemically into one or more other substances. In most chemical reactions, however, two or more substances react to produce one or more new substances. Substances can be thought of as the components of chemical reactions. The outcome of these components is affected by the conditions under which a reaction occurs.

CHEMICAL EQUATIONS demonstrate what occurs in chemical reactions. These equations consist of chemical formulas and symbols that describe the substances that are involved in the reaction. For example, the following is the chemical equation for the rusting of iron:

$$4Fe(s) + 3O_2(g) \rightarrow 2Fe_2O_3(s)$$

This equation states that four atoms of solid iron (Fe[s]) react with three molecules of oxygen gas (O_2[g]) to form two units of solid rust (Fe_2O_3[s]). Experiments that have been performed on this reaction have proven that iron and oxygen always react in these proportions.

All chemical reactions have at least one product and at least one reactant. In the rusting of iron, rust is the *product*, or result, of the reaction. Iron and oxygen are the *reactants*, the substances that undergo chemical change.

The total number of atoms and the kinds of atoms do not change in a chemical reaction. The number of atoms in the reactants is the same as the number of atoms in the products. In this way, chemical equations are similar to mathematical equations. Both sides—of the arrow, in a chemical equation—must balance. Thus, in the equation for the rusting of iron, the reactants contain a total of 10 atoms: 4 atoms of iron and 6 atoms of oxygen. Likewise, the product contains 10 atoms. But the formula of the product is very different from the formulas of the reactants.

CONDITIONS. Some chemical reactions occur spontaneously—that is, when two reactants are simply placed together. The rusting of iron is a spontaneous reaction. Spontaneous reactions occur only when the products are more chemically stable than are the reactants. Rust, therefore, is more stable than iron or oxygen.

Many chemical reactions, however, do not occur spontaneously. They require certain conditions. One of the most common conditions that contributes to chemical reactions is the presence of heat. Heat, a form of energy, can cause substances to become more reactive, or less stable. Solid rust, as demonstrated in the equation shown previously, is fairly stable. But when rust is heated in combination with certain other materials, it becomes metallic iron. This reaction also reveals an important chemical principle—most reactions are reversible. In other words, products can be changed back into reactants.

Heat brings on the chemical reaction known as *combustion*, or burning. Heat causes carbon and hydrogen to combine with oxygen from the air. Combustion produces energy in the form of heat, light, carbon dioxide gas, and water vapor. The blackened remains—of burned logs and marshmallows—are a mixture of carbon and other substances.

Chemical reactions proceed at different rates, according to different conditions. Heat, for example, tends to increase the speed of many chemical reactions. Certain substances, called *catalysts*, can also accelerate the speed of a chemical reaction. The process in which a substance increases the speed of a reaction is called *catalysis*.

Unlike reactants, catalysts remain unchanged by chemical reactions. In most cases, there are several possible sequences of steps by which a reaction occurs. Catalysts participate in some or all of these steps, creating a chemical pathway along which the entire reaction can proceed more rapidly. In this way, catalysts can lower the amount of energy needed to cause a chemical reaction.

An example of catalysis is the effect that nitric oxide (NO) has on the decomposition of ozone (O_3) in the upper atmosphere of the Earth. Ordinarily, ozone decomposes slowly as oxygen atoms and ozone molecules combine and produce oxygen molecules (O_2). The presence of nitric oxide, however, causes the oxygen molecules to be created rapidly.

Catalysts are used widely in industry to speed up chemical reactions that would otherwise take place too slowly. Many useful substances, including gasoline and ammonia, are created through processes that use catalysts, such as platinum and palladium.

Oxidation and reduction

There is an extraordinary range of possible chemical reactions, some that take place naturally every day, and others that must be created in a laboratory. Among the most common—and important in our day-to-day lives—are two related reactions, called oxidation and reduction. Many essential processes that take place in plants and animals depend on a whole series of interdependent oxidation and reduction reactions.

Originally, the term *oxidation* referred to any chemical process in which a substance combines with oxygen. Scientists learned, however, that the type of reaction they were describing could take place, in some cases, without oxygen. Today, oxidation refers to any chemical reaction in which a substance loses electrons. Reduction refers to any reaction in which a substance gains electrons.

Since the electrons released during oxidation must be captured by another substance, oxidation is always accompanied by reduction. This combined transfer of electrons is often called the *redox process.* The formation of water is an example of the redox process. Water molecules are formed when oxygen and hydrogen gases combine.

During the reaction of these gases, hydrogen atoms lose an electron. Therefore, they have been oxidized. The oxygen atoms, on the other hand, gain two electrons—one from each of two hydrogen atoms. The oxygen atoms have undergone reduction. Thus, the formation of water involves both oxidation and reduction.

Metal plating, the process used to make silver-plated objects like this tea service, is a type of reduction reaction.

The rusting of iron is a common example of oxidation. Another example is the combustion of fuels such as natural gas. Oxidation also takes place within the human body, as inhaled oxygen reacts with molecules of food to produce energy, water, and carbon dioxide.

Many important processes rely on reduction. Metal plating, for example, occurs when metal ions are reduced—gain electrons—to form neutral atoms. When a piece of copper is placed in a solution containing positive silver ions, the silver ions pick up electrons from copper atoms, and a coating of silver forms on the copper.

Types of compounds

Chemical compounds may be divided into one of two groups, organic compounds and inorganic compounds. These two groups can be split up into a few smaller groups of compounds, each defined by its atomic structure. Acids and bases are two important groups of compounds. Isomer is a term used to describe different compounds that have the same molecular formula.

Organic compounds

All basic substances that make up living organisms are called organic compounds. Carbon atoms make up the foundation of organic compounds. Most other substances that contain carbon, particularly synthetic substances such as plastics, are also considered organic compounds. The study of compounds that contain carbon is called organic chemistry. (See "Organic chemistry" in Chapter 3.)

Carbon forms more compounds than any other element except hydrogen. The basic reason for this is that carbon atoms have the ability to form an incredible variety of chemical bonds with other carbon atoms and atoms of other elements. Scientists have identified several million organic compounds.

Bar soap, *left,* and butane used in lighters, *above,* are both organic compounds based on hydrogen and carbon. Their vastly different properties result from the difference in one end of their molecules, as shown in the diagrams.

Many important organic chemicals used in industry are obtained from plant and animal sources. For example, coal, oil, and natural gas are produced from the remains of organisms that lived millions of years ago. Other organic compounds present in living matter include amino acids, sugars, and nucleic acids.

Originally, scientists believed that carbon-containing compounds could only be found from living sources. In the early 1800's, however, scientists learned that organic compounds could be created artificially. Nearly all the plastics and synthetic fibers we use every day are organic substances, as are such materials as artificial sweeteners, pesticides, and many useful drugs.

In addition to their ability to form many types of bonds, carbon atoms can also link together into very long chains. These long chains form gigantic molecules called polymers. Polymers make up many important organic compounds. Some polymers, such as starch and wool, occur naturally. Starch is formed by plants from a simple sugar called glucose, and wool is a variety of protein. Other polymers are synthetic. Nylon and polyethylene, a tough plastic material, are examples of synthetic polymers. Rubber, another polymer, occurs naturally. But more than half the rubber used today is made synthetically.

Inorganic compounds

Compounds that do not contain living matter are called inorganic compounds. With a few exceptions, such as the gas carbon dioxide, inorganic compounds do not have carbon atoms. Most inorganic compounds occur in rocks and minerals.

Many inorganic compounds are ionic substances that occur as solids. They include salts and many minerals. Nonmetal elements, such as boron, nitrogen, oxygen, and silicon, make up a wide variety of inorganic compounds.

Zinc oxide, an inorganic compound, is useful as a sunblock.

Although they do not contain living matter, inorganic compounds can be found in living organisms. Blood, for example, contains coordination compounds, an important class of inorganic compounds. *Coordination compounds* contain a central metal atom surrounded by a nonmetal atom or molecule. Blood contains a coordination compound made up of iron atoms that are each surrounded by nitrogen and oxygen atoms.

Acids

Among the most common and important compounds are acids. Acids share certain recognizable properties. For example, they turn litmus paper red, and they tend to corrode metals. Acids also have a sour taste. We come into contact with acids every day. Citric acid is found in citrus fruits such as oranges, and sulfuric acid is commonly used as the fluid in automobile batteries.

Chemists use several definitions to describe the behavior of acids. They are often defined as compounds that produce hydrogen ions when dissolved in water. Acids can also be defined more generally as compounds that can donate a proton when they combine with any other substance.

Citric acid gives oranges their tart flavor.

Acids vary in strength. The strength of an acid is measured by the number of hydrogen ions it produces when it dissolves in water. Stronger acids produce more hydrogen ions. Hydrochloric acid, which helps digestion in the human stomach, is an example of a strong acid. Acetic acid, which is found in vinegar, is a weak acid.

ORGANIC ACIDS contain carbon atoms. They are often obtained from living matter. Organic acids are used in the manufacture of detergents, foods, and soaps. Amino acids, which are the building blocks of proteins, are common organic acids. Others include ascorbic acid, which is vitamin C; and acetylsalicylic acid, or aspirin.

INORGANIC ACIDS do not, in general, contain carbon atoms. They tend to be stronger than organic acids. They are used in plastics and synthetic fibers. Inorganic acids are also used in the refining of petroleum. Nitric acid and hydrochloric acid are common inorganic acids.

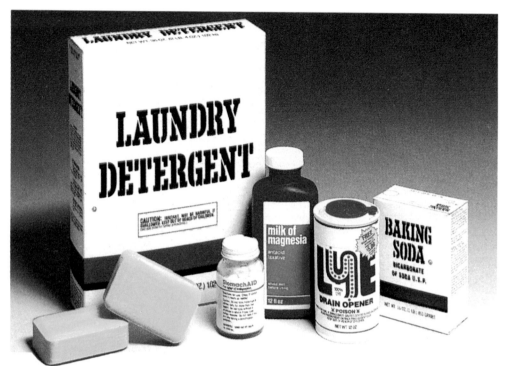

All these familiar products, from laxatives to drain openers, are bases.

Bases

A substance that can react with an acid to neutralize its acidic properties is called a base. Bases taste bitter and they feel slippery when dissolved in water.

Chemists often define a base as any compound that produces hydroxide ions—ions of hydrogen and oxygen—when dissolved in water. They are sometimes more generally defined as any substance that can accept a proton from another substance. It is in this manner that bases neutralize acids.

Bases have many uses in the home. Potassium hydroxide is a base used in making soaps. Many household drain cleaners contain sodium hydroxide. Milk of magnesia, a common antacid, contains the base magnesium hydroxide.

Isomers

In certain cases, two or more substances can be made up of the same number of atoms of the same elements, and yet be completely different compounds. These compounds are called isomers. The difference between isomers lies in the way their atoms are put together. Because the atom arrangement varies, isomers generally show different chemical behavior.

The two types of the gas butane—normal butane and isobutane—are examples of isomers. Both types have the same chemical formula, C_4H_{10}. But because the atoms that make up their molecules are bonded differently, normal butane and isobutane have different boiling points. Normal butane boils at –0.5 °C, while isobutane boils at –11.7 °C.

Chart of Common Compounds

Many chemical compounds are useful in every aspect of our lives. The following chart lists some common compounds, their formulas, and their importance.

Common Compounds

Compound	Formula	Importance
Aluminum chloride	$AlCl_3$	Aluminum chloride is used in manufacturing detergents.
Ammonia	NH_3	Ammonia is widely used as a fertilizer. It is also used in the production of synthetic fibers and in the manufacture of many chemicals, plastics, vitamins, and drugs.
Calcium carbonate	$CaCO_3$	Calcium carbonate is an ingredient of some toothpastes. It is also used in some medicines to reduce stomach acidity.
Carbon dioxide	CO_2	All green plants need carbon dioxide in order to live and grow. Carbon dioxide in the atmosphere helps regulate the Earth's temperature.
Hydrogen fluoride	HF	Hydrogen fluoride, or hydrofluoric acid, is used in manufacturing aluminum. It is also used in the laboratory to separate uranium isotopes.
Hydrogen peroxide	H_2O_2	Hydrogen peroxide is used in the manufacture of many chemical compounds and as a bleaching agent for textiles. It is also used as an antiseptic and skin cleanser.
Magnesium sulfate	$MgSO_4$	Magnesium sulfate is used in medicine and in industry. In its powder form, the compound is known as Epsom salt, which was formerly used as a laxative.
Methane	CH_4	Methane is the main component in natural gas. It is an important industrial compound.
Potassium nitrate	KNO_3	Potassium nitrate is used as a fertilizer, in medicine, and in making gunpowder.
Sodium chloride	NaCl	Sodium chloride, or salt, is necessary for good health. Human blood contains salt, and body cells must have salt to function properly.
Sodium hydroxide	NaOH	Sodium hydroxide, or caustic soda, is widely used in the manufacture of aluminum, industrial chemicals, rayon, paper, and soap. It is also used in petroleum refining.
Water	H_2O	Water is the most common substance on Earth. It covers more than 70 percent of the Earth's surface and fills the air. All living things consist mostly of water.

Mixtures

Many substances consist of combinations of compounds. These substances are called mixtures. Unlike compounds, mixtures vary in composition from sample to sample. For example, spaghetti sauce is a mixture. Some samples of it may be composed of more tomato, some may have more spices, and others may have more water. However, they are all spaghetti sauce.

There are two basic types of chemical mixtures, solutions and suspensions. A solution is a mixture of two or more individual substances that cannot be separated by a mechanical means, such as filtration. A suspension is a mixture whose substances can be separated by filtration. Also, it is possible to recognize a suspension as a combination of two different substances. The different substances in tomato sauce, for example, can be recognized as separate from each other. A solution generally appears as one substance.

Solutions

Solutions occur in three forms. There are liquid solutions, solid solutions, and gaseous solutions.

LIQUID SOLUTIONS are formed when a solid, gas, or liquid is dissolved in a liquid. Examples include water mixed with alcohol, and sugar dissolved in tea. Two liquids that have the ability to form a solution are described as *miscible*. This ability depends on the chemical properties of the liquids and on physical conditions such as temperature and atmospheric pressure. Some liquid mixtures are more miscible than others. Water and alcohol are completely miscible because any amount of the two substances produces a solu-

Sugar dissolved in coffee is an everyday example of a liquid solution.

tion. Oil and water, on the other hand, are not miscible because one will not dissolve in the other.

Gases and solids that dissolve in liquid are described as *soluble*. The substance that is dissolved is called the *solute,* and the substance that dissolves it is the *solvent.* Water is the most common solvent. Other common solvents include acetone and alcohol. In most cases, a solvent and the substance it dissolves have similar molecular structure. For instance, oil dissolves in gasoline.

A given volume of solvent at a particular temperature can dissolve only a certain amount of solute. For example, a particular amount of water can dissolve only a certain amount of salt. Any additional salt remains undissolved in the water. A substance's ability to dissolve in another is called its *solubility*. The solubility of most solids depends on the chemical properties of the substances and on the temperature of the liquid solution. For gases, solubility also depends on pressure.

Solvents have many industrial and scientific applications. They are used in the production of cleaning fluids and such coatings as inks and paints. Solvents are also important in the manufacture of nylon, polyethylene, and many other synthetic fibers.

SOLID SOLUTIONS usually occur as solid forms of liquid solutions. A mixture of melted copper and zinc, for example, is a liquid solution that cools to form brass, a solid solution. When melted silver and copper are mixed and cooled, another solid solution—sterling silver—is produced.

A solid solution usually forms from a liquid solution that has hardened. Zinc and copper melted together and cooled form brass, a solid solution used to make musical instruments, household fixtures, and many other objects.

GASEOUS SOLUTIONS result from the mixture of gases. Air, for instance, is a mixture of nitrogen and oxygen, plus smaller amounts of argon and carbon dioxide. Gaseous solutions are completely miscible—any amount of one gas in a solution can dissolve in any amount of the other. Physical conditions do not affect the ability of gases to form a solution.

Suspensions

The chemical definition of a suspension is a mixture in which the particles of a substance separate from a liquid or gas slowly. These particles consist of many atoms or molecules, so that they can generally be visually recognized. The particles can be thought of as "floating" in the mixture.

There are several types of suspensions. They include: (1) a solid in a gas, such as dust and smoke; (2) a liquid in a gas, such as fog and aerosols; (3) a solid in a liquid, such as muddy or soapy water; (4) a gas in a liquid, such as foam; and (5) a liquid in a liquid, such as latex or water-based paints.

Colloids are suspensions that contain extremely small particles. The particles in most colloids can only be seen through an electron microscope. An example of a common colloid is homogenized milk, which has tiny particles of suspended fat. Colloids also include such familiar products as paint and ink. Blood and many other fluids in living things are also colloids.

The Chemistry of Pollution

When you hear the word pollution, images of smoggy yellow skylines or dead fish clogging an oily river may come to mind. These kinds of pollution are obvious—your nose and eyes tell you there's a problem. Other kinds of pollution, such as acid rain and the depletion of the ozone layer, are not so easy to see and their effects may take years to appear.

What all these kinds of pollution have in common—besides the damage they do to the planet—is that they all result from chemicals. Some chemical substances directly harm the environment. Highly toxic heavy metals, including mercury, zinc, and lead, are produced by factories and coal-burning power plants. Radioactive substances, certain fertilizers, petroleum products, and pesticides are poisonous to animals, plants, and people.

Other types of chemicals damage the environment when they undergo reactions that result in the production of new and harmful substances. The process that results in acid rain, for example, begins when fuel is burned to operate factories, produce electricity in coal-burning power plants, and power automobiles. This combustion produces sulfur dioxide (SO_2), a compound of sulfur and oxygen, and nitrogen oxides, which are compounds of nitrogen and oxygen. When water vapor (H_2O) in the air reacts with these compounds, sulfuric acid (H_2SO_4) and nitric acid (HNO_3) are formed. These

Industrial exhaust reacts with water vapor to produce acid rain like the artificially created acid raindrop at the top left. The deterioration of this statue at the Acropolis in Athens is believed to be caused by acid rain.

weak acids may fall to the ground with rain or snow, killing fish and trees and even damaging stone buildings.

Smog is a serious form of air pollution created mainly by cars and other vehicles. Their exhaust introduces nitrogen oxides as well as hydrocarbons into the air. When activated by sunlight, these compounds undergo a photochemical reaction that produces gases called *oxidants*. One such oxidant, ozone (O_3), forms the chief component in smog. Ozone that is near ground level in smog can irritate people's eyes, noses, and throats and damage lungs.

However, ozone occurs naturally high in the atmosphere. At this level, the ozone forms a layer that actually shields the Earth's surface against the sun's ultraviolet radiation, which can be harmful to forms of life, including humans. Chemicals that break down this protective layer of ozone in the upper atmosphere are one of the most serious causes of pollution today.

These ozone-depleting chemicals are gases called *chlorofluorocarbons* (*CFC's*). Atoms of chlorine, fluorine, and carbon make up CFC molecules. CFC's are commonly used in industry, refrigeration, and air-conditioning systems. Because CFC's are stable gases, they can escape into the upper atmosphere. There, ultraviolet radiation from the sun breaks down CFC molecules, freeing the chlorine atoms from them. A free chlorine atom may in turn react with an ozone molecule, stealing one of its three oxygen atoms. The chlorine atom and the oxygen atom combine to form one molecule of chlorine monoxide (ClO). The remaining two oxygen atoms from the original ozone molecule form one molecule of oxygen gas (O_2). The resulting chlorine monoxide can also act to break down even more ozone. The result is far fewer ozone molecules in the upper atmosphere. In fact, scientists estimate that one chlorine atom can destroy as many as 100,000 ozone molecules.

In June 1990, the world's industrial nations agreed to halt all production of CFC's by the year 2000. Some countries have already limited production. But CFC's can remain in the atmosphere for more than 100 years before they are broken down naturally and the chlorine can wash out of the atmosphere as hydrochloric acid in rain. So even if all CFC production stopped immediately, the threat of ozone depletion would continue for decades.

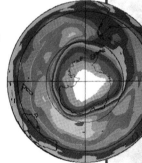

The ozone levels in the upper atmosphere above Antarctica are shown in this computer image of a measurement taken in October 1991. The lowest ozone concentrations appear as pink and white areas.

How chlorofluorocarbons destroy ozone

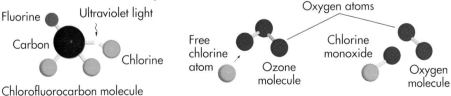

Fluorine

Carbon

Ultraviolet light

Chlorine

Chlorofluorocarbon molecule

Free chlorine atom

Ozone molecule

Oxygen atoms

Chlorine monoxide

Oxygen molecule

Ultraviolet radiation breaks chlorine atoms free from the CFC molecule.

A free chlorine atom steals one of an ozone molecule's oxygen atoms.

Oxygen and chlorine combine to form chlorine monoxide. An oxygen molecule remains.

CHAPTER

3

The Practice of Chemistry

Optical fibers used for fiber-optic communications were developed by chemists.

For many centuries, people have relied on their understanding of chemical processes to make useful products such as glass and medicines. But since the late 1800's, the influence of chemistry has exploded. Today, it touches every aspect of modern life.

Modern transportation needs synthetic rubber, refined metals, and high-energy fuels. Cardiovascular drugs and other medicines, as well as techniques such as gene-splicing, help doctors save lives. Paints, alloys, cements, glasses, plastics, and ceramics are used in construction. All these products and techniques—and countless others—depend on the work of chemists in their laboratories.

Branches of chemistry

Chemists study substances differently according to the questions they want to answer. Many chemists concentrate on special groups of substances, such as organic compounds. Some chemists specialize in analyzing substances to identify the elements and compounds they consist of. Some study chemical changes. Others work to create new substances or make synthetic forms of rare but useful natural materials. Still others apply their knowledge of chemistry in search of ways to use substances and chemical processes in agriculture, industry, medicine, and other fields. Each kind of chemist follows a different branch of chemistry.

Organic chemistry

Chemists who study compounds that contain carbon atoms are involved in organic chemistry. Because carbon atoms can form chemical bonds in many different ways, many kinds of carbon-containing compounds are possible. In fact, scientists have identified several million organic compounds.

Many simple organic compounds are obtained from plants and animals. For example, ethanol is formed by the fermentation of fruits, grains, and vegetables. Petroleum and natural gas consist of hydrocarbons from the remains of marine organisms that lived millions of years ago. Other organic compounds present in living matter include proteins, carbohydrates, lipids, and nucleic acids. All these fundamental groups of substances found in living organisms are based on carbon-atom chemistry. (See "The chemistry of life" in Chapter 9.)

● **hydrocarbon:** *the name used to refer to any organic compound that contains only carbon and hydrogen. All organic compounds are related essentially to hydrocarbons.*

Hydrocarbons form the basis for compounds used to make many types of cosmetics, including theatrical makeup like this girl is wearing.

● **urea:** *a compound consisting of ammonia and carbon dioxide that is produced in the bodies of humans and animals and is present in urine.*

At one time, scientists believed they could obtain carbon-containing compounds only from living sources. Then in 1928, the German chemist Friedrich Wöhler prepared the organic compound urea in his laboratory. Since that time, scientists have discovered numerous ways of making organic compounds from both organic and inorganic materials, and many new organic compounds have been produced in the laboratory, including medicines and polymers used in making plastics, synthetic fabrics, and paints.

Inorganic chemistry

The branch of chemistry involved with any chemical substance that does not have a carbon-to-carbon bond—that is, not an organic compound—is called inorganic chemistry. Most of the elements in the periodic table can react with one another to produce millions of compounds, most of which have never been produced. Inorganic chemists make these new compounds, determine the arrangements of atoms within them, and study how these compounds react with one another.

In industry, inorganic chemists work to develop useful and even life-saving materials. These materials include glass fibers that transmit telephone messages with light, ceramics that lose their electric resistance and become superconductors when cooled, and compounds that stop the growth of cancer cells.

Biochemistry

Biochemists study the chemical processes that take place in living things. Many common elements, including carbon, hydrogen, nitrogen, and oxygen, are present in chemical compounds in the cells of living things. Biochemists try to determine the structures and functions of such compounds.

All organisms contain the organic compounds carbohydrates, proteins, lipids, and nucleic acids. The molecules of these compounds help form cell structures and enable cells to function. Some inorganic substances, such as minerals and water, also play a part in a living cell's growth and maintenance.

Biochemical research covers a variety of life processes. Some biochemists study the large protein molecules called enzymes, which control the speed of chemical reactions in living matter. The enzymes of the human body aid in digestion and muscle contraction, for example. Biochemists identify these enzyme molecules and investigate the means by which they control the chemical reactions involved in these vital processes.

Biochemical research has made it possible to create genetically engineered organisms with particular traits, like these plum-tree seedlings, for use in agriculture, medicine, and research.

Other biochemists research chemical substances that help regulate metabolism. They also study the hormones produced in humans and other organisms. Hormones are chemical messengers that affect many body functions, such as growth and reproduction.

Through the study of the nucleic acid called DNA (deoxyribonucleic acid), biochemists have helped explain the molecular basis of the principles of genetics. Molecules of DNA are present in the threadlike structures in cells called chromosomes. These molecules carry information from one generation of cells to the next. Biochemists have used their knowledge of DNA in a field called genetic engineering to create new proteins and even change the genetic makeup of organisms. (See "Genetics" in Chapter 10.)

Biochemical research has broadened scientific knowledge in many other fields of biology and medicine. Our knowledge of enzymes, for example, aids doctors in diagnosing certain diseases of the bones and liver. Biochemistry also has contributed to the discovery of some antibiotics, which are drugs that destroy disease-causing bacteria. In addition, research in biochemistry has benefited agriculture. Farmers and agricultural researchers have used the findings of research on plants to develop crops of high quality and yield.

Analytical chemistry

Analytical chemists determine the properties of chemical substances and the structure and composition of compounds and mixtures. Much of the science of modern chemistry is built on the results obtained from chemical analyses. Many of chemistry's important applications, whether in helping solve a murder case or testing for lake pollution, rely on the work of analytical chemists.

The principles of analytical chemistry can be applied to many activities, including the discovery of new formulas for perfumes, *below.*

Forensic chemists examine chemical clues found at crime scenes to help in the detection of crime and the prosecution of criminals.

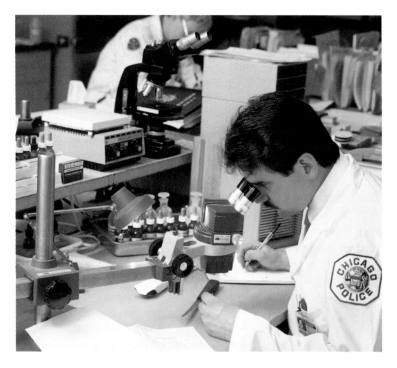

Historically, analytical chemists have performed two types of analysis on a given substance. *Qualitative analysis* identifies the various types of elements and compounds that are present in a substance. *Quantitative analysis* measures the amounts of the different chemicals in a substance. Today, analytical chemists may also study the physical structure and chemical properties of a substance.

Chemical analysis plays a major role in helping maintain high standards for the substances you eat and drink. Food and drug analysis is a specialized field. The analytical chemist often has to deal with complex mixtures of natural products—those made from fruits, cereals, or animals, for example—as well as with synthetic compounds. Many chemicals are added to foods as preservatives, colorants, flavors, emulsifiers (agents that allow liquids to remain mixed), and humectants (moistening agents). Regular analysis ensures that the proper additives in the correct amounts are used. It also is able to detect minute amounts of chemical impurities in food and drugs.

Chemical analysis also plays an important part in the diagnosis of medical conditions. Such clinical analysis, for example, can detect glucose in blood or urine, revealing whether a person is diabetic.

An area of growing importance in chemical analysis is in the detection of crime and the prosecution of criminal cases. This specialized field is known as *forensic chemistry*. The forensic chemist may be able to tell, for example, whether a fire was arson by analyzing ashes and debris for the presence of kerosene, gasoline, or some other inflammable substance. Identifying glass or clothing fragments, the chemical nature of paint flakes, the composition of inks, and hair and blood samples may all produce evidence of guilt or innocence. Forensic chemists also use a technique called *genetic finger-printing* to identify people according to their DNA.

One of the major uses of chemical analysis is in quality control of products, including cosmetics, household cleaners, paints, and metals used to make cars. A chemical analyst can ensure that the correct amounts of chemicals have been mixed. Likewise, pollution control uses chemical analysis to detect pollutants in the air and water around you.

Physical chemistry

Physical chemistry studies the general rules and principles that govern the chemical and physical properties of matter. A physical chemist is primarily concerned with three things: (1) the molecular structure of a substance, (2) whether a particular chemical reaction will occur, and (3) how fast and by what mechanism a reaction will occur. The physical chemist interprets these chemical processes in terms of the physical properties of matter, such as mass, and energy. A field of physical chemistry that is a promising area of research today is *surface chemistry*—the study of the surface properties of chemical compounds. Chemists have learned that surface characteristics are responsible for the ability of catalysts to speed up chemical reactions.

Electrochemistry

A chemist who deals with chemical reactions that involve electricity is an electrochemist. Such electrochemical reactions are used to produce chemicals and electricity as well as to refinish and plate metals.

Some electrochemical processes produce electricity from chemical changes. For example, a series of reactions among the chemicals in a battery produces an electric current. Other electrochemical processes use electricity to produce chemical changes. In a process called *electrolysis*, for example, an electric current is passed through a chemical solution to separate certain elements from the solution. Manufacturers use electrolysis to produce chlorine by passing electricity through salt water. The corrosion of metals is a naturally occurring electrolytic process. Electrochemists study corrosion to develop ways to protect metals.

Photochemistry

Photochemists deal with chemical reactions that result when molecules absorb light. A molecule changes photochemically only if it absorbs the light, not if the light merely passes through it or is reflected by it.

Photochemical reactions are part of many natural processes. In photosynthesis, for example, a green plant converts light energy into chemical energy by absorbing sunlight. The plant uses this light energy to make food out of carbon dioxide and water. (See Chapter 11 for detailed information on photosynthesis.)

Many industrial processes also involve photochemical changes. In photography, for example, some of the silver salts in photographic film absorb light when a picture is taken. The absorbed light chemically changes these salts. When the film is developed, the changed salts produce dark images on the negative.

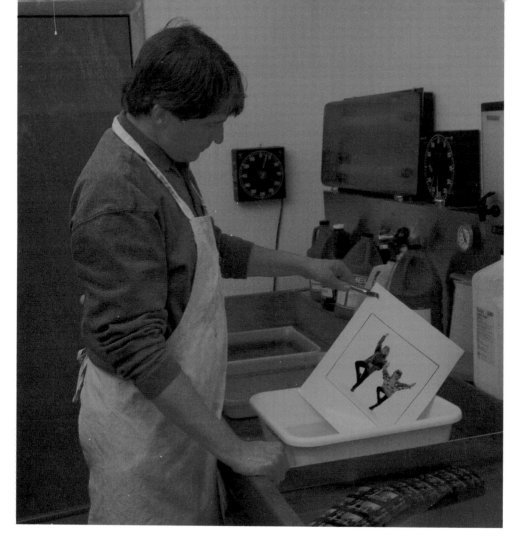

Developing photographs is a familiar application for the principles of photochemistry.

Many photochemists today are involved in researching and developing technological uses for solar energy. Some seek ways to imitate the process of photosynthesis with artificially created molecules. These chemists hope to convert sunlight into electricity more efficiently. Other photochemists study ways to use sunlight to produce such fuels as hydrogen gas and methanol. They are now working to develop a chemical cell that would use the energy of sunlight to break up water molecules into oxygen and hydrogen. The hydrogen that is produced could then be used as fuel. Such cells may one day provide a valuable source of energy.

Chemistry equipment

Chemists use a wide variety of tools and techniques in their research. Specialized instruments and computers help them make accurate measurements. In the same way, chemistry students use particular pieces of equipment as they work.

Basic tools

The following is a list of equipment likely to be found in a high school chemistry laboratory. These tools and techniques—as well as many others—help students explore the composition and structure of substances. In addition to the tools listed below, general supplies such as bowls, corks, glass tubing, hot pads, magnifying glasses, matches, measuring spoons, mirrors, stirring rods, thermometers, and wire are also used extensively in most chemistry laboratories.

Balance

• **Balance.** A balance is a device used to weigh substances. A simple balance consists of a horizontal bar balanced on a thin edge of metal, with a pan suspended on each end of the bar. An old-fashioned weighing scale is an example of this kind of balance.

• **Beakers** are cylindrical glass containers, with a lip for pouring. Beakers often are used for measuring liquids in a laboratory.

• **Bunsen burners** provide an intensely hot flame for heating a solution or finding its boiling point, which is a physical property of a substance. A Bunsen burner consists of a metal tube on a stand and a long rubber hose that connects the tube to a gas jet.

• **Burettes** are used for accurately measuring small amounts of a liquid or gas. A burette is a graduated glass tube, usually with a tap at the bottom.

• **Clamps** are used for holding things together. They usually have opposite sides or parts that can be screwed together to hold something.

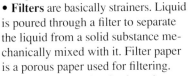

Beaker

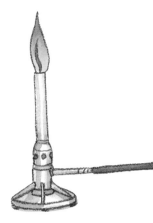

Bunsen burner

• **Distillation condensers** are used in the process of heating a liquid to change it into a gas, and cooling a gas to change it into a liquid.

• **Filters** are basically strainers. Liquid is poured through a filter to separate the liquid from a solid substance mechanically mixed with it. Filter paper is a porous paper used for filtering.

• **Flasks** are thin, bottle-shaped containers often used in laboratories for heating liquids.

• **Funnels** are tapered tubes with wide, cone-shaped mouths. A chemist uses a funnel to pour a substance, such as a liquid or a solid that flows easily, from one container into another.

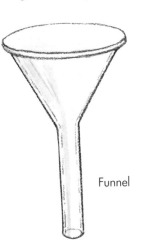

Funnel

Goggles

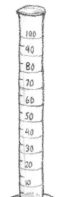
Graduated cylinder

• **Goggles** are a form of eye protection that chemists often wear during experiments or other laboratory procedures.

• **Graduated cylinder**. A graduated cylinder is a container that is open at one end and has markings along its height. Chemists use graduated cylinders to measure the volume of liquids.

• **Hydrometers** are used for finding the density of liquids. A hydrometer usually consists of a glass tube with a weight in the bottom. A chemist measuring the density of a liquid puts the hydrometer in the liquid, then measures its density against a scale marked on the side of the tube.

• **Litmus paper** reacts with a liquid to show whether it is a base or an acid. Blue litmus paper turns red in an acid; red litmus paper turns blue in a base.

• **Magnets** often are used in experiments examining the phenomenon of magnetism or the connection between electricity and magnetism.

• **Medicine droppers** are useful in a laboratory to add one substance slowly to another.

• **Metric rulers and scales**. Science uses the metric system of measurement, so laboratories are equipped with metric measuring devices.

Magnet

• **Pipette**. A pipette is a slender pipe or tube used for transferring or measuring small quantities of liquids or gases. The most common type of pipette is a small glass tube that widens into a bulb at the middle, in which liquid can be retained when the top end is closed with a stopper or a finger.

• **Prisms**, often made of glass, are used to separate white light passing through them into the colors of the rainbow.

• **Ring supports** hold flasks and test tubes. A ring support is attached to a support stand and can be adjusted to different heights.

Test tube

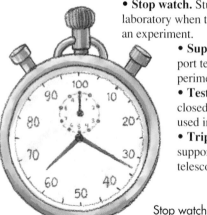
Stop watch

• **Stop watch.** Students use a stop watch in the laboratory when timing is an important part of an experiment.

• **Support stands** are used to support test tubes or flasks for many experiments.

• **Test tubes** are thin glass tubes closed at one end. Test tubes are used in many experiments.

• **Tripod.** A tripod is a three-legged support for an instrument, such as a telescope.

• **Wash bottle.** A typical wash bottle is a small squeeze bottle used to squirt water to rinse solids from the sides of a flask.
• **Watch glasses** are shallow glass dishes used to observe the formation of crystals from a solution and other processes.
• **Wire gauze** is a piece of metal screenlike material placed on a ring stand over a Bunsen burner. The wire gauze supports a beaker when heating substances.

Research devices
A well-equipped high school laboratory will have some or all of the following devices. These devices give greater precision and accuracy to the scientific experimentation done in a high school laboratory.

CALORIMETER. This device is used for measuring the amount of heat given off by or present in a substance or the heat released during chemical reactions. Most calorimeters consist of a can inside another can. The temperature of water in the inner can changes depending on the energy released in the reaction occuring in the outer can. This temperature change can then be measured with a thermometer.

MELTING POINT APPARATUS is a device that measures the temperature at which a solid melts. It consists of an electrically heated tube into which the sample is placed. The chemist puts the tube into the instrument, observes the point at which the substance melts, and records the temperature.

Centrifuge

OSMOMETER. Chemists use an osmometer to measure the pressure exerted by a dissolved material in a solution on a semipermeable membrane separating the solution from another solution or from water. A typical osmometer consists of a bag made of animal tissue, which is connected to a gauge that measures the pressure inside the bag and compares that pressure to a standard equal to one atmosphere.

PH METER is an instrument for measuring the acidity or alkalinity of a solution in terms of a relative concentration of hydrogen ions in the solution. It generally consists of an electrode that is placed in a sample to be tested. A digital display shows the pH of the solution in units 1 through 14.

SPECTROPHOTOMETER is used to measure the concentration of an unknown solution by comparing it to known standards. It allows a chemist to make a precise comparison between solutions based on the intensity of their color.

Specialized equipment

Chemists who work in universities or in industry often perform complex experiments and carry on highly specialized research. They need special devices that are seldom available in high school laboratories.

CENTRIFUGE. A centrifuge is used to separate two liquids mixed together or solid particles that are mixed in a liquid. A typical centrifuge consists of a large wheel connected to an electric motor. The mixtures to be separated are balanced in containers on each side of the wheel. When the motor is turned on, the wheel rotates rapidly and the containers swing out from the center. The heavier liquid or the solid particles move to the bottom of the container, leaving the lighter substances on top.

MASS SPECTROMETER. Chemists use a mass spectrometer to separate ionized atoms or molecules according to their mass and electric charge. Mass

Mass spectrometer

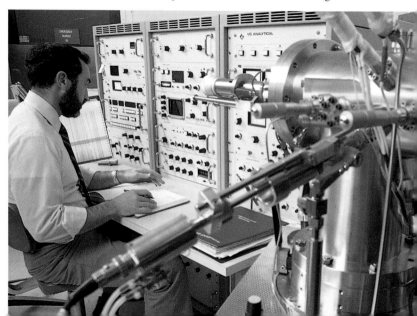

spectrometry gives chemists an effective means of identifying elements, isotopes, and molecules. Chemists also use this technique to determine the chemical composition and structure of more complex substances.

In the basic type of mass spectrometer, a sample of a substance is placed in a vacuum. Electrons bombard the sample, producing ions. Next, an electric field accelerates the ions, which then pass through a magnetic field. The magnetic field separates the ions according to their mass and charge because it deflects lighter ions more than heavier ions. The ions strike a deflector and form a pattern called a mass spectrum.

● **vacuum:** *a space with no matter in it.*

The *mass spectrum* of a compound consists of a series of peaks that differ in height. Compounds can be identified from their mass spectra by the shape and distribution of the various peaks. Most mass spectrometers are combined with a computer that stores, manipulates, and interprets the data.

SPECTROMETER. A spectrometer spreads light into a spectrum of different colors so that scientists can examine it. The atoms or molecules of all substances give off a unique pattern of light when heated. Therefore, chemists can identify a substance or determine its chemical composition by analyzing its light spectrum.

Scientists use spectrometers to examine many different substances. For example, spectrometers may identify chemical substances found at the scene of a crime, detect pollutants in water, or find impurities in steel.

In a typical spectrometer, light enters through a narrow entrance slit and passes through a collimating lens. The collimating lens turns the light into a beam of parallel light rays. The parallel light then travels through a prism, which breaks the light into different colors. A lens focuses the light on an exit slit. Only one color can pass through this slit at a time. To bring the other colors to the exit slit, the prism must be rotated. A circular scale records the angle of the prism. Scientists use this angle to find the light's wavelength. Once they know the light's wavelength, scientists can identify the substance. Some spectrometers have a photomultiplier tube, which measures the brightness of light leaving the slit.

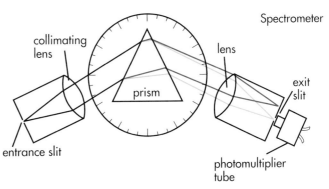

Spectrometer

collimating lens

lens

exit slit

prism

entrance slit

photomultiplier tube

ONE-OF-A-KIND INSTRUMENTS. Some instruments are so specialized that there may be only one of them in the entire world. The intense pulse neutron source and the Argonne-Tandem Linear Accelerator (ATLAS) are two such devices. They help chemists study the basic structure of matter and how molecules and atoms interact to produce specialized types of materials, such as superconducting materials.

Homestyle Chemistry Experiments

You don't need a fully equipped laboratory to "do" chemistry. With just some household items, you can perform the following simple chemical procedures.

Make your own litmus paper

Litmus paper quickly tells you whether a substance is an acid or a base. Blue litmus paper turns red when dipped into an acid. Red litmus paper turns blue when it comes in contact with a base. Litmus paper will show no change of color in a neutral solution, which is neither basic nor acidic.

Did you know you can make your own litmus paper at home, using flowers, vegetables, or fruits? This is because many plants contain natural indicators—that is, substances that change color in the presence of a base or acid. In fact, litmus paper itself changes color because it is impregnated with litmus, a substance obtained from lichens.

For this experiment you'll need a handful of blueberries, shredded red cabbage leaves, water, two saucepans, and paper towels. To make litmus paper that will turn blue in a base, put the blueberries into one saucepan and just cover with water. Boil until the water is dark red. Strain and let the liquid cool. Dip paper towels into the liquid and let them dry. Cut into strips. These strips of paper will act in the same way as red litmus paper—they will turn blue when they come in contact with a base.

To make litmus paper that will turn red in an acid, follow the above procedure using shredded red cabbage leaves instead of blueberries. The strips of paper you end up with will act in the same way as blue litmus paper—they will turn red when they come in contact with an acid.

Try making other indicators using violet petals or red rose petals, beets, carrot peels, cherries, or radish peels. How do they react to lemon juice (an acid)? How do they react to soap (a base)? What can these indicators teach you about other household substances?

Finding starch in foods

In this experiment, you will test for a substance. First, take a small piece of each of the following foods separately: an apple, a potato, oatmeal, bread, crumbled cornflakes, and cheese. Then place each food sample on a sheet of wax paper and add a few drops of iodine solution from a medicine dropper. (You can buy iodine at the pharmacy.) If the food turns bluish-black, it contains starch; if it remains rusty brown, it does not. Foods with large concentrations of starch turn the darkest; those with small amounts turn light blue. Chemists believe this happens because starch captures iodine in its long, spiral-shaped molecules. The spiral molecules with the iodine trapped inside them appear blue. Record your data and findings for each food.

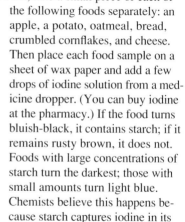

Tarnishing and polishing silver

For this experiment, you need a hard-boiled egg, a silver spoon, a saucepan, aluminum foil, baking soda, salt, water, oven mitts, tongs, and a clean cloth.

Remove the eggshell and egg white from the yolk. Put the yolk on a silver spoon, and leave for at least one hour. When you return, look at the spoon. What has happened to it? It has tarnished where the yolk touched it. That happened because sulfur in the egg yolk combined with silver in the spoon to create the compound silver sulfide (Ag_2S). This compound is what you see as tarnish.

Now, line the inside of the pan with aluminum foil, shiny side up. Put the spoon in the saucepan and cover it with several inches of water.

Add a teaspoon of baking soda and a teaspoon of salt. Boil for about 10 minutes. Remove from the heat and, using oven gloves and tongs, take the spoon out of the water. Rub the spoon with a clean cloth. The tarnish should wipe off easily.

This occurs because an electrochemical reaction took place while the water was boiling. During the reaction, the baking-soda-and-salt solution acted as an electrolyte. That is, while dissolved in water, it conducted an electric current that helped break up the silver sulfide into silver ions and sulfur ions. Some of the aluminum from the foil dissolved as ions as well. The sulfur ions were attracted to the surface of the aluminum foil, forming a dark film of aluminum sulfide. The silver ions in the silver sulfide returned to the surface of the spoon.

Separate the molecules in sugar

To separate the substances in a compound, you'll need a metal pie pan, some aluminum foil, and one of the burners on top of your stove.

Begin by putting a teaspoon of sugar on a square of foil in the pie pan. Place the pan on the burner and turn the heat on low. As the sugar heats, it first melts and then begins to boil. Bubbles form and pop over the boiling sugar.

Now, using a pot holder, place a cooled glass upside down over the bubbling sugar. Notice the clouds of steam that fill the glass. Carefully remove the glass and touch the inside with your finger. Water has formed inside the glass.

Once the sugar stops bubbling, turn off the burner and let the pan cool. Then examine the sugar—or what's left of it. Instead of the tiny, white grains you began with, you should now see a pile of dry, dark bubbles. What do you think this substance is?

It might help you to know the chemical formula for sugar: $C_{12}H_{22}O_{11}$. In other words, sugar is made of carbon, hydrogen, and oxygen atoms. When you heated the sugar, these components were separated. Some of the oxygen and hydrogen atoms combined to form water. (Remember the steam that formed when you held the glass over the boiling sugar?) The rest escaped into the air. Therefore, the black substance remaining on the pie pan must be carbon. If you like, use another simple chemist's tool—a magnifying glass—to examine the carbon. What does it look like?

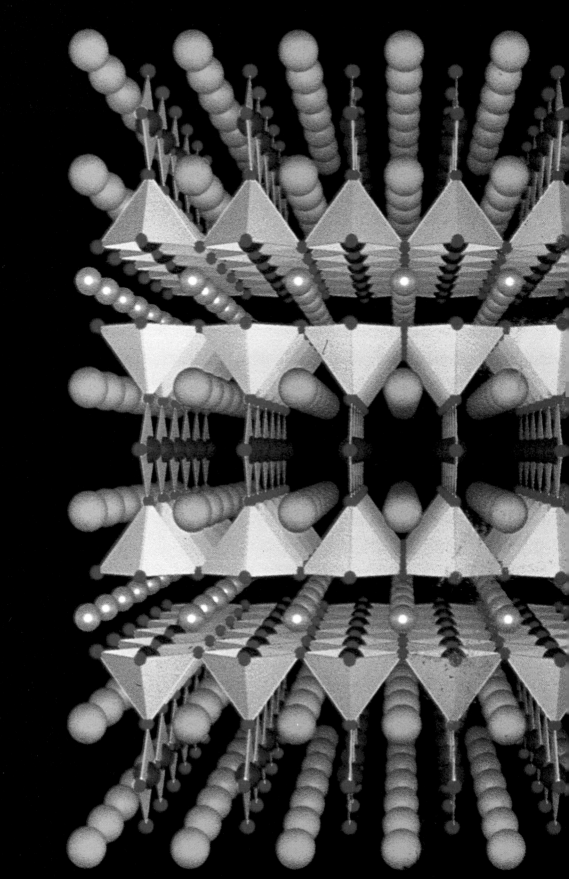

Physics

- **Mechanics: Force and Motion**

- **Nature of the Atom**

- **States of Matter**

- **Energy**

- **Time and Relativity**

CHAPTER

4

Mechanics:
Force and Motion

Physics is a science that investigates how things work. Physics studies matter, force, and energy: what they are and how they affect one another. Mechanics is the branch of physics that studies bodies in motion and at rest. Mechanics examines the effects of forces on bodies, which are stated in Newton's three laws of motion. Scientists apply the principles of mechanics in many ways: to design tiny computer parts and huge dams, to predict the movements of celestial bodies, to study the motion of atomic particles, and much more.

A mechanical clock works because energy stored in a coiled spring is released slowly, moving its parts.

Basic concepts of physics

The basic concepts of physics include physical quantities, measurements, and vectors. The laws of physics are based on changes that physicists observe in certain *basic* physical quantities, such as time, mass, length or distance, electrical charge, temperature, brightness, and amount of a substance. Mechanics uses three of the basic quantities—time, mass, and distance—to define *derived* quantities, such as velocity, acceleration, force, energy, work, power, and momentum. These basic and derived quantities are discussed in greater depth later in this chapter.

Every quantity in physics—such as mass, energy, or power—has size or magnitude. The size or "how much" of a quantity is known as its *scalar* property, because some type of scale is required to measure it.

Scales are based on a recognized *standard unit of measure*. In mechanics, the three standard units are *meter* (m) for distance, *kilogram* (kg) for mass, and *seconds* (s) for time. Each standard unit has been defined carefully by an international organization based in France. All scientific instruments that measure physical quantities do so in these units. Measurements are expressed in numbers and units. For example, we might speak of a runner weighing 70 kilograms running a distance of 100 meters in a time of 10 seconds. The unit (kilogram, meter, and second) identifies the type of quantity being measured (mass, distance, and time). The number gives the size of the quantity.

Despite official international acceptance of these standard units, engineers in the United States and some former British colonies may use an old British system of measurement. This system uses foot-pound-second units of measurement.

Some quantities require an added property of *direction* to describe them fully. For example, when plotting the location of a weather balloon, a scientist must specify its position as 30 degrees northeast and 20 miles away from the weather station. A quantity described by both size and direction in this way is called a *vector quantity*.

Mass

In physics, mass and matter are related but different. *Matter* is the physical "stuff" of nature, the molecules and atoms of solids, liquids, and gases. *Mass* is the amount of matter in a substance. A train, for example, has more mass than an automobile. Mass usually is measured in kilograms.

Mass has two special properties—inertia and gravity. An understanding of these two properties is essential to understanding force and Newton's three laws of motion.

The mass, or amount of matter, of these popcorn kernels remained the same before and after they were popped. Popping caused that mass to extend over a greater area, increasing the kernels' volume but not the mass itself.

INERTIA is an object's tendency to resist change in its motion. Because of inertia, a motionless object stays still unless some force makes it move. Inertia also makes a moving object continue in the same direction at a constant speed unless some force changes its motion. The more mass an object has, the greater its inertia. Forces that change an object's motion first must overcome the *inertial mass* of the object. The greater the force required to move, stop, or deflect a body, the greater its mass or inertia. This is the reason it takes more force to stop a locomotive than to stop an automobile, even if both are moving at the same speed.

GRAVITY is the property of mass that attracts it to other masses. For example, objects that are near or on the Earth are pulled toward it. Scientists usually refer to the mutual attraction between any two bodies as *gravitation*. The force exerted by the Earth on objects is called gravity, or force of gravity. Gravity acts on objects at a distance and does not require contact. The force of gravity is discussed later in this chapter.

Force

Force in mechanics refers to the push or pull exerted on a body with mass. Because forces are applied in a particular direction (for instance, up or down), they are *vector quantities*.

Force can be exerted either by contact or at a distance. *Mechanical* forces act when one body touches another—for example, when two balls collide. *Action-at-a-distance* forces require no contact to influence an object. For example, Earth's gravity attracts the moon from a distance.

Force of gravity

Gravitation is the force of attraction that acts between objects because of their mass. The gravitational attraction that an object has for objects near it is called the force of gravity. In the 1600's, the English scientist and math-

Objects near the Earth are pulled toward it by the planet's gravitational attraction, or force of gravity. Sir Isaac Newton realized that the same force of gravity that pulls an apple from a tree could hold planets in their orbit around the Earth.

This astronaut's mass is the same in outer space as it was on Earth. Because the gravitational force acting on that mass has changed, however, so has the astronaut's weight.

ematician Sir Isaac Newton formulated the universal law of gravitation to explain how the planets move. In addition, the law showed that tides resulted from the unequal gravitational attraction of the moon and sun on Earth's oceans and large lakes.

Newton's law of universal gravitation states that the gravitational force between two masses is proportional (directly related) to the size of their masses. The larger the masses, the larger the gravitational force between the two objects. Also, the gravitational force is inversely (oppositely) proportional to the square of the distance between them. This means that if the distance between two objects doubles, the gravitational force between them decreases to one-fourth of its original value.

Weight

Weight is the force exerted on a mass by a planet's gravity. Mass is not the same as weight. An object's mass remains constant but its weight may change. An object's weight depends on (1) the distance between the object and the center of the planet, (2) its mass, and (3) the mass of the planet. An astronaut, for example, may weigh 180 pounds on Earth but only 30 pounds on the moon. Yet the astronaut's mass remains the same. Units used to measure weight include newtons, pounds, and kilograms.

Motion

Motion occurs when an object changes its location. Motion is relative rather than absolute. An object may be in motion in regard to another object, but standing still in regard to a third object. For example, if you are riding on a train and pass a person standing near the tracks, that person will see you and everyone else on the train as being in motion. But to you, the person sitting beside you on the train will be at rest.

The difference in motion between yourself and the object that you are looking at is called *apparent motion*. For example, if you are in a car and another car is moving slightly faster than yours, you will see the other car as being in a small apparent motion relative to your car. Your car becomes your *frame of reference*.

Kinematics

Kinematics is the study of an object's motion but not the forces acting on the object. For instance, kinematics describes the motion of the Earth around the sun while ignoring the gravitational force holding Earth in orbit.

Motion is relative— that is, it depends on your frame of reference. To the person standing on the sidewalk, both people on the bicycle are moving. To the child on the back of the bike, the cyclist stays in the same place but the person on the sidewalk slowly moves out of sight.

In kinematics, an object's movement is the path it follows along a line or trajectory curve during a specified time. Five basic types of movement are studied in kinematics. *Translation* or *linear motion* occurs along a line— for example, a jet taxiing down a straight runway. *Parabolic motion* follows a symmetrical, arched curve—for example, a fly ball hit into the air. *Circular motion* or *revolution* is motion around a central point—for example, the moon revolving around Earth. *Rotation* is the spinning of a body on its own axis—for example, the Earth rotating on its polar axis. *Oscillation* is a repeated back-and-forth motion across a center line or point—for example, a simple pendulum swinging.

In kinematics, only four quantities are required to describe motion: displacement, time, velocity, and acceleration.

DISPLACEMENT is a vector quantity involving both direction and distance. Displacement is measured in meters or feet. For example, two runners start out from the same point and run 100 meters in opposite directions, one east and one west. They are both 100 meters from their starting point, but their individual displacements are different: One is 100 meters east and the other is 100 meters west.

TIME is a scalar quantity measuring the duration of an event in seconds. Time is used to measure rates of change, or speed.

The velocity of these baseball players is different because they're moving in different directions. As one sprints forward and the other slows down, both are accelerating because their velocities are changing.

VELOCITY describes both the speed of a body and its direction. *Speed* describes how fast a body is moving. An object's average speed is the distance traveled divided by the time it takes to move this distance. The equation $v = d/t$ is used to find average speed. (In this equation, v stands for average speed, d stands for distance, and t stands for time.) An object's *instantaneous speed* is its speed at a particular moment. Speed often is measured in meters per second (m/s).

Velocity, however, describes an object's direction as well as its speed. For example, the speed of a northbound train might be 30 meters per second. Its velocity, however, would be 30 meters per second due north.

ACCELERATION describes how much an object's velocity changes in a period of time. It is measured in meters per second per second (m/s²) or feet per second per second (ft/s²). For instance, if a car travels 3 m/s in the first second, 6 m/s in the second second, and 9 m/s in the third second, the car is said to have a constant acceleration of 3 m/s². The velocity of the car has increased 3 m/s in each second.

When an object slows down, its velocity decreases. This change also is acceleration, sometimes called *negative acceleration* or *deceleration*. An object accelerates if its speed, direction, or both change. When the two runners move along a curved section of a race track, their velocity changes because their direction changes. This is true even if their speed remains constant. So, the runners have accelerated.

When both the speed and direction of an object are constant, its velocity is *uniform* and its acceleration is zero. If the speed or direction change, the velocity is *variable*. Acceleration also can be uniform or variable and expressed as either average or instantaneous.

The Physics of Driving

The principles of mechanics are in operation all around us, at all times. We walk, work, eat, and even sleep according to these principles. It is easy to overlook the influence of mechanics on everyday life, but observing how these laws commonly operate is one of the best ways to understand them. Sir Isaac Newton discovered the concept of universal force while spending some time alone in the country. Today, you can get a clear demonstration of the laws of mechanics by taking a ride in a car.

Getting started

Even before the engine starts, certain basic conditions influence your car. For example, it is not floating, as it would in space. But neither is it drawn into the Earth. This is because the force of gravity, which pulls your car toward the Earth, is equal to the normal force, or the force of the concrete resisting the pressure of the car.

Your car also is not moving. Newton's first law states that an object at rest will stay at rest unless a force moves it. This is known as the principle of inertia. Your car's inertia keeps it from moving because no significant force—such as an extremely powerful wind—is currently strong enough to move it.

Your ride begins after the engine starts, the gears fall into place, and the tires turn. You can thank Newton's third law of motion for that pleasurable feeling of progress. This law states that for each action there is an equal and opposite reaction. Your tires are pushing against the road, by way of friction. So the road, in turn, pushes back against your tires, propelling your car forward.

Soon your car reaches the speed limit, and the accelerator switches to cruise control. Your car now has a set velocity, which is its speed and direction. According to Newton's first law, your car's inertia would keep it at this velocity forever unless an outside force acted on it. Luckily, there are a number of outside forces. Air resistance, for example, drags across the entire surface of your car. Meanwhile, the tires slow the car in friction against the road. And if you travel up a hill, gravity draws backward against your car.

Taking a curve

As your car approaches a curve in the road, you know that Newton's first law says your car's inertia will try to keep it moving forward in a straight line. So how will you manage the turn? Newton's second law says that forces change the motion of objects. So your car will need an additional force to make the turn.

When a car turns, it actually is traveling around part of an imaginary circle. The force that compels an object to move in a circular path is called centripetal force. The main centripetal force that changes the motion of your car and allows it to turn is the friction of the tires. This friction, of course, is always present. But when your car's wheels turn, the force changes direction, swinging your car around the curve.

Several factors affect the way a car takes a curve. If the pavement is slick, the centripetal force—friction—is reduced, and your car may skid off the road. If your car is particularly heavy, it may have more difficulty making the turn. Newton's second law says that a heavier object requires more applied force to change its motion than a lighter object does. So a heavier car requires more friction to turn, especially at high speeds.

Highway engineers bank, or slant, roads to the inside of curves for these reasons. A banked road adds the normal force—the resistance of the road—to the force of friction,

As a car approaches a curve, its inertia will tend to keep it moving in a straight line. Centripetal force is needed to put the car on a circular path, or to change its linear velocity into angular velocity. The driver may feel pulled outward as the car turns; this "pull" sometimes is called centrifugal force.

increasing the centripetal force on your car and making it easier to complete the turn.

Coming to a stop

After you have completed the curve and your car has resumed its speed, you see a stop sign ahead. What happens next? You can figure that out by applying your understanding of mechanics. You know that to slow and eventually stop the car, the forces resisting your car's inertia must be increased. The brakes on your car will take care of that job. Brakes create additional friction against your wheels and provide the necessary force to stop your car.

You might notice that as your car slows, you feel pushed forward. This is because you and your car are separate bodies, with separate inertia. Your car's speed decreases, but your body continues at a constant speed. Fortunately, your car slows gradually. The friction of your legs against the seat and the restraint of your seat belt create forces that enable your body to come to rest comfortably. If the intersection is clear, you and your car can start the whole process over again.

Newton's three laws of motion

In the 1600's, Sir Isaac Newton proposed three laws of motion that revolutionized physics. Newton's laws express the relationship among force, mass, and acceleration. These laws explain why forces applied to matter can hold bodies at rest, set them in motion, and change their rate and direction of movement. Newton's laws describe the ideal motion of objects, without accounting for air resistance or other friction. Even so, scientists use these laws to describe a variety of motions, from balls bouncing to rockets lifting off.

Mechanics uses Newton's three laws of motion to study larger bodies that are either at rest or moving much slower than the speed of light. The motions and interactions of molecules, atoms, and atomic particles are described by the laws of *quantum mechanics* (see Chapter 5). The motion of bodies that travel near the speed of light is covered by *relativity theory* (see Chapter 8).

THE FIRST LAW states that a motionless object will remain at rest unless an outside force acts on it. Also, an object traveling in a straight line will continue to do so unless an outside force deflects or stops it. This tendency to remain at rest or moving in a uniform straight line is an object's inertia.

Mass affects an object's degree of inertia: The greater an object's mass, the harder it is to make the object move or to change its velocity. Therefore, unless force is applied, a motionless book on a table stays at rest and a speeding interplanetary probe moves in a straight line with constant velocity.

One force that commonly stops a moving object is *friction*. For example, if you push your chair back, it will not go on moving across the floor forever. Friction caused by the floor will stop the chair. An object that has no outside force acting on it is in *equilibrium.*

THE SECOND LAW describes how an object changes its velocity (speed, direction, or both) when force is applied to it. This law states that an object accelerates in the direction of the force. For example, if someone kicks a soccer ball toward the west, the ball will move toward the west.

Newton's second law also says that any change of motion depends on the magnitude of the force applied and the mass of the object. It takes less force to change

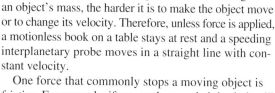

To demonstrate inertia, balance a coin on a card at the end of your finger. Without touching the coin, flick the card out from under it. The card will move because you applied force to it, but the coin will stay still because no force has been applied.

An object changes its velocity (in direction, speed, or both) when force is applied, and the amount of change depends on the amount of force. The harder a tennis player hits the ball, the faster it will return across the net.

the direction of an object with little mass than an object with much mass. A tennis player, for instance, applies force with a tennis racket to return a served ball (a small mass). The harder the player hits the ball (the more force applied), the faster it changes direction and increases speed (the greater the change in velocity or acceleration).

Newton's second law can be written as the equation $F = ma$, where F stands for applied force, m stands for mass, and a stands for acceleration. Force sometimes is measured in *newtons*. One newton is the amount of force required to make a 1-kilogram object accelerate 1 meter per second squared, or 1 kg-m/s².

THE THIRD LAW of motion states that for every action, there is an equal and opposite reaction. This law can be written as the equation $F = -F'$. In this equation, F and F' stand for forces that are equal and opposite. This means that all forces occur in pairs. These forces do not cancel each other out because they act on different bodies. One example is walking; a person's foot pushes against the ground (action), and the ground pushes back on the foot (reaction). In a rocket, exploding gases propel it forward (action), while the rocket pushes on the gas, ejecting the gas backward (reaction).

Statics and dynamics

Statics and dynamics are the branches of mechanics that study the effects of forces on bodies at rest or in motion. Statics deals with bodies at rest or moving at a constant speed in a constant direction. Such bodies are in equilibrium (that is, all forces acting on the body cancel out). For example, if you hold a telephone receiver against your ear, the force of gravity pulls the receiver down against your hands. But the receiver doesn't fall, because your hand pushes it up with equal force. The two forces balance out, and the receiver stays at rest against your ear.

Dynamics is the branch of mechanics that describes bodies that are not in equilibrium because of a force acting on them. This condition is covered by Newton's second law. The body's motion is nonuniform or variable because the force accelerates the body, changing its velocity either in speed, direction, or both. In our examples,

As the force of gravity pulls a parachute jumper down, the resistance of air pushes the parachute up.

the body is assumed to be rigid—this means it does not lose its shape under the forces that make it move.

One of the key concepts in dynamics is the effect of gravitational force, the chief force in the motion of satellites and planets. In the early 1600's, the Italian astonomer and physicist Galileo discovered that if air resistance did not exist, all masses would fall toward the Earth with the same acceleration, known as *g*. This *g* is a constant: *9.8 m/s² or 32 ft/s².*

Accelerated translational motion

● **center of gravity:**
*point in an object
where the force of
gravity appears to act.*

Accelerated translational motion occurs when force acts on a body's center of gravity, which changes its speed along a straight line.

VERTICAL ACCELERATED TRANSLATIONAL MOTION is illustrated by a ball thrown vertically into the air. On the way up, the velocity of the ball decreases (decelerates) because of the pull of gravity. At the highest point, the ball's velocity is zero. On the way down, the ball's velocity increases. The downward acceleration of the ball remains constant at *g = 9.8 m/s² or 32 ft/s².* This means that in each second of fall, the velocity of the ball will increase by about 10 m/s, although air resistance will slow it down somewhat.

FREE FALL AND WEIGHTLESSNESS occur when gravity is the only force operating on a body. Objects falling in Earth's atmosphere are never in a true state of free fall because another force, air resistance, also acts on them. Weightlessness occurs when no forces are supporting a body. In reality, the falling body does have weight, but the weight cannot be felt. For example, when you dive off a diving board, you feel as though you were weightless.

TERMINAL VELOCITY is the maximum velocity a falling body can attain before resistance of the medium through which it is falling balances the force of gravity. For example, a sky diver free falling before opening a parachute may reach a terminal velocity of about 200 mph (320 kph).

This ball picked up speed as it fell toward the ground, slowed as it climbed through the air, and came to a brief stop before falling again. These changes in velocity are characteristic of vertical accelerated translational motion.

ESCAPE VELOCITY is the minimum velocity necessary for a body projected vertically to escape gravitational pull. For example, an interplanetary probe leaving Earth must reach an upward velocity of about 11 km/s (7 miles/s or 25,000 mph) to reach outer space.

Projectile motion in a plane

Projectile motion results when an object is launched at an angle to the ground as the force of gravity tries to pull it down. A projectile is an object that moves freely through space after an initial push.

An example is the path of a fly ball hit at an angle to the ground. As the ball moves forward, it travels upward and then downward, along a *parabolic* path in a plane perpendicular to the ground. The trajectory, or path, the ball follows is a symmetrical, arched curve. The curve's high point lies midway between its point of departure and point of return to Earth. The ball's horizontal velocity is constant, but its vertical velocity varies because gravity is pulling it down. The horizontal distance the ball travels depends on the initial velocity and initial launch angle.

Circular motion

Circular motion occurs when an object moves in a circle around a central point. Examples of circular motion include a car driving around a curve in a road, a weight swinging around on a string, and a satellite in circular orbit around the Earth. In dynamics, circular motion is an example of nonequilibrium or accelerated motion because the object's direction changes even if its speed does not. According to Newton's second law, a force must be at work to cause this continuous change in the direction of motion.

This wagon wheel moving in a circle around a central point is an example of circular motion.

Oscillation

● **equilibrium point:**
point of rest.

Oscillation occurs when an object repeatedly moves back and forth across an *equilibrium point* or *line*. Common examples of oscillation are a metronome, a simple pendulum, and an object vibrating on a spring. Oscillation also is called *vibration*.

Because the object's velocity (either its speed or direction) varies as it moves, oscillation is a case of nonequilibrium or accelerated motion. The force acting on the body is called the *restoring force* because this force seeks to return the body to its equilibrium position.

● **potential energy:**
stored energy.
● **kinetic energy:**
energy of movement.

An oscillating object possesses potential and kinetic energy. For an object attached to a spring, for example, its *potential energy* depends on how far it is from the equilibrium point. When the object is moving, it possesses *kinetic energy* due to its velocity. The kinetic energy is greatest as the mass passes through the equilibrium point. Energy is discussed in more detail later in this chapter.

An oscillating object's *amplitude* is the distance the object travels from its equilibrium point. The *period* is the time it takes to complete one cycle, or move from its high point to its low point and return to its high point. The *frequency* is the number of cycles completed in a unit of time.

The person wielding this sledgehammer is doing work by swinging it downward—applying force in the same direction as the sledgehammer's motion.

Simple harmonic motion is an example of oscillation. An object on a vertical spring can be set into simple harmonic motion by pulling the mass down a distance and letting go. Another example of simple harmonic motion is the motion of vibrating strings on a musical instrument.

Work and energy

Force applied to an object changes its motion or position. These changes can in turn result in work, energy, power, and momentum. These common terms have special meanings in physics.

WORK in everyday usage usually means muscular exertion or mental effort. In physics, work is done only when force is applied to an object in the same direction as the object's motion. When this happens, there is displacement. For example, when you wheel your bicycle out of the garage, the force you apply to the handle bars pushes the bike in the same direction as you are walking. Work equals force multiplied by distance, or $W = Fd$.

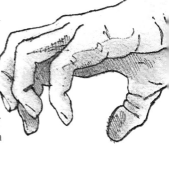

A ball's potential, or stored, energy is converted to kinetic energy when it falls. Energy is never created or destroyed, only converted from one form to another.

No work is done if a person simply holds an object because there is no displacement. If you substitute 0 for d in the equation above, you see that $W = 0$. Likewise, no work is done if a person simply carries an object horizontally. That is because the object's motion is horizontal to the ground, yet the force holding it is perpendicular to the ground.

Work is a scalar quantity. In the metric system, work is measured in *joules*. One joule is the amount of work done when a force of 1 newton moves something 1 meter. You do about 1 joule of work if you pick up an apple from the ground. One joule equals 1 *newton-meter*. For example, if you push a box 10 meters across the floor with a horizontal force of 40 newtons, you do 400 joules of work (40N x 10m = 400J). In the British system, the *foot-pound* is the most common measurement of work. One joule equals 0.7376 ft.-lb., and 1 foot-pound equals 1.356J.

ENERGY is the ability to do work. In fact, energy is measured in the same units as work, joules. In mechanics, work can produce two types of mechanical energy: kinetic and potential. *Kinetic energy* is the energy of movement. When work makes an object move, the object receives kinetic energy. A book falling from a shelf, an arrow shooting from a bow, and a train chugging westward all exhibit kinetic energy. An object's kinetic energy depends on its mass and speed. The larger or faster the body, the more kinetic energy it possesses.

This relationship between kinetic energy, mass, and velocity is written in the equation $KE = (1/2)mv^2$. In this equation, KE stands for kinetic energy, m stands for mass, and v stands for velocity. For example, a 1,000-kilogram auto moving at 20 m/s has kinetic energy of $1/2(1,000 \text{ kg})(20 \text{ m/s})^2 = 200,000$ J. By contrast, a 1,000-kilogram auto moving at 10 m/s has kinetic energy of $1/2(1,000 \text{ kg})(10 \text{ m/s})^2 = 50,000$ J. This explains why a fast-moving car will skid for longer after the brakes are applied than a slow-moving car will. Kinetic energy can be converted back into work. For example, a wrecker's ball can swing with kinetic energy to exert a force to break down the wall of a building.

Potential energy is stored energy. For example, a book lifted to a high shelf has gravitational potential energy. If the book falls, its potential energy is transformed into kinetic energy. Thus, the work done in lifting the book is regained as kinetic energy. The higher an object is, the more gravitational potential energy it has. This can be expressed in the equation $PE = mgh$, where *PE* stands for potential energy, *mg* stands for an object's weight, and *h* stands for height.

According to the *law of the conservation of energy,* energy is not created or destroyed. Energy is only transformed from one form to another. Work, kinetic energy, and potential energy can be transformed into one another. For example, when someone shoots a stone from a slingshot, the potential energy in that person changes to the potential energy of the stretched band. When the band is released, its potential energy turns into kinetic energy as the stone shoots forward. When the stone hits a target, the energy becomes heat energy.

POWER is the rate at which work is done. Power is the amount of work done divided by the time taken to do it: $P = W/t$. If two people each push a box of the same weight the same distance, the one who pushes the box faster gets the work done in less time and exerts the greater power. In the metric system, power is measured in *watts*. One watt is one joule per second. Another measurement of power is the unit horsepower (hp). One horsepower equals 746 watts.

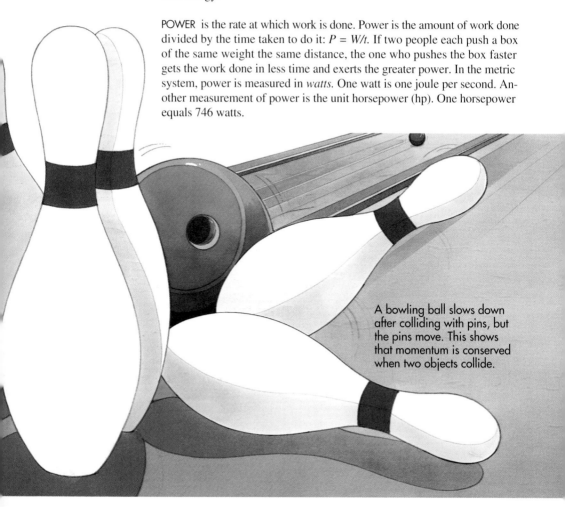

A bowling ball slows down after colliding with pins, but the pins move. This shows that momentum is conserved when two objects collide.

MOMENTUM. A moving object has momentum as well as velocity. In physics, an object's momentum is its mass multiplied by its velocity. The equation for linear momentum is $p = mv$, where p stands for momentum, m stands for the object's mass, and v stands for velocity. The larger the mass and velocity of a body, the greater its momentum. An automobile with a mass of 1,000 kilograms driving north at 5 meters per second has a momentum of 5,000 kilogram meters per second toward the north. A truck with a mass of 5,000 kilograms must drive north at only 1 meter per second to have the same momentum as the car.

When two bodies collide, their motions change. Familiar collisions are the action of billiard balls striking one another in a game of pool or a pitched ball being hit with a swung bat. The greater an object's momentum, the greater force required to change that momentum.

Momentum is conserved when two objects collide. If no external forces act during the collision, the change in momentum is zero. This is an example of the *law of conservation of momentum*. This law implies that the total momentum of two balls just before they strike each other, for example, equals the total momentum just after the collision. As one ball loses momentum and slows down, the other gains momentum and speeds up. To analyze a collision it is essential to determine whether it was elastic or inelastic. An *elastic collision* is one in which no energy is lost during the collision. Some energy is always lost to friction in objects larger than gas molecules, but if you think of two objects colliding with a spring between them, it will give you an idea of a totally elastic collision. The compressed spring would return energy to the bodies as they rebounded. An *inelastic collision* is one in which energy is lost due to friction or deformation of the bodies. Then, the kinetic energy after the collision is less than before. An example is when two autos collide and damage each other.

MACHINES are tools that help do work. Simple machines do work by increasing, decreasing, or changing the direction of force applied to an object. The law of conservation of energy states that the work a tool does is equal to the energy put into it, minus energy lost to friction. No machine can multiply energy or work, only force.

A *pulley* is an example of a simple machine. A pulley is made of a fixed support (also known as a *block*), plus a wheel and a rope or chain (together known as the *tackle*). The more pulleys or ropes used, the greater the load that can be moved and the less force required to move it. Even a small, portable block and tackle can lift heavy weights. Other simple machines include the lever, inclined plane and wedge, screw, and wheel and axle.

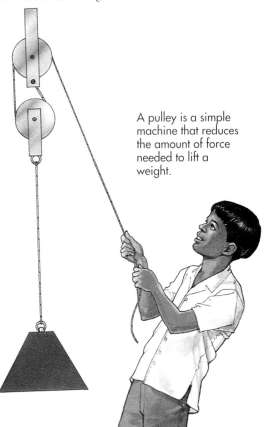

A pulley is a simple machine that reduces the amount of force needed to lift a weight.

Fluids

● **manometer:**
measures the pressure of gases or vapors.

● **barometer:**
measures air pressure.

In physics, a fluid is a substance that can flow, such as a liquid or gas. The laws of *hydrostatics* describe the behavior of liquids at rest. *Pressure* is the amount of force divided by the supporting area. A fluid's pressure at a point depends on the fluid's density and how deep that point is below the surface. Pressure gauges, such as manometers and barometers, measure pressure according to the heights of columns of fluid.

PASCAL'S LAW states that a fluid in an enclosed container transmits the same pressure to all portions of the fluid, including the container walls. This principle is used to transmit a force through a fluid from one container to another. Hydraulic brakes, pumps, and other equipment operate on this principle.

● **hydraulic brake:**
brake in which fluid under pressure operates the mechanical parts.

ARCHIMEDES' PRINCIPLE states that an object fully or partly immersed in a fluid is lifted by a *buoyant force*. This buoyant force equals the weight of the fluid displaced by that object. From this principle, it follows that a floating body displaces an amount of liquid equal to its own weight. If the average density of a body is less than that of the fluid, the body can float. A hydrometer uses Archimedes' principle to measure the specific gravity of a fluid. Archimedes also discovered that the amount of water displaced by an immersed body is equal to the body's volume.

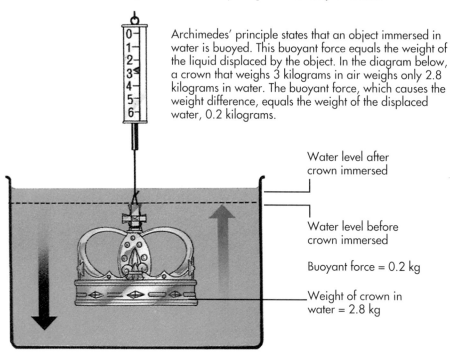

Archimedes' principle states that an object immersed in water is buoyed. This buoyant force equals the weight of the liquid displaced by the object. In the diagram below, a crown that weighs 3 kilograms in air weighs only 2.8 kilograms in water. The buoyant force, which causes the weight difference, equals the weight of the displaced water, 0.2 kilograms.

Water level after crown immersed

Water level before crown immersed

Buoyant force = 0.2 kg

Weight of crown in water = 2.8 kg

Useful equations

Linear velocity: $v = d/t$
    v is the velocity, d is distance moved, t is the time taken to travel that distance.

Linear acceleration: $a = (v_1 - v_0)/t$
    a is the acceleration, v_1 and v_0 are the initial and final velocities respectively, t is the time (in seconds).

Force and acceleration: $F = ma$
    F is the force, m is the object's mass, a is the acceleration.

Linear momentum: $p = mv$
    p is the object's momentum, m is the object's mass, v is the velocity.

Newton's law of universal gravitation: $F = Gm_1m_2/d^2$
    F is the gravitational force (in newtons), G is the universal gravitational constant, m_1 and m_2 are the masses of the objects, d is the distance between the objects' centers of mass.

Minimum escape velocity: $v_e = (2GM/r)^{1/2}$
    v_e is the escape velocity, G is the gravitational constant, M is the mass of the planet, r is the radius of the planet.

Mass/weight relationship: $W = mg$
    W is the weight of the object, m is the object's mass, g is the acceleration of the object due to gravity.

Power of a machine: $P = W/t$
    P is the power, W is the work done, t is the time taken to do the work (in seconds).

5

Nature of the Atom

All matter, whether solid, liquid, or gas, is composed of atoms. In elements, atoms are the smallest unit of matter that retain that element's properties. Tiny as atoms are, they consist of even smaller subatomic particles: protons, neutrons, and electrons. In turn, protons and neutrons consist of smaller particles. Scientists have given these elementary particles futuristic-sounding names, such as gluons, gravitons, hadrons, muons, and neutrinos. Two branches of physics are involved with these particles: particle physics, which studies them in general, and quantum mechanics, which describes their energy and motion.

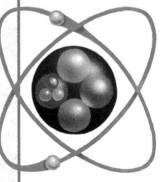

Helium atom

Structure and properties of an atom

Atoms are made up of *subatomic particles*, which include the three basic parts of atoms: protons, neutrons, and electrons. Protons and neutrons are found in the center, or *nucleus*, of the atom. One or more electrons move about in the space surrounding the nucleus.

Protons and *neutrons* in the nucleus are called *nucleons*. (The simplest atom, that of hydrogen, has only one proton and no neutrons.) The proton and neutron have roughly the same mass. Together they make up nearly all the atom's mass. The proton carries a positive electrical charge, while the neutron has no electrical charge. The diameter of the nucleus is about 100,000 times smaller than the diameter of the whole atom. This means that atoms are composed mainly of empty space.

A complete atom has one *electron* for every proton. Electrons circle the nucleus at high speeds in certain orbits, or *shells*. The shells are numbered 1 through 7, starting with the one closest to the nucleus. Each shell can hold only a certain number of electrons. Those closest to the nucleus hold electrons with the least energy, while those farthest from the nucleus hold electrons with the most energy. Electrons have a negative electrical charge and are attracted by the protons' positive charge. Because electrons have kinetic energy, however, they resist the attraction and do not fall into the nucle-

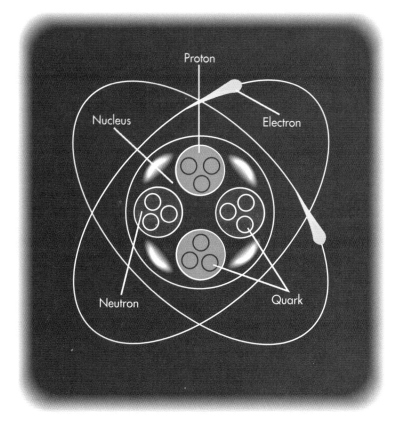

The subatomic particles that make up atoms are grouped into three families: quarks, leptons, and bosons. An atom's protons and neutrons are made of quarks; its electrons are a kind of lepton; and bosons transmit forces between particles.

us. Electrons have very little mass, only about 1/2,000 the mass of a proton or a neutron.

In physics, the properties of all atoms are described by atomic number, atomic mass, atomic weight, and electrical charge. Some atoms also exhibit radioactivity. (For more details on the structure and properties of atoms, see Chapter 1.)

Families of particles

Protons, neutrons, and electrons are among the hundreds of subatomic particles identified by scientists so far. Many of these are *unstable particles*, which exist only briefly before decaying and becoming other particles. Physicists have grouped subatomic particles into three major families: (1) quarks, (2) leptons, and (3) bosons. Quarks, leptons, and bosons are *elementary particles*—that is, they do not seem to be made up of smaller units. Elementary particles are too small to measure, but scientists estimate that they are more than 100 million times smaller than atoms.

QUARKS are particles that make up neutrons and protons. Scientists do not know for sure how many kinds of quarks exist, but at the present time they believe that there are six. The two main types are called *up* (or *u*) and *down* (or *d*). A neutron consists of two d's and one u. A proton consists of two u's and one d. Quarks do not seem to exist singly, but always in combination with other quarks. When quarks combine, they form other particles called *hadrons*. Quarks carry an electric charge that is either one-third or two-thirds the charge of an electron.

LEPTONS. Physicists have identified six kinds of leptons, including the electron. Two other kinds of leptons, *muons* and *taus,* seem to differ from an electron only in mass. A muon is about 207 times as heavy as an electron, and a tau is 3,490 times as heavy. Like electrons, muons and taus carry a negative electric charge. The other three leptons are kinds of *neutrinos,* tiny particles that have no electric charge and are too small to measure.

BOSONS transmit forces between particles. The known bosons are *photons, gluons,* and *W particles* and *Z particles* or *weak bosons.* Photons are particles of light. They carry the electric force that keeps electrons within atoms. Gluons transmit a force that binds quarks together. W particles and Z particles can change one type of quark or lepton into another. Physicists predict the existence of two other kinds of bosons. One, the *graviton,* is thought to transmit gravity. Little is known about the properties of the other predicted particle, the Higgs boson.

Quantum mechanics

The science of mechanics based on Newton's laws was unable to explain many of the interactions between and with subatomic particles. In the first 30 years of this century, a new theory called quantum mechanics was developed through major theoretical contributions from the physicists Albert

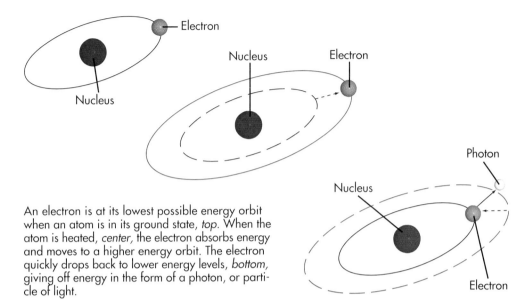

An electron is at its lowest possible energy orbit when an atom is in its ground state, *top*. When the atom is heated, *center,* the electron absorbs energy and moves to a higher energy orbit. The electron quickly drops back to lower energy levels, *bottom*, giving off energy in the form of a photon, or particle of light.

Einstein, Niels Bohr, Louis de Broglie, Erwin Schrödinger, Werner Heisenberg, and Wolfgang Pauli.

When an element is heated, its atoms give off light. This light does not include the full spectrum of colors found in a rainbow or prism. Instead, atoms from each element produce their own unique set of colors or *spectral lines*. Physicists could not explain this phenomenon until they theorized that energy at the subatomic level exists in tiny packets called *quanta*. This idea is expressed in the equation $E = hf$. (E is energy; h is the universal Planck's constant, 6.626×10^{34} joule-seconds; and f is the frequency of the quantum particle). A single packet of energy is a *quantum*.

ELECTRON ENERGY LEVELS. Quantum mechanics shows that electrons can move only in certain orbits around the nucleus. Each orbit has a particular value of energy. When an electron is in a specific orbit, it exists at a stable energy level and does not release or absorb energy. Therefore, electrons are limited to certain energy levels called *quantum states*. Just as water seeks its lowest possible level, electrons seek the lowest energy state. When all the electrons in an atom are at their lowest energy level, the atom is said to be in its *ground state*.

If outside forces act on the atom, the electron can jump to another orbit. When matter is heated, electrons absorb energy and move to an orbit of higher energy. The atom is then in an *excited state*. But atoms rarely stay excited for more than a fraction of a second. Electrons quickly drop to orbits of lower energy until they reach their ground states once again. At each succeeding drop, the electron gives off a quantum of energy in the form of light. This bundle of energy is called a *photon*. The energy of the photon equals the difference between the higher and lower energy levels of the electron. These photons are what produce the spectral line colors that had puzzled physicists.

Light is a stream of separate photons, which have characteristics of both waves and particles.

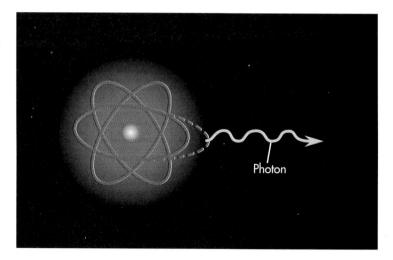

Photon

WAVE-PARTICLE DUALITY is perhaps the most unusual feature of the quantum theory. Scientists have discovered that particles such as electrons also behave like waves. At the same time, these waves also behave like particles. Electrons and other atomic particles are associated with waves called *matter waves*. Matter waves have a specific wavelength. Also, scientists once believed that light was a wave emitted as a continuous flow. But quantum mechanics explains that light is a stream of separate photons that have characteristics of both particles and waves.

These phenomena illustrate the wave-particle duality feature of quantum theory. The wave-particle nature of electrons implies that it is impossible to know both a particle's exact location and its precise velocity. Physicists can only predict probable locations and velocities of particles. This is because in order to make such measurements, physicists must shine light at a particle to "see" it. But the light's energy disturbs the particle and changes its velocity. So, the more accurately scientists try to measure the position of a particle, the less accurately they can measure its velocity, and vice versa. This lack of exactness is known as the *Heisenberg uncertainty principle*.

Forces in the nucleus

The quantum rules that govern the motions of electrons apply to protons, neutrons, and all other subatomic particles in the nucleus. The force that keeps the nucleons together, however, differs greatly from the electrostatic attractive force between electrons and protons.

Because all protons in the nucleus have a positive charge, they should repel one another and fly apart. Neutrons carry no charge. However, neutrons and protons are held together by a powerful force called the *strong nuclear force*, also known as the *strong interaction*. The strong nuclear force overcomes the mutual repulsion of the protons and binds the nucleons tightly together. The huge energy involved in this strong interaction is called the *binding energy* of the nucleus. The binding effect of this nuclear force dies off quickly unless the nuclear particles are extremely close. For example, strong nuclear force does not affect electrons.

This powerful binding energy can be overcome only by radioactive decay or by artificially splitting the nucleus with high-energy particles. Scientists have built huge electromagnetic machines known as *particle accelerators* to bombard the nucleus of an atom with a high-energy beam of particles. These collisions disrupt or even split the nucleus and knock particles loose. Nuclear physicists have developed a wide variety of detectors to trace the motion and speed of the particles emitted. Through the use of particle accelerators, they have discovered more than 100 different kinds of subatomic particles in the nucleus.

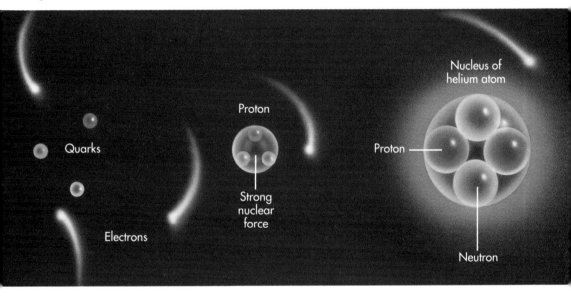

The strong nuclear force binds quarks to make up an atom's protons and neutrons. The same powerful force also holds protons and neutrons together to form the nucleus.

NUCLEAR FISSION. One of the predictions of the special theory of relativity was that matter could be transformed into energy. This idea is expressed in Einstein's famous equation $E = mc^2$ (energy equals mass times the speed of light squared). In 1942, this prediction was confirmed in the first large-scale nuclear fission experiment, conducted at the University of Chicago. Nuclear fission is the splitting of a heavy nucleus into two medium-sized nuclei. Fission can occur spontaneously or by bombarding the nucleus with a high-speed neutron. For instance, when the uranium isotope 235 is struck by a neutron and splits into two, it releases two or three neutrons and tremendous amounts of energy in the form of light, heat, and gamma radiation.

If the emitted neutrons in turn split more atomic nuclei, they produce a chain reaction that can produce an atomic bomb explosion. Fission was used

Nuclear Energy

In the early 1900's, scientists discovered that great energy holds an atom's protons and neutrons together in the nucleus. They realized that if they could release and control that energy, a new power source would be available. Today, nuclear energy provides about 6 percent of the world's *commercial energy* (energy produced by businesses and governments and sold to the public). And if such disadvantages as cost and hazardous waste can be overcome, nuclear energy could supply far more of the world's power.

Nuclear power plants

Although "energy from the nucleus" may sound a bit mystical, nuclear power plants are similar in basic ways to conventional plants that burn fossil fuels such as coal or oil. Both are types of thermal power plants, which use the force of steam from boiling water to generate electricity. All that is re-quired to boil water and create steam is heat. So thermal power plants—which generate most of the world's energy—are like huge furnaces, varying only in the fuel they use.

Instead of burning a fossil fuel such as coal or oil, nuclear power plants use the metal uranium. Uranium is particularly effective in *nuclear fission,* a process in which the nuclei are split to release their energy. Fission takes place in a nuclear reactor. A *nuclear reactor* bombards a certain amount of fuel, usually a type of uranium, with neutrons, a kind of subatomic particle.

Nuclear fission takes place when a bombarding particle splits the nucleus of a uranium atom. When a uranium atom breaks apart, a certain number of *free* neutrons are released. A free neutron can split another uranium nucleus, releasing even more free neutrons. This process is a *chain reaction.*

Each time a uranium nucleus splits apart,

Inside a nuclear power plant, a nuclear reactor bombards fuel, usually uranium, with neutrons. When the nucleus of a uranium atom splits, energy escapes as heat. This heat boils water and produces steam, which in turn spins turbines that run an electric generator. Steam leaving the turbines is cooled back to water by cold water piped from a cooling tower.

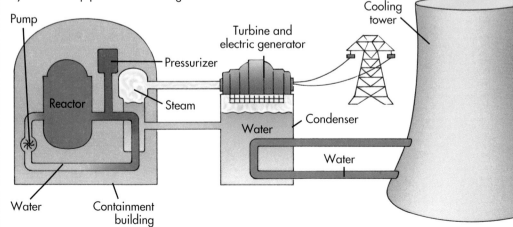

Pump
Pressurizer
Reactor
Steam
Water
Containment building
Turbine and electric generator
Water
Condenser
Cooling tower
Water

energy escapes. During a chain reaction, this energy becomes tremendous. Most of this energy is released in the form of heat.

A nuclear power plant uses the heat generated by fission to boil large amounts of water near the reactor. The boiling water produces steam, which pipes carry to the plant's turbines. Pressure from the steam rotates the turbines, which in turn run a generator that converts the movement into electricity.

Advantages and disadvantages

Compared with other kinds of energy, nuclear energy has advantages and disadvantages. One advantage is that nuclear power plants use less fuel than fossil-fuel plants. Also, fossil fuels pollute the air during use, but uranium does not.

Nuclear energy also poses disadvantages, however. Nuclear power plants cost more to build than conventional plants. Also, accidents have occurred at nuclear power plants.

A serious accident occurred in 1979 at the Three Mile Island nuclear power plant in Pennsylvania when the reactor's cooling system broke down. The reactor's core, which contains the nuclear fuel, was destroyed. A total core meltdown that might have released poisonous radioactive material into the air was avoided.

The worst nuclear accident in history occured in 1986 at Chernobyl in Ukraine, which was then part of the Soviet Union, where an explosion tore apart the reactor. A large amount of radioactive material was released into the air. Official reports said 31 people died and 200 were seriously hurt, but many people believe the casualties were higher.

A further drawback is that nuclear fission produces hazardous waste. Fission of uranium produces strontium 90, cesium 137, and barium 140, substances that remain radioactive and dangerous for about 600 years. Plutonium, another product of fission, remains radioactive for thousands of years.

One disposal plan suggests recycling some nuclear wastes into fuel for reactors. Another plan calls for storing radioactive waste underground. In the United States, no such storage site has been selected.

Fusion

In theory, people should be able to get nuclear energy from a process called fusion. Fusion occurs when two lightweight nuclei combine. The combined nuclei form the nucleus of a heavier element, changing some matter into energy as they do so. Fusion occurs naturally in stars, including the sun.

On Earth, scientists can create fusion reactions that produce a great deal of energy by applying intense heat. These reactions are called *thermonuclear reactions.*

Thermonuclear reactions occur only in an unusual state of matter called plasma. *Plasma* is a gas of free electrons and free nuclei. If plasma containing lightweight nuclei is heated to many millions of degrees, the nuclei fuse. In fusion experiments, scientists usually use plasmas made from tritium or deuterium. Both of these fuels are isotopes, or forms, of hydrogren.

Scientists have not yet created a container that can hold the superhot plasma during fusion. The container must be able to hold extremely hot plasma, yet its walls must be very cold to avoid melting. But if the plasma touches the container's cold walls, fusion will stop.

Scientists have tried to achieve fusion at room temperatures, known as cold fusion. Few experts expect cold fusion to become a reality before the year 2000, however.

Nuclear fission occurs when a neutron strikes a heavy nucleus, such as that of a uranium atom; splits the nucleus; and starts a chain reaction. Vast amounts of energy are released during fission.

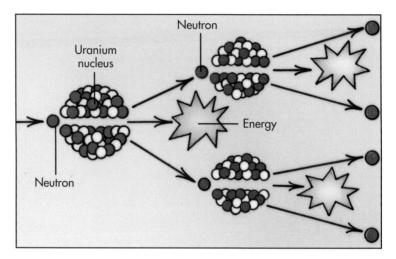

in atomic bombs dropped by the United States on Japan in 1945. If the chain reaction is controlled, however, enormous fission energy can be harnessed to produce electricity. Nuclear power plants generate millions of kilowatts of energy through controlled nuclear fission.

NUCLEAR FUSION also can be used to produce nuclear energy. This process involves fusing the nuclei of two lighter elements to form a heavier nucleus composed of less mass than the sum of the masses of the two lighter nuclei. Two hydrogen atoms, for example, can be fused to produce one helium atom. The "lost mass" is transformed into energy in the form of heat, light, and radiation. Fusion fuels the stars, including our own sun. However, the fusion of atomic nuclei requires temperatures of hundreds of millions of degrees. (See the special feature "Nuclear Energy" in this chapter for more information on nuclear fission and fusion.)

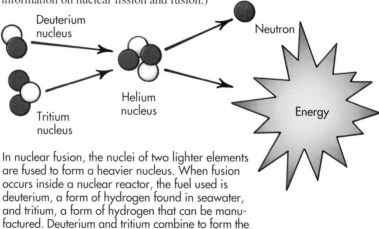

In nuclear fusion, the nuclei of two lighter elements are fused to form a heavier nucleus. When fusion occurs inside a nuclear reactor, the fuel used is deuterium, a form of hydrogen found in seawater, and tritium, a form of hydrogen that can be manufactured. Deuterium and tritium combine to form the nucleus of a heavier element, helium, releasing a neutron and a huge amount of energy.

States of Matter

These bottles consist of solid matter; the substance they contain consists of liquid matter.

Elements and compounds can exist in one of three states, or phases, of matter: solid, liquid, or gas. The state of a substance depends on the amount of energy its atoms and molecules possess. It also depends on the strength of the forces holding the atoms and molecules together. Depending on the amount of pressure, substances usually change phase at specific temperatures if energy is added or subtracted. Unusual phases of matter include colloids, liquid crystals, gas plasma, supercooled and superfluid liquids, and superconductive solids.

Solids

A solid is a substance that has a fixed shape and volume. Solids are held together by *cohesion,* which results from the attractive forces between their atoms and molecules. As a result, solid substances are rigid and hold their shapes unless deformed by external forces. Two principal types of solids exist: "true" or crystalline solids and amorphous solids.

Crystalline solids, or *crystals,* consist of atoms and molecules that are arranged in regular three-dimensional lattices—like eggs in a stack of egg cartons. This structure is determined by the chemical bonds between the adjacent atoms and molecules. One way crystalline solids may form is when a substance evaporates. They also may form when a gas or liquid solidifies. Most crystalline solids melt at specific temperatures to become liquids. Examples of crystalline solids include metals, ice, salt, diamond, and many plastics.

Amorphous solids, in contrast to true solids, have no crystalline structures nor specific melting points. Glass, carbon black, and many resins are examples of amorphous solids.

The atoms or molecules of a solid vibrate, *inset,* but are held together by attractive forces. As a result, a solid, such as sunglasses, holds its shape unless warped by outside forces.

● **carbon black:** *a powdery soot that forms from incomplete burning of natural gas and oil.*

Strength and hardness are important properties of solids. The forces that bind atoms and molecules give solids their *strength.* Bonds between atoms generally are stronger than bonds between molecules. As a result, the strongest solids are collections of single atoms, such as most metals and diamond. Molecular solids—such as plastics, ice, and some metals and alloys—are softer and melt more easily. The strength of a solid is determined by measuring its *elasticity*—how it behaves when stretched or compressed.

The *hardness* of a solid depends on the strength of the bonds between its atoms or molecules. Hardness is measured on the *Moh's scale* of 1 to 10. The hardest natural substance, diamond, measures 10 on the scale. Talc, the softest natural substance, measures 1. Some metals are soft enough to be shaped easily. *Ductile* metals can be stretched into wire without breaking, while *malleable* metals can be hammered or rolled into thin sheets. The hardness of metals can be changed by exposing them to heat in different ways. *Annealing* increases a metal's ductility; *tempering* reduces its brittleness; and *quenching* increases its hardness and brittleness.

Liquids

Liquids are substances that have a fixed volume, but not a fixed shape. The attractive forces between the atoms and molecules of liquids are too weak to hold the particles in fixed positions. Instead, liquids' atoms and molecules move about at random, permitting liquids to flow and assume the shape of their container. Unlike solids, liquids cannot be stretched. They can be compressed, however. All liquids exert pressure, depending on their depth and density. Three important properties of a liquid are 1) surface tension, 2) adhesion, and 3) capillary action.

● **density:** *mass in a unit volume.*

Surface tension

Surface tension enables a liquid to behave as if it had a "skin." Inside a liquid, each atom and molecule is attracted equally in all directions; however, atoms or molecules on the surface experience few attractive forces from the outside. As a result, the outer atoms and molecules are pulled inward and toward each other, keeping the surface of the liquid taut. It is this surface tension, or "skin," that enables certain insects to walk on water; these insects are too light to break the surface tension. Surface tension varies from liquid to liquid. In water, surface tension can be reduced by adding a detergent. The soap molecules spread throughout the solution, reducing the adhesion between neighboring water molecules.

● **solution:** *a mixture formed by dissolving.*

Because of surface tension, liquids assume a shape with the least possible surface area. This is why soap bubbles and raindrops tend to be spherical.

A liquid's atoms or molecules move about at random, *inset,* but are drawn together at the liquid's surface. This surface tension produces a "skin" that a light insect, such as the water strider, can walk on.

Adhesion and wetting

Adhesion results from the attraction of a liquid's atoms or molecules to the atoms or molecules of another substance. This property allows liquids to "wet" a surface. Water spreads over glass and wets it because its adhesion to glass is greater than its own surface tension. In mercury, however, the surface tension is greater than its adhesion to glass. On a glass plate, mercury forms beads and does not wet the surface.

Capillary action

Capillary action (capillarity) refers to the tendency of liquids to move into or out of tiny, hollow passageways called capillaries. Examples of capillaries include slender tubes and fine pores in solid material. Paper towels, for instance, have millions of capillaries between their fibers, enabling them to

Fogged-up windows illustrate adhesion. Water molecules that condense out of the air are more attracted to glass molecules than they are to one another. Adhesion causes the water to spread over the glass.

Florists use the capillary action of liquids to dye flowers. If a flower stem is placed in a mixture of water and food coloring, the liquid will rise through the stem and color the flower's petals.

absorb water. Plants use capillary action to draw water from the soil into their roots.

Capillarity depends on surface tension. If the capillary walls strongly attract the molecules of the liquid's surface, the liquid will move up the tube or pore. If the liquid's molecules are more strongly attracted to each other than to the capillary walls, the higher surface tension will repel the liquid from a capillary. Water will move up a capillary tube, for instance, while mercury will move down. The narrower the capillary, the greater its ability to absorb or repel a liquid.

Gases

A gas is a substance that has no shape or size of its own and can expand to occupy the space of its container. Because cohesion in a gas is almost zero, its atoms or molecules are far apart and move relatively freely. Thus, a gas can be expanded or compressed to a much greater degree than can a solid or liquid. Unlike liquids, gases fill the entire volume of a closed container. Collisions of atoms and molecules with the walls of the container give rise to *gas pressure*.

Kinetic theory of gases

The kinetic theory of gases is based on several assumptions: (1) gases consist of atoms and molecules moving rapidly and randomly in all directions; (2) each gas particle has a kinetic energy that depends on its temperature—the hotter it is, the more kinetic energy; (3) as gas molecules bounce off one another, they lose no energy; (4) the attractive forces between gas molecules are almost zero; (5) the volume of a gas molecule is so small compared with the volume of the whole gas that it can be ignored; (6) the time a gas molecule is involved in a collision is so small compared with the time between collisions that it, too, can be ignored; (7) the pressure exerted by all the gas molecules on the walls of a container is the average force they exert per unit area.

Real gases

A gas that conforms to all the kinetic theory's assumptions is called an *ideal gas*. In practice, no gas is entirely ideal. Real gases vary somewhat from the ideal-gas assumptions. Under high pressures, the molecules of a gas become attracted to each other and their volume can no longer be ignored. Likewise, at very low temperatures gas molecules have much less kinetic energy and become attracted to one another.

The atoms or molecules of a gas move about in all directions, *inset.* Blimps and other airships contain a lighter-than-air gas, usually helium, that allows them to overcome their own weight and rise from the ground.

In fact, below a particular temperature, called the *critical temperature*, a gas is known as a *vapor*. This vapor can be condensed into a liquid if the pressure is increased. For example, carbon dioxide can be converted easily to a liquid because its critical temperature is 88.7 °F. (31.5 °C), a little more than room temperature. Nitrogen, however, is more difficult to condense because it must be cooled to a critical temperature of –233 °F. (–147 °C) before it can be liquefied.

Measuring pressure

The pressure of air around us is known as *atmospheric pressure*. In physics, atmospheric pressure often is measured with a mercury barometer. This instrument consists of a long tube filled with mercury, placed open end down in a container of mercury. The mercury in the tube drops slightly, creating a vacuum in the tube's sealed end. Changes in atmospheric pressure act on the surface of the mercury in the container, raising or lowering the mercury in the tube. Pressure is measured in millimeters of mercury (mm Hg). *Standard atmospheric pressure* is measured at 760 mm Hg, which is equal to about 14.7 pounds per square inch or about $1.01 \times 105N/m^2$.

An *aneroid barometer* works on the same principle as the mercury barometer, but its vacuum is contained within a drum. Changes in air pressure cause the drum to change shape and to move a pointer that registers the pressure on a scale.

Changes of phase

Depending on temperature and sometimes pressure, matter can change its phase. That is, it can change from a solid to a liquid or gas, or vice versa. At absolute zero (–459.67 °F. or –273.15 °C), all matter is in the solid phase. As the temperature of a substance increases or decreases, so will the kinetic energy of its atoms and molecules. This change in kinetic energy enables substances to change in phase.

The *melting point* is the temperature at which a solid, when heated, becomes a liquid. This temperature is equal to the *freezing point* at which the liquid, when cooled, becomes a solid. For example, the melting point of ice is the same as the freezing point of water. Sometimes, a solid passes directly into the gas phase without first melting. This process is called *sublimation*. Iodine and frozen carbon dioxide (dry ice) are examples of solids that sublimate. When a solid melts under pressure but refreezes when the pressure is released, it undergoes *regelation*.

At the *evaporation* temperature, a heated liquid becomes a gas. This is the same as the *condensation* temperature, at which a cooling gas becomes a liquid. Near the surface of a liquid, some molecules always have enough energy to break free and enter the vapor or gas state. This vapor exerts a pressure on the liquid called the *vapor pressure*. Heating the liquid allows more surface molecules to break free. When the vapor pressure equals the atmospheric pressure, a liquid boils and evaporates. This is why in low atmospheric pressure the boiling point is lower and in pressure cookers the boiling point rises.

The kinetic energy of ice-cube molecules increases with heat. Eventually, the vibrating molecules of the solid begin to move more freely and the ice cubes melt. Continued heat causes the water molecules to speed up, until the liquid becomes a gas.

What's All the Fuss About Superconductors?

A coil made of superconducting ceramic material, which usually is brittle and hard to shape, was developed by researchers at Argonne National Laboratory in Illinois. Researchers made a paste of ceramic material and silver powder, which they formed into a coil. They solidified the paste by heating it.

Imagine riding a train that travels faster than 300 miles (480 kilometers) per hour, floats above its track, and creates only the slightest vibration or noise. You could have the opportunity sooner than you think—development of such a train is well underway in Germany, Japan, and the United States. These trains, a type of *magnetic levitation transportation system* (*maglev*), will rely on extraordinary materials called superconductors. The maglev may be the most thrilling example, but superconductors have many possible applications, which are likely to influence the way we live in years to come.

Superconductivity is a phenomenon in which certain metals, organic compounds, and ceramics conduct electricity without resistance. Any material that shows this ability is called a superconductor. In most of these materials, superconductivity occurs only at temperatures near absolute zero, which is the lowest possible temperature, −459.67 °F. (−273.15 °C). But scientists have developed certain ceramics that become superconductors at temperatures as high as −164 °F. (−109 °C).

In an ordinary conductor such as copper, electrical resistance occurs because electrons moving through the material collide with other particles and scatter. As a result, energy is lost in the form of heat. The electrons in a superconductor, however, are able to flow through the material freely without bumping into other particles.

Superconductors have another special property. Under certain conditions, superconductors are pushed away by magnetic fields. So a superconductor placed over a magnet will float, suspended over the magnetic field.

The first superconductors were discovered in 1911 by the Dutch physicist Heike Kamerlingh Onnes. He found that if he cooled mercury with liquid helium, the mercury's electrical resistance disappeared. Onnes investigated the capacity for storing electricity in a superconductor by forming a ring of mercury and trying to maintain a flow of electricity around the ring. Scientists soon found that certain other metals and alloys also could act as superconductors.

Three American physicists—John Bardeen, Leon N. Cooper, and John Robert Schrieffer—developed the modern theory of superconductivity and received the 1972 Nobel Prize for physics for their work. This

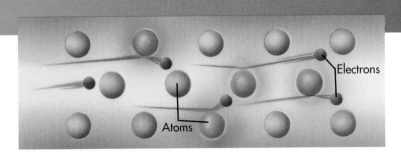

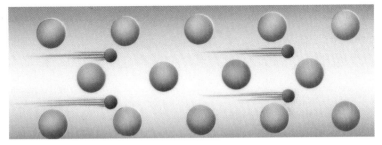

In an ordinary conductor such as copper wire, *top,* an electric current encounters resistance. Flowing electrons strike atoms in the conductor, losing energy to the atoms in the form of heat. In a superconductor, *bottom,* an electric current meets no resistance. The electrons can flow through the material without bumping into atoms or losing energy.

theory says that a superconductor has no electrical resistance because its electrons form pairs. These pairs travel in groups along paths that enable them to avoid collisions with other particles within the superconductor.

The first ceramic superconductor was discovered in 1986 by West German physicist J. Georg Bednorz and Swiss physicist K. Alex Müller. Since then, scientists have developed several others. These ceramic materials have a wider variety of applications because they become superconductors at higher temperatures than metals or alloys.

The uses of superconductors are practically limitless. They already have proven valuable in devices that detect magnetic fields on land and underwater, in magnetic resonance imaging (MRI) units, and in particle accelerators, which speed up atomic particles.

But scientists predict that superconductors soon will have much more common applications. In addition to the maglev train, they may be used in automobile engines that produce very little heat and in smaller, lighter engines for ships.

Superconductors also may enable engineers to create computers that run much faster than ones we use today. And these computers could be powered by superconducting electrical lines that transmit over vast distances with no loss of power.

Scientists currently are working toward the development of a ceramic superconductor that can operate at much higher temperatures, requiring no more equipment than an air conditioner. Once they accomplish this, the superconductor may become as common as the light bulb.

Intermediate states of matter

Some substances are neither solid, liquid, nor gas but intermediate states of matter. Colloids and liquid crystals are such substances.

● **solvent:** *substance that can dissolve other substances.*

● **suspension:** *a mixture in which tiny particles of a solid remain suspended without dissolving.*

COLLOIDS are solutions containing large molecules or clumps of molecules. The solvent is known as the *dispersing medium*. The substance in the solvent is called the *disperse phase*.

A colloid is an intermediate state between a solution and a suspension. The dispersing medium and the disperse phase in a colloid can be a solid, liquid, or gas, creating eight basic types of colloids. When the dispersion medium is a solid and the disperse phase a gas or liquid, the resulting colloid is a *gel* or *foam* and has a large surface area for absorption. For example, charcoal is a solid foam colloid used to filter unwanted odors or gases. Colloids formed in gas dispersion mediums include smoke and mist.

A colloid, such as electrorheological (ER) fluid, *above right*, consists of fine particles suspended in a liquid. When surrounded by an electric field, the ER fluid stiffens into a gel, *above left*. Researchers hope to capitalize on this characteristic to construct buildings better able to withstand earthquakes.

LIQUID CRYSTALS, as the name suggests, are an intermediate state between a liquid and a solid crystal. In a liquid crystal, the atoms and molecules are arranged in a pattern similar to a solid but this pattern can be made fluid by

A digital electronic watch displays the time in digits that form when electric current passes through patterns of liquid crystal.

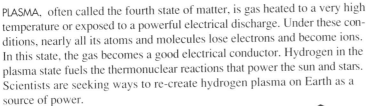

changes in temperature or electrical fields. Liquid crystals that change color as temperatures rise or fall are used to make temperature indicators. Voltage-sensitive liquid crystals create the images seen in electronic displays.

Unusual states of matter

Some substances are solid, liquid, or gas but have unusual properties; these substances include gas plasma, supercooled and superfluid liquids, and superconductive solids.

PLASMA, often called the fourth state of matter, is gas heated to a very high temperature or exposed to a powerful electrical discharge. Under these conditions, nearly all its atoms and molecules lose electrons and become ions. In this state, the gas becomes a good electrical conductor. Hydrogen in the plasma state fuels the thermonuclear reactions that power the sun and stars. Scientists are seeking ways to re-create hydrogen plasma on Earth as a source of power.

SUPERCOOLED LIQUIDS are liquids that fall below their normal freezing temperature without forming solids. However, if a supercooled liquid is shaken or a small particle added to it, its temperature rises to the freezing point and the liquid becomes solid. In clouds, supercooled water droplets can freeze in the form of ice crystals that eventually become heavy enough to fall as snow.

SUPERFLUIDS are liquids cooled to a temperature where they have almost no viscosity, or thickness; and nearly unlimited ability to conduct heat or cold. At present, scientists cannot completely explain this phenomenon. However, superfluids appear to have much in common with gases. The superfluid isotope helium 4, for instance, is so light that it "crawls" up and over the walls of its container.

Snowflakes result when supercooled water in clouds freezes.

At very low temperatures, liquid helium becomes a superfluid light enough to "crawl" up and over the walls of its container.

SUPERCONDUCTIVE SOLIDS result when certain solids (usually metals, alloys, or ceramics) are cooled to the *transition temperature*. At this temperature they lose all resistance to the flow of electrons. Such materials become superconductors of electric current and are used to produce high-current electromagnets. The main difficulty is that the transition temperatures for many materials are extremely low. Scientists are currently searching for materials with higher transition temperatures. Scientists have discovered materials with superconducting transition temperatures of up to −164 °F. (−109 °C).

Energy

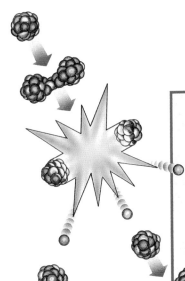

7

The nucleus of an atom can be split to produce nuclear energy.

Energy is the ability to do work. Energy takes many forms—the kinetic energy of a moving object, the radiant energy of light, the nuclear energy of an atom. Most of the energy we use had its source in the sun. It was transmitted to Earth in the form of sunlight, which was converted to the chemical energy now locked in fossil fuels. Or, plants used it to make the food that sustains all animal life. Without the energy in the universe, no human life would be possible.

The potential, or stored, energy of a spring such as a Slinky® can be converted to kinetic energy.

What is energy?

For many years, scientists considered energy and matter as separate. In recent years, however, scientists have come to regard matter and energy as different aspects of the same thing. For example, electromagnetic radiation behaves as a wave, yet has properties of particles. Also, measurements of nuclear reactions indicate that bursts of new energy are accompanied by loss of mass in the nuclei. Therefore, scientists now accept the *principle of conservation of mass-energy*, which states that energy can be developed from matter and turned into matter, but the sum of energy and matter remains the same. (See "Quantum mechanics" and "Forces in the nucleus" in Chapter 5.)

Energy takes many forms. *Potential energy* is stored energy. An elastic object such as a spring gains elastic potential energy when it is stretched or compressed. Potential energy can be converted to *kinetic energy*, the energy of movement. For example, the stretched or compressed spring's potential energy is converted to kinetic energy when the spring is released. (See "Work and energy" in Chapter 4.)

Heat energy is a form of kinetic energy because the temperature of a substance depends on the motion of its atoms or molecules. The faster the molecules move, the hotter the substance is. *Radiant energy* consists of waves. Most types of radiant energy are emitted by atoms when electrons fall from higher to lower energy levels. Radiant energy is released in waves of different lengths, from the long radio waves through the short gamma rays. (See "Electromagnetic radiation" in this chapter.)

Sound energy consists of vibrations in the molecules of air, water, or another medium. It can be considered another special form of kinetic energy.

Electrical energy is found in matter that has gained or lost an electric charge. If two objects with different levels of electrical energy are joined by a conductor, an electric current flows between the two objects until they are at the same energy level.

Chemical energy is stored in the bonds between the atoms that make up the molecules of a substance. When the substance undergoes a chemical reaction, it may release energy and produce a new substance with less chemical energy. Or, it may absorb energy (usually in the form of heat) to produce a new substance that has greater chemical energy.

Nuclear energy results from a change in the nuclei of atoms through nuclear fission or fusion. Energy released in a nuclear reaction can take the form of heat, light, and other radiation. (See "Forces in the nucleus" in Chapter 5.)

● **conductor:** *substance that allows the transfer of electric charges.*

● **nuclear fission:** *splitting a nucleus by bombarding it with a high-speed neutron.*

● **nuclear fusion:** *fusing the nuclei of two light elements to form a heavier one.*

Heat

Heat is an important form of energy. Every material thing possesses internal energy. A substance consists of atoms and molecules that are always in motion, giving the substance internal energy. If a substance's atoms or molecules move slowly, the object has low internal energy; it is cold. If its atoms or molecules move rapidly, the substance has high internal energy; it is hot. The energy that is transferred between two objects because of a temperature difference is called heat.

Temperature is a measurement of a substance's internal energy. Although theoretically a temperature of absolute zero is possible, this state cannot be reached in practice. No upper limit to temperature has been determined; the temperature at the center of the sun is about 27 million °F. (15 million °C), and larger stars are hotter.

● **absolute zero:** *a theoretical temperature, –459.67 °F. (–273.15 °C), at which no molecular movement occurs.*

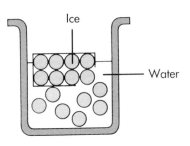

Heat causes solids, such as ice, to melt. As an ice cube melts, *inset,* its internal energy increases and its molecules begin to move faster.

32° F. (0° C)

Ice

Water

Formation of heat

All material objects can be sources of heat, and all the other forms of energy can be converted to heat. The sun is the Earth's most important source of heat energy and the Earth's interior is also very important. Various chemical reactions, particularly combustion, change chemical energy to heat. Nuclear reactions and the flow of electricity also produce great quantities of heat. Another major source of heat is kinetic energy produced by the friction of two surfaces rubbing together.

In turn, heat can be converted into other forms of energy. For example, steam engines powered by heat result in kinetic energy.

● **combustion:** *the act or process of burning.*

Heat capacity

The specific heat capacity of a substance is the amount of heat required to raise the temperature of 1 gram of the substance by 1 degree Celsius. The heat capacity of a substance varies slightly depending on its temperature range. The total amount of heat energy that any body gains or loses depends on its mass, its specific heat capacity, and its change of temperature.

Transfer of heat

Heat passes from one place to another in three ways: through conduction, convection, or radiation.

Conduction is the process by which heat moves from one part of a body to another. Atoms in the hotter part of a solid, or in a hot solid touching a cool one, vibrate faster and strike neighboring atoms. These atoms then vibrate faster, striking others and passing the energy along until all the atoms are moving at the same level of energy—that is, they have the same temperature. In conduction, heat energy is passed from atom to atom without the atoms themselves changing place. Metals transfer heat by conduction particularly well because their electrons are relatively free to move.

In *convection*, heat is transferred by the movement of a heated material. Convection occurs in liquids and gases. During convection, the heated part of the substance expands, becomes lighter, and rises. Cooler molecules

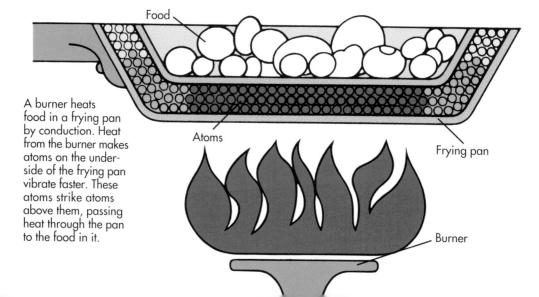

Food

A burner heats food in a frying pan by conduction. Heat from the burner makes atoms on the underside of the frying pan vibrate faster. These atoms strike atoms above them, passing heat through the pan to the food in it.

Atoms

Frying pan

Burner

move nearer the source of heat, taking the place of the expanding ones. In turn, they are heated, expand, and move higher. The flow of heated molecules away from a source of heat and the flow of cool molecules toward it form a *convection current*. The current continues to flow until all the molecules reach the same temperature.

Radiation is energy emitted as waves or particles. All moving molecules create waves of radiant energy, known as *infrared rays*. Hot objects give off more infrared rays than cold objects. In conduction and convection, moving particles transfer heat. In radiation, heat can be transferred through a vacuum, which has no particles. All ob-

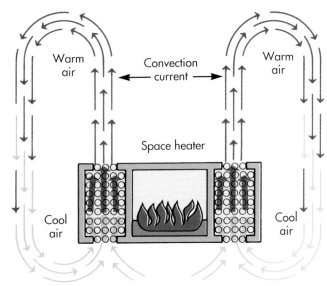

A space heater warms air by convection. Heated air rises and cool air takes its place, creating a convection current.

jects also absorb heat radiation. A cold object in warm surroundings absorbs more radiant energy than it emits until its temperature matches that of the surroundings. Then, it emits as much energy as it receives.

Insulation is a way to control the transfer of heat by keeping it in or out of a place or substance. Conduction of heat can be limited by materials

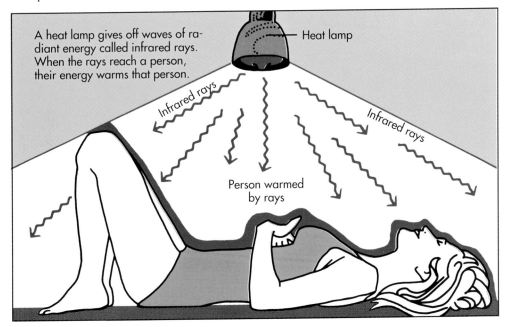

A heat lamp gives off waves of radiant energy called infrared rays. When the rays reach a person, their energy warms that person.

Heat lamp

Infrared rays

Infrared rays

Person warmed by rays

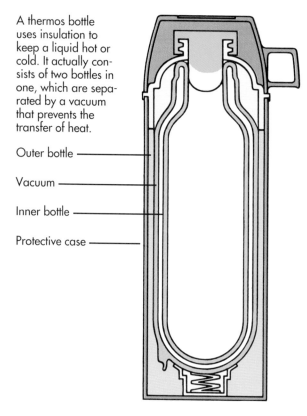

A thermos bottle uses insulation to keep a liquid hot or cold. It actually consists of two bottles in one, which are separated by a vacuum that prevents the transfer of heat.

Outer bottle ————

Vacuum ————

Inner bottle ————

Protective case ————

such as plastic and wood, in which atoms do not move freely in response to heat. Convection currents can be controlled by separating cold and hot areas with a block of "dead air," as between a storm window and inner window. Heat traveling by radiation can be reflected by white or polished surfaces such as white clothing.

Effects of heat gain or loss

When a substance gains or loses heat, its temperature rises or falls. It also may change in size or state.

Molecules usually contract when they cool. As molecules are heated, however, they move more rapidly and tend to separate. The substance—whether gas, liquid, or solid—expands. If a gas is in a closed container and thus prevented from expanding, its pressure will increase. The expansion of solids because of heat must be taken into account when large structures such as bridges are designed, because structures that lack room to expand could bend or break.

All substances require heat to make them change state from solid to liquid and then to gas. As substances change from gas to liquid and then to solid, they give up heat. (See "Changes in phase" in Chapter 6.)

Sound

Sound consists of waves that transmit kinetic energy through a medium. These waves are set off by vibrations of an object, such as a person's vocal cords, a rotating motor, or the skin of a drum. Any substance that touches the vibrating object also vibrates, sending waves in all directions. Because sound consists of movement within a medium, it cannot travel through a vacuum, such as outer space.

Waves are of two types, transverse and longitudinal. In *transverse waves*, the vibrations occur at right angles to the direction in which the waves travel. You can see this type of wave by holding a rope at both ends and moving it up and down or from side to side. Light waves and ocean waves are transverse waves.

In *longitudinal waves*, the vibrations occur in the same direction that the waves travel. They do this by alternately pushing against the medium in which they are traveling, compressing it, and then moving back, allowing

When a drumstick hits a drum, the skin of the drum vibrates. This vibration sets off waves we call sound.

the medium to expand. You can see this type of wave in a coiled spring with one end fixed and one end moving back and forth. Some sections of the spring have many coils compressed together, while other stretches have coils spread apart. A region that is compressed is called a *compression*; a region of expansion is called a *rarefaction*. Sound waves are longitudinal waves.

Sound waves

Sound travels in a series of compressions and rarefactions. A single wave consists of a single sequence, or cycle, of compression and rarefaction. A sound wave's *frequency* is the number of cycles produced by a vibrating object each second. A more rapid vibration produces a higher frequency. Frequency is measured in hertz (Hz). As the frequency increases—that is, as the number of cycles per second rises—the wavelength decreases, and the distance between one compression and the next gets shorter.

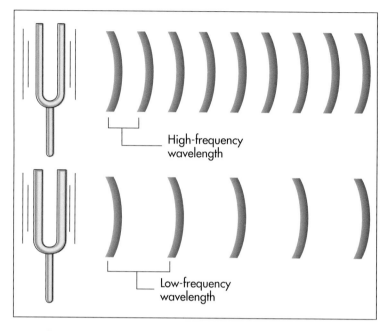

High-frequency
wavelength

Low-frequency
wavelength

A rapidly vibrating object, *top,* produces sound waves
with a higher frequency than those produced by a slowly
vibrating object, *bottom.* A sound wave's frequency is
also known as pitch.

Pitch is a subjective term that corresponds to frequency. Notes described
as having high pitch have high frequency; those with low pitch have low
frequency.

Waves with frequencies below the range of human hearing are called *in-
frasonic waves,* and those with frequencies above human hearing range are
ultrasonic waves. Some animals can hear sounds in these frequencies. For
example, many bats use ultrasound to navigate.

Intensity is related to the energy flowing in a sound wave. Intensity is the
amount of power that passes each second through a given area perpendicular to the direction of the sound wave. Intensity is measured in *decibels*
(dB). The subjective term *loudness* corresponds to intensity. People generally perceive sounds of greater intensity as louder. However, the human
ear is less sensitive to sounds of high and low frequencies, so a wavelength
in these ranges is usually perceived as softer than a mid-range wavelength
of equal intensity.

Musical sounds produced by certain instruments, such as strings and
pipes, can be described by a third characteristic. Musicians call this aspect
sound quality or *timbre* produced by overtones. A scientist might refer to
standing waves. A standing wave is produced when a wave and its reflection combine and form a wave pattern that appears to be standing still. For
example, when a string vibrates, it sets off a wave that is reflected from

each end of the instrument. The two waves cross each other, and cancel out each other's vibrations at points called *nodes*. Each section of the string between the nodes vibrates separately. The resulting sound combines the waves set off by the string and by all its separate sections.

When sound travels

The speed of sound depends on the medium through which the sound waves travel. Some media transmit sound waves faster than others, depending on their density and elasticity, also called *compressibility*. In general, sound travels faster through liquids and solids than through air. However, the speed of sound in air increases with temperature.

A sound wave hitting a surface is reflected at the same angle at which it strikes the surface. Sound is reflected by any surface. However, because sound waves can be as long as several yards or meters, the surface must be sizable. When a sound wave strikes a small surface, only part of it is reflected. The rest is bent and scattered. This is called *diffraction*. A sound also is diffracted when it passes the edge of an obstacle or through an opening. This is why we can hear sounds from around a corner.

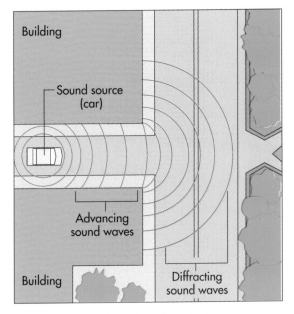

Sound waves traveling along the side of a building spread around the building's corner. This action, known as diffraction, means people can hear sounds from around a corner.

As a whistling train approaches a listener, *left,* the whistle's sound waves are compressed and its frequency, or pitch, seems to increase. As the train moves away, *right,* the whistle's sound waves spread out and the listener hears its pitch drop.

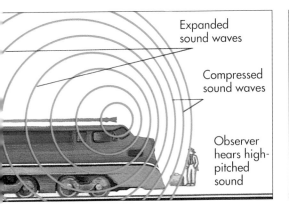

Expanded sound waves

Compressed sound waves

Observer hears high-pitched sound

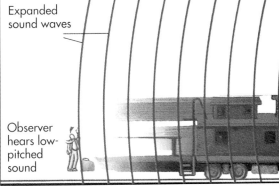

Expanded sound waves

Observer hears low-pitched sound

When a sound wave leaves one medium and enters another in which the speed of sound differs, the direction of the wave also changes. This change in direction is called *refraction*.

The *Doppler effect* refers to the perceived frequency when the source of sound moves relative to the listener. For example, if the whistle sounds on a train moving toward a listener, the time between successive compressions or rarefactions is shortened the closer it gets, so the frequency seems to increase. As the train moves away, the time between cycles lengthens, so the frequency seems to decrease.

Interference occurs when two sound waves pass through the same point. If their compressions and rarefactions coincide, the waves reinforce each other, and the sound becomes louder. If the condensations of one wave coincide with the rarefactions of the other, the waves cancel out each other and the sound weakens. Sometimes the same two waves will reinforce each other at certain points in the cycle and cancel out each other at other points. The result is a sound that gets louder and softer at regular intervals. These variations in loudness are called *beats*.

Resonance occurs whenever one body is made to vibrate at its own natural frequency by impulses received from another body vibrating at the same frequency. Well-made musical instruments take advantage of resonance, for example, in the choice and shape of wood in a violin, guitar, or piano.

Electromagnetic radiation

Electromagnetic radiation is a form of energy that results from changes in the energy levels within atoms. Visible light is a form of electromagnetic radiation. Other types are radio waves, microwaves, infrared radiation, ultraviolet radiation, X rays, and gamma rays.

Electromagnetic radiation is a wave that is formed by both an electric field and a magnetic field, which are at right angles to each other and to the

Electromagnetic radiation moves in waves. A wave's frequency depends on its wavelength, or the distance between one high point and the next. The wave below has a lower frequency than the wave at the bottom of the next page because its wavelength is longer.

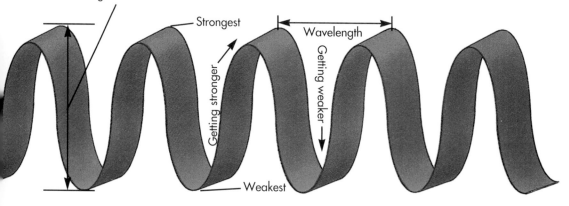

Strength of the magnetic field

Strongest

Wavelength

Getting stronger

Getting weaker

Weakest

direction of the wave. But under certain circumstances, particularly when this radiation strikes a substance, electromagnetic radiation behaves like a stream of particles. For practical purposes, therefore, electromagnetic radiation can be considered as either waves or particles of energy, depending on the situation. The particles, or packets, of energy are called *photons*. (See "Quantum mechanics" in Chapter 5.)

Electromagnetic radiation as waves

Electromagnetic radiation waves move in a pattern like that of ocean waves. A given point in the wave moves up and down, forming equal-sized curves, at a steady rate in the direction of the wave. The distance between one high point, or *crest*, and the next is called the *wavelength*. The number of times per second that crests pass a fixed point is the frequency. The shorter a wavelength is, the higher is its frequency. The velocity of a wavelength depends on its wavelength and frequency. Electromagnetic waves range in length and frequency, with the shortest wavelengths billions of times shorter than the longest ones. Visible light has wavelengths in the middle of the range.

Like sound waves, electromagnetic waves passing through a narrow opening or around edges of an obstacle defract. In some media, radiation may encounter irregular molecules or small objects. The random reflections or diffractions that result are called *scattering*. Electromagnetic waves can also reinforce and interfere with each other.

Electromagnetic radiation as particles

Electromagnetic radiation behaves like a stream of particles when ultraviolet radiation strikes certain metals. When this happens, the metals emit electrons. This is called the *photoelectric effect*. Quantum mechanics explains that radiation's energy is transmitted in individual packets called *quanta* or photons. When a photon enters an atom, it can strike an electron with enough force to knock the electron out of its orbit, leaving the atom with a positive charge. The amount of energy in a photon depends on the frequency of the radiation.

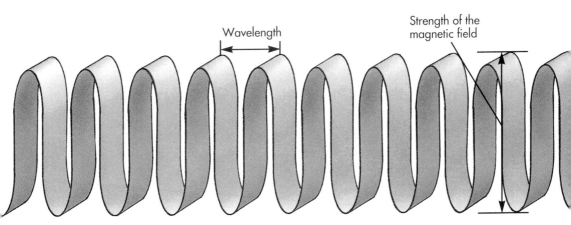

Wavelength

Strength of the magnetic field

Putting Light to Work

One of the most impressive tools in modern medicine is a light that can do the work of a surgical knife. Delicate eye operations that were once high-risk have become routine with the help of this tool. Remarkably, the same tool can be used to play music, cut metal, and transmit information. This versatile device is the *laser,* which not long ago was described as "a solution looking for a problem." Today, of course, the laser easily can be regarded as the solution to a great number of problems. It might even be considered a simple solution, based on our understanding of light.

The laser is a device that produces a very narrow, powerful beam of light. The word *laser* stands for *l*ight *a*mplification by *s*timulated *e*mission of *r*adiation. These words describe the key processes in the creation of laser light.

Laser light is special because it is *coherent.* That means that it spreads little and is *monochromatic* (single-colored). Light from most sources, such as a flashlight, spreads rapidly and fades after a short distance. On the other hand, a typical laser beam expands to a diameter of only 1 meter after traveling 1,000 meters, or only 64 inches per mile.

Light consists of waves, and the color of light is determined by its *wavelength* (the distance from one peak of a wave to the next). Ordinary light includes many different wavelengths and, therefore, many different colors. When these colors merge the light appears white. Laser light consists of waves with a very narrow range of wavelengths. So a laser beam usually appears as only one color.

A laser beam can travel great distances because its waves move *in phase*—that is, all the peaks move in step with one another. When light waves are in phase, they can be directed to move in a narrow path and in one direction, enabling a laser beam to maintain its intensity. Ordinary light, which is *incoherent*, consists of light waves moving in different directions and at many different wavelengths, so it cannot move in phase.

Coherence gives laser light its amazing versatility. A compact disc (CD), for example, can store a huge amount of information because it is read by a tightly focused laser beam. As the disc spins, a laser beam reflects off microscopic pits in the disc's surface. These reflections vary, creating a digital code that represents the information on the disc.

CD's can hold information other than music. Large quantities of information previously stored in books are now also available on CD-ROM (compact disc read only memory). Today's public libraries, for example, are likely to contain CD-ROM versions of directories, encyclopedias, and newspaper articles in addition to the traditional print versions.

Lasers are important to *fiber-optics communication,* technology that transmits telephone and television signals, and other data around the world. In fiber-optics communication, the electrical signals of telephone calls or television pictures are changed into *pulses,* or bursts, of laser light. Strands of glass called *optical fibers* conduct the laser light, with each fiber carrying as much information as several thousand copper wires could handle.

Scanners at supermarket checkouts use laser beams. A laser beam identifies the product by scanning the lines and spaces of the product's bar code. The laser sends this information to a store computer, which finds the product's price and relays it to the register. Bar-code scanners also are used in libraries to keep track of books and in post offices to sort mail.

Scientists can measure distance with lasers by measuring the amount of time it takes a laser beam to reach a distant object and reflect back. They even used a laser beam to measure the distance between Earth and the moon. In 1969 and 1971, astronauts put mirrored devices called *laser reflectors* on the moon. Scientists focused a high-powered laser from a telescope on Earth to the laser reflectors on the moon, which reflected the beam back to Earth. By measuring how much time it took the beam to return to Earth, scientists worked out the distance between Earth and the moon to within 2 inches (5 centimeters). The distance they arrived at is about 238,000 miles (383,000 kilometers).

The concentrated light of a laser can generate tremendous heat. In industry, this heat is put to many uses. Industrial lasers generating thousands of watts of power cut such materials as metals, ceramics, cloth, and plastic. They also weld metals, drill holes,

and strengthen materials by heating them.

And how do lasers do the work of a surgical knife? Through their heating power, lasers can be used to make extremely precise cuts and to seal cuts with little damage to surrounding tissue. So eye surgeons often use lasers to close off broken blood vessels in the back of the eyeball.

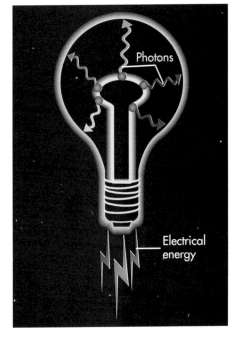

Ordinary light is produced when atoms in the filament of a light bulb emit tiny bundles of energy called photons, *right*. These photons travel in waves of different wavelengths and go in all directions. Laser light is produced as photons bounce between a mirror and a partial mirror, *below*. The light builds in intensity and shoots out through the partial mirror, its waves in phase and traveling in the same direction.

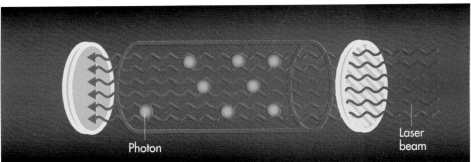

Visible light

Visible light is a very small part of the electromagnetic spectrum. One unit scientists use to measure wavelengths of light is the *nanometer,* which equals one billionth of a meter, or 1/25,000,000 inch. Wavelengths in the visible spectrum range from about 700 nanometers for deep red to about 400 nanometers for deep violet. Radiation frequency is measured in hertz (Hz), or number of cycles (one complete wavelength passing a checkpoint) per second. Deep violet light, with the highest frequency, has a frequency of about 750 trillion hertz. Visible light exhibits all the usual properties of electromagnetic radiation, including wave-particle duality, reflection, refraction, diffraction, dispersion, and interference. A medium that stops light is *opaque;* a medium that allows light to pass through without distortion is *transparent;* and a medium that allows light rays to pass through but scatters and diffuses them is *translucent.*

● **wave-particle duality:** *the tendency of waves sometimes to behave as particles and particles sometimes to behave as waves.*

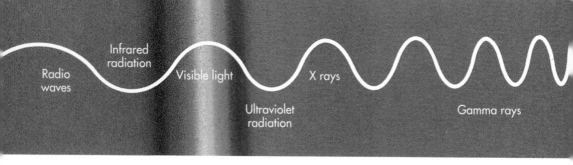

Radio waves

Infrared radiation

Visible light

Ultraviolet radiation

X rays

Gamma rays

Visible light is only a small part of the electromagnetic spectrum, which includes such waves as gamma rays and infrared rays.

BRIGHTNESS AND SHADOW. The unit used to measure the brightness of light is the *candela* (cd). One candela is the amount of light emitted by a source at a specific frequency and intensity. Because opaque objects stop light, they cast shadows. If a light were extremely small, its light could be completely absorbed or reflected by an opaque object, producing a shadow equally dark at all points, with sharp edges. In reality, most sources emit enough light so that some passes or bends around the edges of the opaque object. The usual shadow, therefore, has a darker region called the *umbra;* the partial shadow is the *penumbra.*

REFLECTION. Almost all surfaces reflect some visible light. Some surfaces reflect only certain wavelengths, so they appear to have the color of the reflected light. Two statements, referred to as the *laws of reflection,* hold true about all light rays that strike a reflecting surface. First, both the incoming, or *incident,* ray and the reflected ray are in the same plane as each other and an imaginary line called the *normal,* which is perpendicular to the surface at the point where the incident ray hits it. Second, the angle between the incident ray and the normal equals the angle between the reflected ray and the normal. Because most surfaces are uneven, they reflect light rays in random directions. Very smooth surfaces, such as polished glass, reflect the light so evenly that they can form images.

A material's color depends on the range of wavelengths it reflects or absorbs. We see a surface as white, *left,* if it reflects all the colors in the spectrum. A surface appears yellow, *center,* if it absorbs most colors but reflects yellow. A black surface, *right,* absorbs all colors and so reflects none.

REFRACTION. Like all other forms of electromagnetic radiation, light passing from one transparent medium to another can be refracted. An observer looking at a straw in a glass of water sees a bend in the straw at the water's surface. This is because light travels slower in water than in air; light emerging from it to air is refracted toward the water's surface.

COLOR AND SPECTRA. A rainbow reveals the range of wavelengths, each with its own color, that make up visible light. When all these colors combine, they form white light. These colors can split apart when passing through a medium that refracts different wavelengths at different rates. As they emerge from the medium, the wavelengths no longer appear as a unit but rather as a range of colors flowing gradually from red to violet. The splitting of light is called *dispersion.* A rainbow is formed when sunlight passing through raindrops is dispersed. A triangular block of glass or plastic, called a *prism,* has the same effect. A *spectrometer* is a device that uses prisms and lenses to disperse a beam of light into its spectral colors. It is useful in identifying chemical substances that have been heated to a glow. (See "Specialized equipment" in Chapter 3.)

Not all the colors of the rainbow are necessary to form white light. Mixing together just three shades—red, green and blue—has the same result. For this reason, these colors are known as the three *additive primary colors.* Three colors that produce black when combined are known as the *subtractive primary colors.* The subtractive primary colors are magenta (a red), cyan (a blue), and yellow.

LUMINESCENCE is a process through which a substance glows when its electrons are excited by energy other than heat, such as chemical reactions within an organism. There are two types

A pencil set in a glass of water, *right,* appears to bend because light passing from the water is refracted.

of luminescence. *Fluorescent* materials glow only while being exposed to extra energy. Many gases, liquids, and solids become fluorescent when exposed to radiation or electrically charged particles. TV picture tubes, for example, have fluorescent screens. *Phosphorescent* materials glow long after they receive extra energy. For example, phosphorescent paint absorbs energy from sunlight and later emits it as a greenish glow that slowly fades.

Electricity

Electricity is a form of energy that is based on the flow of electrons through substances. Every atom is composed of tiny particles, including protons, electrons, and neutrons. A proton has a positive electric charge, and an electron has a negative electric charge. Neutrons have no charge. Ordinarily, an atom has an equal number of protons and electrons, and so is electrically neutral. An atom's protons and neutrons cluster together in the nucleus of the atom and the electrons orbit them, held in place by their attraction to the positively charged protons. However, atoms can lose or gain electrons. Atoms that acquire electrons acquire a negative charge. Atoms that lose electrons acquire a positive charge. Any charged atom is called an *ion*.

A light bulb lights up when electric current passes through a coil of wire, or filament, inside the bulb, *inset.*

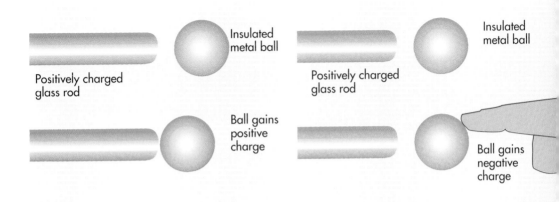

An object may be electrically charged by contact, *above left*. When a positively charged glass rod touches an insulated metal ball, the ball gains a positive charge. An object also may be charged by induction, *above right*. If the positively charged glass rod is placed near the metal ball, the ball will gain a negative charge if touched by a person on the ground.

Every charged particle is surrounded by an *electric field*, a space in which the charge has an effect on other charged particles. Particles with unlike charges attract each other, while particles with like charges repel each other. If a substance has ions of both types, the charges cancel each other out and the substance has no significant overall charge. But if a substance has many ions of one kind, it can become positively or negatively charged. In the substance, particles with like charges repel each other. (See "Structure of an atom" and "Properties of an atom" in Chapter 1.)

Static electricity

When some substances rub together, one rubs electrons from the other and each acquires a charge of static electricity. For example, combing your hair on a dry day will result in electrons moving from your hair to the comb. Because the positive charges on individual strands repel each other, your hair may stand out. The negatively charged comb, held close, will attract strands to itself.

An object with a static electric charge may pass the charge to another object by *contact*, in which charged particles move directly between objects. For example, in the above illustration, you may hear a spark of electricity jump between the comb and your hair. A charge may also be passed along by *induction*, in which a second object is induced, or drawn, to acquire a charge. If the negatively charged comb is held near a small scrap of paper, all the positive ions in the paper will be attracted to the surface close to the comb. The paper will now have two regions of charge, one positive and the other negative.

Current electricity

Current electricity is the continuous flow of electric charges. Electrons move more freely through some substances than others. Substances that transmit current are *conductors*. A gas, liquid, or solid (particularly a metal) can conduct electric current if it has enough free electrons or ions. In an *insulator*, such as glass or rubber, the electrons are too firmly bound to their nuclei to permit a current to flow through. A substance such as silicon that transmits a current better than an insulator but not as well as a conductor is a *semiconductor*. A material's *conductivity* refers to how easily it conducts a charge; its *resistivity* refers to its tendency to oppose the flow of an electric charge. Conductivity does not depend on the size and shape of the conductor.

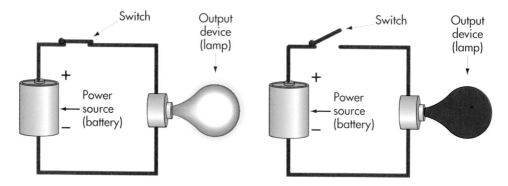

When a switch is on, electric current can flow from a power source to an output device such as a lamp and back again, *above left*. This path is called a circuit. When a switch is off, electric current cannot flow because the circuit has been broken, *above right*.

An electric current begins with some nonelectric form of energy being converted into an electromotive force (EMF). For example, a battery converts chemical energy into an EMF. One terminal of the battery has a negative charge, and the other has a positive charge. There is a *potential difference*, or difference in potential energy, between the terminals. If a conductor is connected to both terminals, electrons flow from the negative terminal through the conductor to the positive terminal. (The current is said to flow in the opposite direction, from positive to negative.) Every conductor has some resistance, which changes some of the electrical energy flowing through it into heat. To put the rest of the electrical energy to work, an output device such as a motor or lamp is placed between the energy source and the conductor.

The path of the electrons from the energy source and back again is a *circuit*. The EMF, or push, from the energy source is measured in *volts* (V). The amount of electric charge passing a fixed point in the circuit per second is the *current;* it is measured in *amperes* (amp). The resistance of the conductor and any load on the circuit is measured in *ohms*. The greater the resistance on the circuit, the slower the electric charge passing through it and the lower the current. The lower the resistance is, the more quickly the charge flows through and the higher the current is. The relationship among current, resistance, and voltage is known as *Ohm's law.*

A *direct current*, or DC, is one that flows in one direction. An *alternating current*, or AC, is one that reverses direction at regular intervals. The standard frequency of electricity in North America is 60 Hz AC, which means that the current changes its direction of flow 60 times every second.

Applications of electricity

Electricity can be put to work as it is converted to other forms of energy, such as heat and light. Electric current produces heat in direct proportion to the strength of the current and the amount of resistance. The heat energy can be passed along by conduction, convection, or radiation. In an incandescent lamp, electricity is converted to light when a metal filament with high resistance is heated to a white-hot glow. In a fluorescent lamp, electrons stimulate gas atoms. The gas atoms emit ultraviolet light, which in turn stimulates substances called phosphors to glow. (See "Transfer of heat" in this chapter.)

Magnetism

Magnetism is a force that is produced by a moving electric charge. It is a fundamental property of matter and is characteristic of all substances, although only some are strongly magnetic. Magnetism is not itself a form of energy. Yet it is not independent of electricity. Magnetic effects are caused by electric charges and result from movements of electrons in the atoms of certain substances, which are called *magnets.*

Iron filings clinging to a magnet line up along its magnetic field. This bar magnet has a three-dimensional magnetic field.

Characteristics of magnets

Every magnet has two poles, a *north pole* and a *south pole*. The position of the poles may vary; for example, on a bar magnet, they are on opposite ends, while on a disk magnet, they are on opposite faces. Like poles repel each other, and unlike poles attract each other. The force between the poles of two magnets depends on the strength of the individual magnets and on the distance between them. The closer two magnetic poles are, the more strongly they attract or repel each other. If a magnet is divided between its poles, it forms two smaller, complete magnets. Magnets may be either permanent or temporary.

The region in which the effects of a magnet can be felt is the *magnetic field*. A magnetic field can be represented by imaginary field lines, which indicate its strength and direction.

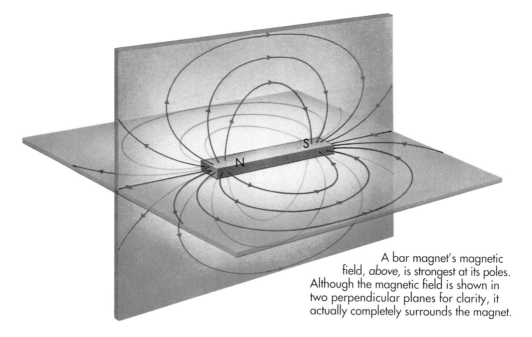

A bar magnet's magnetic field, *above*, is strongest at its poles. Although the magnetic field is shown in two perpendicular planes for clarity, it actually completely surrounds the magnet.

Where the lines are closest together, the force is strongest. The magnetic field of a bar magnet is strongest near the magnet's poles. Magnets that are free to move within the field of a more powerful magnet will align themselves, north pole to south pole and vice versa, with the stronger magnet. The Earth itself is a magnet, with its magnetic poles close to the geographic poles. This explains why a compass needle's tiny, movable bar magnets always point north.

Nature of magnetism

Any substance has magnetic characteristics owing to its atomic structure. Every electron has an electric charge and by its motion creates a magnetic field. Usually, electrons are arranged so that their magnetic fields cancel each other out. In some substances, however, the fields do not cancel out.

A compass needle is a magnet that lines up with the Earth's magnetic field and points north.

Each atom is, in effect, a tiny magnet or *dipole*. Materials that contain many atomic dipoles are *ferromagnetic*.

Dipoles can line up with one another in regions called *domains*. In most cases, the domains are arranged randomly. If all the dipoles in a large number of neighboring domains point in the same direction, however, the combined effect is an overall magnetic field in the material. This alignment of magnetic domains may occur naturally, as in lodestone and other magnetite ores. It may be brought about in iron or other ferromagnetic materials by placing them within the field of a

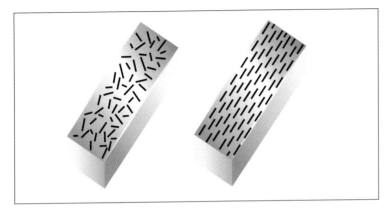

The domains of a non-magnetized iron bar, *far left*, point in random directions. The domains of a magnetized iron bar, *left*, line up in one direction.

permanent magnet, but this effect ceases when the magnet is removed. These materials are said to be *magnetically soft*. The alignment may be spurred in other ferromagnetic materials by stroking the material with a permanent magnet or by placing it inside a coil of wire carrying a large direct current. The current creates a strong magnetic field, and the field then induces a magnetic field in the material. Materials in this group, which includes steel, are *magnetically hard*.

When a magnetically hard material is magnetized, it becomes a permanent magnet. However, even permanent magnets can be demagnetized if the magnetic domains lose their common alignment. This can be done by (1) striking the magnet to knock domains out of place; (2) heating it to near its melting point to make individual atoms vibrate and move out of alignment; and (3) placing the magnet inside a coil of wire carrying an alternating current and reducing the current to zero to reverse the magnetic field and destroy the overall effect.

Useful equations

Electrical energy: $E = IVt$
E is the energy, I is the current flowing through the conductor, V is the potential difference across the conductor, t is the time of flow

Heat energy: $Q = mct$
Q is the amount of heat energy, m is the mass of the object, c is the specific heat capacity, t is the temperature increase

Velocity, frequency, and wavelength: $v = fl$
v is the velocity, f is the frequency, l is the wavelength

Energy and frequency: $W = hf$
W is the energy of a photon, h is Planck's constant, f is the frequency

Ohm's law: $R = V/I$
R is the resistance, V is the voltage across the circuit, I is the current

8

Time and Relativity

Throughout the history of physics, scientists have struggled to connect discoveries in apparently separate fields. Recognizing connections between electricity and magnetism, for example, revealed these phenomena to be different aspects of the same principles. By the end of the 1800's, Isaac Newton's ideas had revealed many of the forces at work in the world. Many scientists assumed almost all laws governing the physical universe had been discovered. In the 1900's, however, the discoveries of quantum mechanics and especially the theories of Albert Einstein changed our understanding of mass, energy, space, and even time.

Sand clock

Time

For many years, science investigated time only to perfect its measurement. The nature of time seemed self-evident—specifically, that it flowed in one direction and always, everywhere, at the same rate. Today, scientists no longer think of time as absolute. Experiments using extremely accurate methods to measure time have supported theoretical arguments that time flows slower or faster for different observers in the universe. The relativity theory, which first argued that time is relative, is discussed in detail later in this chapter.

Instruments to measure time periods shorter than a day came into use at least 4,000 years ago. These instruments probably were sundials, which tell time according to a shadow cast by a pole. Mechanical clocks appeared in Europe in the 1200's. Apparently based on Chinese timekeeping devices, they used falling weights and sets of gears to measure time. At their best they were accurate only to the hour, and they often were not at their best, requiring frequent resetting. With the invention of the pendulum clock in the mid-1600's, clocks became more reliable. Minute and second hands were added to these clocks later.

In the 1700's, navigators on the open seas determined their whereabouts according to the position and rising time of stars, so it was essential that they have the accurate time. British concern for safeguarding ships resulted in the invention of a *chronometer*, a clock or watch with an accuracy of better than one second per week.

Devices that tell time by the shadow cast by a pole, such as the Egyptian time stick, were probably the first clocks.

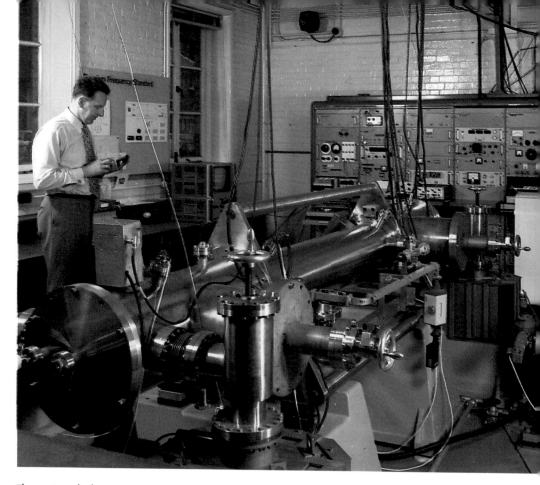

The cesium clock is a complex but extremely accurate timekeeping device, which scientists used to define the second as 9,192,631,770 oscillations emitted by an atom of cesium-133.

Although mechanical clocks continued to be improved, no significant change in time measurement came until the 1900's. Then scientists began to develop clocks based on natural physical processes, such as the vibration of certain crystals and atoms. An atomic clock is the most accurate modern timekeeper. When certain changes occur in the atoms of some elements, radiation of a particular frequency is emitted. Frequency is the number of oscillations (vibrations) per second, so the second can be defined as a particular number of oscillations of a particular radiation. The second now is defined as the duration of 9,192,631,770 oscillations emitted by an atom of cesium-133. The use of the cesium clock standard enables scientists to measure time independently of Earth's motion.

Relativity

The experiment that eventually led Einstein to devise the special theory of relativity was conducted in 1887 by American physicists Albert Michelson and Edward Morley. Their purpose was to find the difference in speed between a light beam traveling in the same direction as the Earth's movement around the sun, and another beam traveling at right angles to that direction. They expected to find that the light beam traveling with the Earth's motion moved faster than the other. To their surprise, they discovered that both beams traveled at exactly the same speed. The speed of light was constant, regardless of the frame of reference. Scientists tried to make this finding

● frame of reference: *the position from which a person observes something.*

consistent with Newton's laws of physics. Up to 1887, Newton's law of gravity had accounted for almost all discoveries concerning motion on Earth and in the sky. Scientists had no reason to expect a flaw in his ideas.

Special theory of relativity

Einstein's special theory of relativity, written in 1905, changed the way we think about mass, energy, space, and time. To understand the theory, you need a lot of imagination. But the basis for the theory is a phenomenon that you can see for yourself. If you bounce a ball on a moving train, the ball behaves just as it would if you bounced it on the ground. Einstein attributed this to the relativity principle. The *relativity principle* says that when two systems are in uniform motion relative to each other, the laws of physics are the same in both systems.

● **uniform motion:** *motion when an object's speed and direction are constant.*

Einstein saw that the Michelson-Morley experiment meant that light also must behave the same in the two systems. So, he said that light always travels at 186,282 miles (299,792 kilometers) per second, whether the source of light is moving or still. He described the relativity principle as true for all phenomena, mechanical or electromagnetic.

Einstein declared that Newton's laws were incomplete. Although Newton's ideas hold true in the everyday world, at very fast speeds they do not. Einstein showed that an object's mass increases as it approaches the speed of light. The theory also shows a relation between a body's energy and mass ($E = mc^2$). This has practical importance in the liberation of the energy in the nucleus of the atom. (See "Forces in the nucleus" in Chapter 5.)

According to the theory of relativity, no material object can move as fast as light. That is because as the object nears the speed of light, its mass increases. As its mass increases, the object needs more and more energy to move. At the speed of light, its mass would become infinite. So, it would need an infinite amount of energy to keep going—more energy than exists in the entire universe!

Einstein's special theory of relativity is his most famous because it changed our ideas of time. In everyday life, 10 minutes seem like 10 minutes, whether you spend them sitting on a train or in a classroom. But Einstein showed that time is not absolute; it is different for somebody moving very fast than it is for someone standing still.

For example, imagine you are sitting in a train that is moving almost as fast as light. (Of course, such a speed is impossible in the real world.) You see a beam of light travel from near the ceiling to a mirror on the floor, then back up again. According to your clock, six seconds pass while this is happening. But someone standing outside the train also times the light beam's journey. That person insists that it took 10 seconds.

Who is correct? Both people are correct. On the train, the light beam did travel down and up in six seconds. But the person outside the train saw the beam travel farther. That person saw the light move sideways as well as down and up, because the train was moving across that person's line of vision. In each case, the light beam was traveling at the same speed. But because the person outside sees it travel farther, it must take more time to do so. This relationship between time, distance, and the velocity of light is seen in the equation *time = distance/velocity*. In the same way, two events that

According to the theory of relativity, a clock moving relative to an observer appears to run slower than a stationary clock. This illustration shows a clock experiment performed in an imaginary train traveling 150,000 miles (240,000 kilometers) per second.

150,000 miles (240,000 kilometers) per second

6 seconds pass

In the train, a pulse of light travels from a flashlight near the ceiling to a mirror on the floor, then back up again. If the distance between the flashlight and the mirror is 560,000 miles, then the pulse travels a total of 1,120,000 miles. The observer's clock shows that 6 seconds pass, so the velocity of light is about 186,000 miles per second.

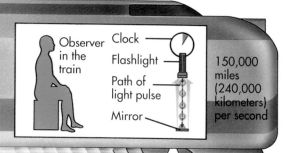

Observer in the train

Clock

Flashlight

Path of light pulse

Mirror

150,000 miles (240,000 kilometers) per second

6 seconds pass

Outside the train, an observer sees the light pulse travel 1,860,000 miles rather than 1,120,000 miles. This is because the pulse moves sideways as well as down and up. The stationary clock shows that 10 seconds pass as this happens, so the velocity of light is still about 186,000 miles per second.

Path of light pulse

150,000 miles (240,000 kilometers) per second

10 seconds pass
Stationary observer and clock

seem simultaneous to you on the train may not be simultaneous for the person on the ground.

Suppose this speeding train has a clock big enough to be seen from the ground. According to Einstein, if you compared that clock with a clock in a station you pass, the station's clock would be running slower than the train's. But to people in the station, the train's clocks would be running slower.

How can this be? According to Einstein, the movements of anything traveling at high speeds slow down in the eyes of people standing still. To you on the train, everything seems to move the way it would normally. But in fact, you are talking more slowly than you would outside. Your heart is beating more slowly. You're even aging more slowly! Even the smallest particles, such as electrons, are moving slower. So, matter itself is affect-

To people standing in a station, a train moving almost as fast as light, *bottom,* would appear shorter than it would if it were standing still.

ed. A clock, like everything else, is made of atoms. The particles in these atoms have slowed down. So, the train's clock seems slow to people in the station outside.

But why does the station's clock seem slow to you? This is where Einstein's thinking gets really tricky. You are on a moving train and the people outside are standing still. But from your point of view, it is the buildings and people and trees outside that are whipping past the train, not the other way around. To you, the station looks as if it was passing you at nearly the speed of light, not the other way around. So, the station's clock slows down for you.

Also, to people in the station the moving train will look shorter than it really is. Ordinarily, nothing moves or changes much in the time it takes light to get to us. But if the train is moving almost as fast as light, the human mind can't decide exactly where the ends are. So, the moving train looks shorter than it would if it were moving slower, or standing still.

In Einstein's new view of the universe, space and time are not separate, but together make up *space-time.* We often describe the physical world in terms of three dimensions: length, width, and height. Einstein explained that time is a fourth dimension that also applies to the physical world.

Even scientists have difficulty imagining space-time. The term *space-time* does not mean that time behaves exactly like space. For example, we can move through space but not through time. On the other hand, relativity says that space behaves like time in some ways. For example, as we look at a star with a telescope, we are not seeing the star as it is now. Instead, we are seeing light that left that star long ago. In a sense, we are gazing at the distant past.

Einstein used mathematics to prove his theory, but it has since been supported by experiments. In studies of atomic particles accelerated to near the speed of light, the atoms slowed down, just as Einstein predicted atoms in

The Twin Paradox

Remember the story of Rip Van Winkle, who fell asleep for 20 years? When he woke up, he found that he had remained the same age but those around him had grown older. His own daughter was now nearly as old as he was!

Believe it or not, such a thing could be possible according to Einstein's theory of relativity, under certain conditions. If time is relative, Einstein argued, then aging is relative too. Someone traveling at close to the speed of light would age more slowly than people on Earth.

This extraordinary idea is illustrated in Einstein's twin paradox. Of course, you know that twins are very nearly the same age. They may be born several minutes apart, but they age at the same rate throughout their lives.

But what happens if one twin gets into a spaceship and travels to a star 25 light-years away? Suppose a woman travels to the star at nearly the speed of light, while her twin brother remains at home on Earth.

According to clocks on Earth, a little more than 50 years go by before the spacefaring twin returns to her home planet. She bounds out of the spaceship and runs to meet her twin brother, who is now an old man.

How can this happen? The spaceship was moving at such speed that its clocks ran slow relative to clocks on Earth. To the space traveler, the journey took only one year, and she aged only one year. Meanwhile, her twin brother on Earth has been aging according to Earth's clocks, so he has aged 50 years while she's been away.

At one time, some scientists believed that this story contradicted the theory of relativity. After all, they argued, relativity says that from the space traveler's point of view it is Earth's clocks that run slow. So why should the space traveler age less than the twin on Earth, rather than the other way around?

The answer lies in the fact that the astronaut's motion was not uniform in relation to Earth's. Her spaceship's velocity changed, both in speed and direction. The spaceship had to leave Earth's atmosphere, accelerate to nearly the speed of light, turn around at the star, head back to Earth, and eventually slow down to land.

Under relativity, if the spaceship and Earth moved uniformly in relation to each other, the spaceship's time would slow down for people on Earth. At the same time, Earth's time would slow down for the space traveler. Because of the spaceship's changing velocity, this situation does not apply. From Earth's point of view, clocks on the spaceship ran slow. And the space traveler agrees that more time passed on Earth than on the spaceship.

When this problem is analyzed in detailed mathematical formulas, it shows that for the space traveler, most of the 50 years passed on Earth during the short time she was turning around at the star.

The end result is that the twins now find that one of them is 49 years older than the other! This situation is known as the twin paradox. But it is a paradox only if you cling to the idea that time is absolute. As Einstein has shown us, depending on where we are and how we're moving, we each have an individual sense of time.

the moving clock would do. In other experiments, particles accelerated to 86 percent of the speed of light doubled their mass, just as Einstein's theories described.

General theory of relativity

The special theory of relativity explained a lot, but it was inconsistent with Newton's theory of gravity. Einstein tried to make the theory consistent with Newton's ideas, but in 1915 he abandoned the attempt in his general theory of relativity.

Einstein showed that gravity is not a force, but a result of the curving of space-time. Einstein explained that a planet or other large body curves space-time around itself, much as a bowling ball placed on a mattress would dent the mattress. This warping of space-time causes smaller objects to move in curved paths toward a massive object, just as marbles would roll toward the bowling ball because of the dent in the mattress. Planets such as the Earth are not made to move in curved orbits by the force of gravity, but follow as straight a path as they can through curved space-time. This path is called a *geodesic*.

● **orbit:** *the path a planet follows when circling the sun.*

To make his point, Einstein described this experiment: In an elevator at rest in space, a ball is floating. The elevator begins moving up, toward the

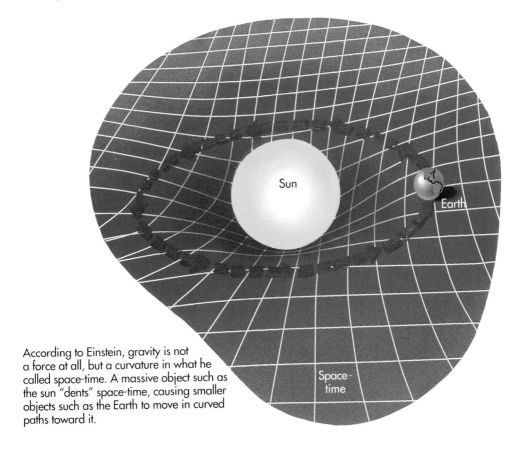

According to Einstein, gravity is not a force at all, but a curvature in what he called space-time. A massive object such as the sun "dents" space-time, causing smaller objects such as the Earth to move in curved paths toward it.

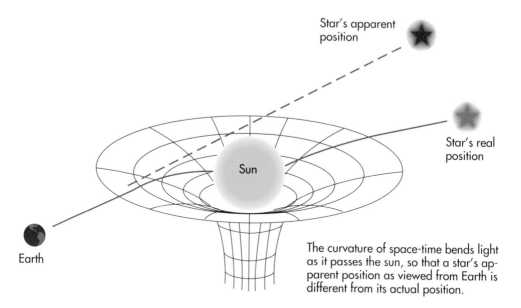

Star's apparent position

Star's real position

Sun

Earth

The curvature of space-time bends light as it passes the sun, so that a star's apparent position as viewed from Earth is different from its actual position.

ball. Eventually, the ball collides with the elevator's floor. To an observer outside, it looks as if gravity acted on the ball. In reality, the observer's frame of reference (the elevator) moved. Therefore, it makes no difference whether an object is acted on by gravity or by an accelerated frame of reference. From this principle, Einstein reasoned that matter in space curves space-time about itself.

As with Einstein's special theory of relativity, his general theory has been supported by evidence beyond his mathematics. Einstein produced an equation that showed how much the sun curved space-time. For most planets, including Earth, Einstein's equation predicted the same orbits as Newton's law of gravitation. But in the case of Mercury, the planet closest to the sun, Einstein's equation showed that its orbit should shift every time it completely circled the sun. Scientists had noticed the orbit's tiny shift before, but could not explain it under Newton's laws. This was the first proof of general relativity.

Einstein also predicted that the curve in space-time bends light as it passes the sun. This has been confirmed during solar eclipses, when photographs taken of the sky showed stars in slightly different positions than when the sun is shining.

Einstein also pondered the nature of the universe. The theory of relativity predicted that the universe was either expanding or contracting. But because all the scientific evidence of the day pointed to an unchanging universe, Einstein altered his equations to match that thinking. He later referred to this as the biggest blunder of his life when American astronomer Edwin Hubble showed that the universe is expanding. (See "The theory of a dynamic universe" in Chapter 21.)

Unified theories

Einstein's theories are not the last word in explaining the forces at work in the universe. For the last 40 years of his life, Einstein tried to work out a *unified field theory*, a theory that would unify all the forces of nature. When Einstein died on April 18, 1955, papers filled with his latest field theory calculations were found on a table in his hospital room.

Today, physicists believe that there may be an underlying unity among three of the basic forces of the universe: the strong nuclear force, the weak nuclear force, and electromagnetism. The strong nuclear force binds the nucleus together. The weak nuclear force is responsible for the radioactive decay of many kinds of atomic nuclei. Electromagnetism holds electrons to the nucleus. Theories that attempt to establish this underlying unity are referred to as *grand unified theories* (GUT's). GUT's consist of mathematical statements that describe these forces as a single unified force. According to GUT's, the underlying unity occurs only at extraordinary high energies, like those that existed in the earliest moments of the universe. At lower energies, such as those existing today, the superforce appears to act as three different forces.

Researchers are also testing *supergravity theories*, which would include the fourth fundamental force, gravitation. Such theories show that physicists once again hope that a few basic laws will unify all our knowledge about how the world works.

An experiment to test GUT's directly would require energy about a trillion times higher than is now available, but some predictions were confirmed in experiments with a particle accelerator, *inset.* A particle accelerator smashes particles together at extremely high energies. Curving green trails, *left,* mark the paths of subatomic particles created by the collision of a proton and a neutrino.

PART

Life Sciences

3

- **What Is Life?**
- **Cells: Life's Building Blocks**
- **The Plant World**
- **The Animal World**
- **Other Organisms**
- **The Human Body**

What Is Life?

Ameba

The question seems simple enough. Yet scientists and scholars have been researching, theorizing, and debating the subject for thousands of years. Some people think the answer involves more than just the principles of science. They believe that philosophy and theology also play a major part. And a question that may cause even more controversy than "What is life?" is "How did life begin?" These questions fascinate us because no matter how we answer, no one can prove that we are right or wrong. Although the answers to these questions remain shrouded in mystery, over the years, scientists have come up with some elegant theories.

Defining life

Are the things you see around you living or nonliving? This book, of course, is nonliving. The cat purring beside you is living. The difference is obvious. But biologists, although they have a vast knowledge of living things, find that the definition of life isn't always so obvious—sometimes the dividing line between living and nonliving things is quite obscure. For example, a virus is lifeless by itself because it does not grow, metabolize, or respond to its environment, but it can reproduce once it enters a living cell.

Instead of trying to reach a precise definition of life, scientists focus on the characteristics that seem to distinguish living things. No single characteristic tells us what life is, but together they form a composite that generally sets living things apart from nonliving things. Nearly all living things share the following characteristics:

• Growth. Growth in living things is more than simply an increase in size. Living things are able to produce organic molecules that become part of their structure.

• Metabolism. Living things undergo chemical processes to produce the materials and energy necessary for life.

• Reproduction. Living things are able to produce more of their kind sexually or asexually.

• Movement. Almost every living thing moves, either by moving from place to place or undergoing internal movements such as circulation or the movement of organs.

• Responsiveness. Living things react to their changing environments.

• Adaptation. Most living things are able to adjust to changes in their living conditions. Adaptation helps an organism survive and reproduce in its particular environment.

Living things share common traits that set them apart from nonliving things: growth, metabolism, reproduction, movement, responsiveness, and adaptation.

The origin of life

Almost every culture has a story to tell about the creation of life. In most of these stories, one or more powerful gods are responsible for all that exists. But since each group of people views the world in a different way, no two creation stories are exactly the same. Scientists deal with the natural world, with things that can be observed and measured, so science has no way of testing these stories. And these stories cannot all be true. But since creation stories can be neither proved nor disproved, it's possible that there's some truth in each of them.

There are three main theories scientists have used to explain how life began. The theory of spontaneous generation—the idea that life suddenly arose from nonliving matter—was a common belief for thousands of years. The theory, which originated in ancient times, maintained that lower forms of life began in nonliving matter. For example, people believed that flies could emerge fully developed from dust and mud or from decaying meat. Scientists developed this theory as a result of drawing incorrect conclusions from what they thought they saw happening.

During the mid-1600's, an Italian scientist named Francesco Redi demonstrated that meat sealed in closed jars—and thus protected from flies—would not produce flies. However, in spite of Redi's experiments and the work of other scientists, many people continued to believe that microscopic forms of life could arise spontaneously, and the argument raged on for another 200 years.

Finally, during the mid-1800's, French chemist Louis Pasteur settled the controversy. He demonstrated that even the tiniest bacteria always grow from other bacteria and do not spring into life spontaneously. After Pasteur's experiments, most scientists accepted the principle that all life comes from existing life.

More recently, scientists have proposed several theories of how life began. They believe that life arose on the Earth more than 3-1/2 billion years ago. These modern theories on the origin of life obviously are not based on direct observation, but scientists have used their knowledge of living things and their understanding of the early physical conditions on Earth to develop these ideas.

The two most widely accepted theories of the origin of life are the theory of panspermia and the theory of chemical evolution. *The theory of panspermia* claims that spores—specialized reproductive cells—from some other part of the universe landed on the Earth and began to develop. However, some scientists doubt that spores could survive a journey through the harsh conditions of outer space. And even if this theory is correct, it explains only the origin of life on Earth and not how all life began.

Nevertheless, recent evidence may prove that this theory is valid—at least in part. Scientists have found certain organic molecules in dust particles from outer space. With help from the early Earth's environment, these molecules may have laid the foundation for life on Earth.

The theory of chemical evolution was developed during the 1920's by Russian biochemist Alexander I. Oparin and British biologist J. B. S. Haldane. This theory proposes that life developed through a series of chemical

Chemist Louis Pasteur, *above*, proved through his experiments that living things do not emerge from nonliving things.

reactions in the atmosphere and oceans early in the Earth's history. This theory is more widely accepted today than the theory of panspermia.

Understanding chemical evolution

In order to understand the theory of chemical evolution, we need some knowledge of the elements of life. The most common elements in living things are carbon, hydrogen, nitrogen, oxygen, phosphorus, and sulfur. Other elements are present in smaller amounts.

The chemistry of life

Water, the simplest chemical compound of importance to living things, makes up 50 to 95 percent of most organisms and is an essential part of many life processes. Most chemical reactions within organisms can occur only in a water solution, and water is also a part of many such chemical reactions. In addition, water moves nutrients within organisms.

Most of the principal compounds in living things—except water—contain carbon. Almost all living material consists of about 50 kinds of carbon molecules, plus the macromolecules—large, complex molecules—formed from them. The four main types of macromolecules are carbohydrates, lipids, proteins, and nucleic acids.

CARBOHYDRATES consist of carbon, hydrogen, and oxygen and serve as the principal energy source for most living things. Carbohydrates also provide the basic material from which many other kinds of molecules are made.

LIPIDS consist primarily of carbon and hydrogen. The best-known lipids are animal fats and vegetable oils, both rich sources of energy. Many kinds of organisms store food in the form of lipids. Other lipids form the basic structure of cell membranes.

Macromolecules consist of smaller molecules: Sugars are found in carbohydrates, fatty acids in lipids, amino acids in proteins, and bases in nucleic acids.

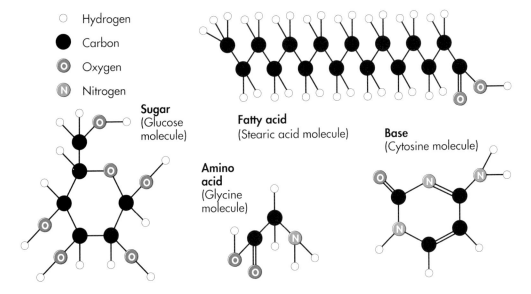

○ Hydrogen

● Carbon

◉ Oxygen

Ⓝ Nitrogen

Sugar (Glucose molecule)

Fatty acid (Stearic acid molecule)

Base (Cytosine molecule)

Amino acid (Glycine molecule)

PROTEINS are the most common—and most complex—macromolecules in living things. They are important structural parts of the tissues of cells and of the substances between cells. They are also the most varied—human beings have thousands of different proteins. Proteins in the form of enzymes also play an essential role in the control of chemical reactions in the body. Proteins are made up of one or more long chains called polypeptides, which consist of many small molecules called amino acids. All amino acids contain carbon, hydrogen, nitrogen, and oxygen.

● **polypeptides:** *a molecular chain of amino acids.*

NUCLEIC ACIDS store and transmit the information necessary for producing proteins. They consist of long chains of smaller molecules called nucleotides, which consist of a nucleic base (adenine, guanine, cytosine, or thymine), a sugar, and a phosphate group. There are two types of nucleic acids: DNA (deoxyribonucleic acid) and RNA (ribonucleic acid). DNA carries the hereditary information that an organism passes on to its offspring—it determines that a cat will produce a cat, not a dog. DNA has a nucleotide consisting of one of the four bases plus deoxyribose, a form of sugar. RNA, serving as a pattern for building proteins, transmits DNA's instructions. RNA consists of a nucleotide that has adenine, guanine, cytosine, or uracil plus ribose, a more complex form of the sugar contained in DNA. A more detailed explanation of how DNA and RNA function in a cell appears later in this chapter.

Primeval soup

We know that the early Earth was hardly an ideal home for life, so something must have changed in order for life to develop and survive. In the 1920's, Alexander I. Oparin proposed that the early Earth's atmosphere contained little or no free (uncombined) oxygen. Because hydrogen is the most abundant element in the universe, many scientists believe that the early Earth's atmosphere had large quantities of hydrogen. If so, the hydrogen-containing compounds formaldehyde, hydrogen cyanide, and water would also have been abundant. According to the theory of chemical evolution, energy from such forces of nature as sunlight, ultraviolet radiation, radiation from the decay of radioactive substances, lightning, and heat from volcanoes provided energy for reactions among these compounds, which then produced simple biological molecules, such as sugars and amino acids. The theory proposes that these molecules then combined and formed more complex molecules. Finally, the theory claims that those molecules organized to form membrane structures that were capable of isolating structures in which biochemical reactions could occur—a step toward the first organism. But what caused these molecules to interact—and then to form organisms?

Scientists propose the following sequence of events: Over many, many years, the Earth underwent significant changes. The mountainous and volcanic Earth started to cool, and pools of water collected in valleys. Then, as the atmosphere itself cooled, this water was lifted by evaporation and fell back down in the form of rain. Rain water then washed over the Earth's surfaces, extracting salts and minerals from the rocks. This water, now rich in minerals, filled the cracks and crevices of the Earth, turning tiny streams into pounding rivers, filling valleys and canyons, and finally forming great bod-

In the fertile waters of Earth's early oceans, simple molecules interacted to form macromolecules. Scientists call these waters the "primeval soup," and some claim this process marked the beginning of life.

ies of water—the oceans. In these waters, the simple molecules started to interact—again with the help of energy from sunlight, lightning, and volcanoes—forming macromolecules. Thus, these ancient bodies of water, teeming with salts, minerals, and complex molecules, have come to be known as the "primeval soup."

Proving chemical evolution

Proposing a theory is an important step in the scientific method, but the theory must be proved. In 1953, two American chemists, Stanley L. Miller and Harold C. Urey, provided the first experimental evidence showing how macromolecules could have formed on Earth.

For one week, Miller and Urey subjected a mixture of ammonia, hydrogen, methane, and water—the molecules of early Earth's atmosphere—to the energy of high-voltage sparks. At the end of that week, they discovered that amino acids and other simple biological molecules had formed. Since then, this experiment has been conducted time and time again, and researchers have produced most of the simple building blocks that make up the macromolecules of living cells.

While the experiments of Miller, Urey, and others help explain how large, complex molecules could have formed—and thrived—when the Earth was young, many questions remain unanswered. Scientists still do not know how life itself came to be. They are still trying to find out how biological molecules could have become organized into unicellular organisms. This crucial step—from complex molecules to even the simplest forms of life—remains a mystery.

● **unicellular:** *made up of a single cell.*

From molecules to organisms

Many scientists propose that the next stage in chemical evolution might have been the grouping of certain macromolecules within a protective bubble membrane, forming what scientists call a protocell. Studies have shown that structures similar to biological membranes form spontaneously in a mixture of lipids and water. The mere presence of the right type of molecules seems to bring about the formation of these biological membranes.

Scientists propose that the membrane surrounding the protocell had small openings that allowed a two-way exchange of certain materials—between the inside and the outside—of this nonliving cell. Eventually, these proto-cells developed ways to synthesize their own nutrients. Perhaps they took in very simple nutrients from the outside environment and then combined them into usable food. This method would be similar to photosynthesis, the process used by green plants today. (See "Photosynthesis" in Chapter 11.)

Over a period of about 200 million years, according to the theory, proto-cells acquired another important feature—the ability to reproduce, to make other protocells exactly like themselves. The key to this ability was the for-mation of the complex molecule RNA, which became part of the protocell. Just like the RNA in cells today, this RNA could select certain amino acids and other chemical building blocks from its environment and assemble tiny protein molecules. These protein molecules could then start the process of making more RNA. So at one point, RNA and proteins were the two chief features of protocells. The RNA was the control center, while the protein molecules served as food and building materials. During this period, but probably after the formation of RNA, another giant molecule evolved—the wondrous DNA. DNA carries the instructions that tell RNA what kind of protein to make.

Does the theory of chemical evolution explain the origin of life on Earth? All scientists can say is—maybe.

The theory of evolution

Most scientists agree that life on Earth began in the "primeval soup." Simple molecules became complex molecules, complex molecules became unicel-lular organisms, and unicellular organisms became more complex, multi-cellular organisms. Over the ages, these complex organisms acquired char-acteristics that helped them respond to changing environments. This evolu-tionary process eventually produced all the Earth's species.

The pictures on these two pages show some examples of the wide range of complexity of life on Earth.

Green algae

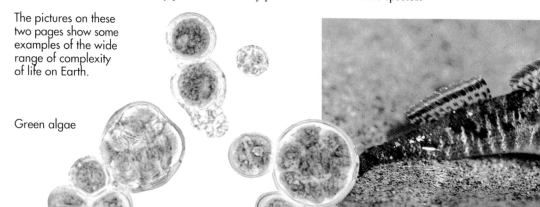

However, some people believe in a theory called *scientific creationism,* which cites evidence that the world began through an act of creation. Scientific creationists maintain that it is improbable that life itself or complex organisms could have evolved through natural processes. They believe that fossil evidence fails to show any one kind of organism in transition to any other kind of organism. They say that this lack of evidence for gradual change is predicted in the creation theory and supports the view that each form of life was always unique within genetic limits—that birds were always birds, for example, and human beings always human beings.

● **genetic:** *having to do with origin and traits of organisms.*

From cells to species

While the origin of life on Earth is still in question, scientists know how life has developed over time. Scientists now estimate that more than 2 million species of living things inhabit the Earth. Yet with all their differences, these organisms have much in common. According to the theory of evolution, different environments have resulted in variations among species. Certain traits

Red-tailed hawk

Woolly monkey

Dragonfly

Mudskipper

Python

are more suited to certain environments and the organisms that have those traits survive and pass them to their offspring—this is how different species have arisen. But because all species evolved from common ancestors, living things remain basically alike.

The theory of evolution is made up of several ideas, including the basic proposal that species undergo changes in their inherited characteristics over time. These changes transformed some of the species that lived long ago into the species living on Earth today.

According to evolutionary theory, the first unicellular organisms probably resembled today's mud-living bacteria called *methanogens*. These unicellular organisms didn't need free oxygen to survive, and they were protected from the sun's ultraviolet rays by mud and water. Life continued in this primitive form for about 3 billion years. Eventually—perhaps through chemical reactions—these unicellular organisms produced the first plantlike organisms. These plantlike organisms brought life to the surface of the Earth.

Although scientists know very little about them, these primitive plantlike organisms dominated the seas for hundreds of millions of years. And throughout that time, they used photosynthesis to obtain the energy they needed. One of the by-products of photosynthesis is oxygen.

Over billions of years, oxygen built up in the Earth's atmosphere. High up in the atmosphere, the sun's ultraviolet rays converted some oxygen into a gas called ozone. The atmospheric oxygen and the ozone formed from it filtered the sun's lethal ultraviolet rays, which previously had made life on land impossible. Thus, by producing oxygen, these early plantlike organisms paved the way for life on the surface of the Earth. Many different and more complex forms of life quickly took advantage of the new surface conditions. Along with the development of these early plantlike organisms came the beginnings of animal life. Thanks to oxygen-producing plantlike organisms, animal life could now develop and survive.

In this way, according to the theory of evolution, many forms of life— both plants and animals—came from one unicellular organism. This branching process, called *speciation,* produced the more than 2 million species of living things on Earth today.

Another idea related to evolution is *gradualism*—the belief that evolutionary changes take place slowly over periods of time ranging from decades to millions of years. Most scientists think that evolution continues today at a similar pace.

However, the fossil record indicates that many species appear virtually unchanged over millions of years and then, relatively abruptly, are replaced by new species. In the 1970's, a few scientists advanced the theory of *punctuated equilibrium* to explain this phenomenon. This theory suggests that a new species might evolve rapidly in geographic isolation and invade the territory of the parent species, which then becomes extinct in competition with the new one.

● **population:** *a group of individuals of the same species living in the same environment.*

Natural selection

Most evolutionary change is caused by the interaction of two processes: mutation and natural selection. Mutation produces random, or chance, variation in the genetic makeup of a species or population. Natural selection, also known as "survival of the fittest," determines which random changes will endure, according to the degree to which they contribute to the individual's struggle for life. At the same time, natural selection eliminates variations that make a species less likely to survive.

The behavior and physical makeup of some organisms enable them to thrive under conditions that are unique to their environment. Because the supply of food, water, and other necessities of life for all the organisms produced is limited, living things are in constant competition. They also face such dangers as being destroyed by predators or wiped out by changes in their environment. In any community, some members of a species have

A mutation can become beneficial if a species' environment changes. Before the mid-1800's, most peppered moths in Great Britain were light-colored because predators couldn't see them against the light-colored trees. But when soot from smokestacks blackened the trees, the mutant black peppered moths gained the advantage. Today, most peppered moths in Great Britain are dark.

traits that help them in the struggle for life while others have traits that are less suitable. All these traits are largely inherited and are passed on, in turn, to the individual's offspring.

However, individuals whose behavior or physical traits do not suit their environment are less likely to survive and reproduce, so the genetic factors responsible for these undesirable traits tend to be weeded out over time. Gradually, over thousands of years, a population's collection of genetic traits alters, so the average anatomy, physiology, and behavior of the population alters too. The better-adapted individuals have more offspring than those who are less well adapted, so the number of better-adapted individuals increases. Evolution—through natural selection—is taking place.

In the study of evolution, it is important to remember that populations evolve, but individuals do not. Animals do not fight each other into extinction. The factor that counts most is reproductive success. So the fittest animals are simply those with the most surviving offspring, and not necessarily the biggest, strongest, or fastest.

If the environment changes, different traits or combinations of traits may become more—or less—favorable to survival, and the overall character of the species may change. In this way, a species survives in its environment and avoids extinction. If two populations of a species live in different environments, they will probably develop differently. Eventually they may differ so much that they become two separate species. Charles Darwin, who formulated several theories on evolution, believed all species evolved in this way.

● **anatomy:** *the structure of an animal or plant.*

● **physiology:** *all the functions and activities of a living thing.*

The living environment

As we have learned from our study of evolution, organisms need certain things to survive. For example, all living things must have water. But not all organisms have the same needs. If they did, there would be a constant struggle for a limited supply of the basic essentials of life, such as food, habitat, and mates, and only a few organisms would survive.

Organisms thrive in environments, or habitats, that meet their specific requirements. The conditions necessary for life are generally categorized according to physical and biological factors. Scientists speak of two types of environments in which organisms live: the physical environment and the biological environment.

Such features as climate, geological formations, and soil make up an organism's physical environment. The physical environment determines which kinds of plants and animals can live in a given place. In general, areas with a warm climate and plenty of water can support a wide variety of living things. However, only species with very specific traits can live in extreme environments.

Other living things in the same habitat form the organism's biological environment. All the members of a species living in a particular area form a population; all the animal and plant populations that inhabit the area make up a community. The various populations in a community relate to one another in many ways. In the most basic relationship, organisms obtain nutrients and energy by eating other organisms. Some kinds of animals eat

In order to survive, all living things require certain conditions. Wolves are capable of surviving in almost any habitat, except for deserts and tropical forests. But because of competition from humans, most wolves live in sparsely populated northern regions, such as Alaska, Minnesota, Canada, China, and Russia.

plants, and others eat animals that eat plants. In addition, some types of bacteria and fungi get nutrients and energy from nonliving matter, such as the decaying remains and waste matter of other organisms. An organism's food sources, reproduction, growth, and behavior are all related to its biological environment.

Scientific classification

For the convenience of science, living things are divided into related groups in an orderly arrangement known as scientific classification. The classification is based on the judgment of biologists who have studied many organisms—both living and preserved. Classifications often differ in details because biologists sometimes disagree on how different groups of organisms fit into this scheme. Scientists use Latin and Greek words in scientific classification because early scholars used these languages and because they are "dead" languages and so do not change over time.

Seven groups make up a system in scientific classification—kingdom, phylum or division, class, order, family, genus, and species. The kingdom is the largest group. Until the 1960's, most scientists formally recognized only two major kingdoms—Animalia, the animal kingdom, and Plantae, the plant kingdom. But as they learned more about the microscopic world, scientists realized that a two-kingdom classification system was not precise enough. Today, most biologists use a system that recognizes five kingdoms: Animalia, Plantae, Fungi, Protista, and Monera. For specific information on these five kingdoms, see chapters 11, 12, and 13.

ANIMALIA is the largest of the kingdoms. Animalia consists of multicellular organisms that generally take in and digest their food. Animals depend on other plants or on animals that eat plants for food. Animals have the most complex body features of all living things. This kingdom has more than 1 million named species.

PLANTAE includes such multicellular organisms as flowering and nonflowering plants, grasses, and trees. There are more than 350,000 species of plants.

This blue whale is part of the Animalia, or animal, kingdom, which includes more than 1 million species.

The Plantae, or plant, kingdom includes this hibiscus and more than 350,000 other species.

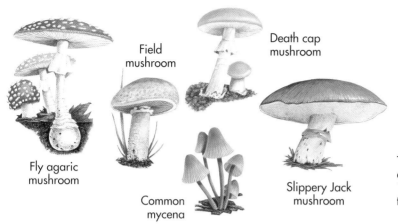

Field mushroom

Death cap mushroom

Fly agaric mushroom

Common mycena

Slippery Jack mushroom

These mushrooms are examples of the 100,000 species in the Fungi kingdom.

FUNGI are multicellular organisms that obtain their food from dead or living organic matter. They include molds and mushrooms. There are more than 100,000 species of fungi.

MONERA—also called Prokaryotae—is made up of bacteria, including cyanobacteria (also known as blue-green algae). Monerans are simple unicellular organisms that can only be seen with a microscope. Monerans differ from living cells in that they lack specialized parts called organelles. (See "Organelles" in Chapter 10.) There are more than 10,000 known species in this kingdom.

PROTISTA includes unicellular microscopic protozoans such as diatoms, ameba, and paramecia, as well as multicellular algae. Scientists divide protists into groups based on how they move. The Protista kingdom has more than 100,000 species. Unlike monerans, unicellular protists contain organelles similar to those in multicellular organisms.

● **protozoans:** *unicellular organisms.*

● **diatoms:** *unicellular aquatic algae with hard shells.*

Cyanobacteria, *below right,* shown here enlarged about 200 times, belong to the Monera kingdom. The ameba, *below left ,* is one of the 100,000 species belonging to the Protista kingdom.

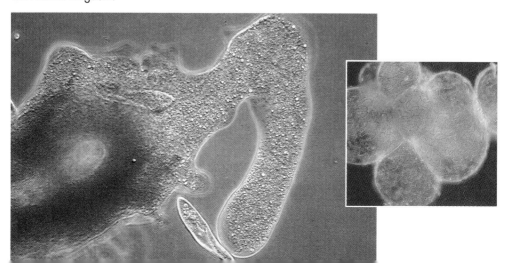

Extinction Is Forever

Throughout the history of life, species have come—and gone. The living things that inhabit the Earth today are only a tiny fraction of all the species that have ever existed. Scientists believe that an incredible 4 billion species of plants and animals have lived and died since life on Earth began. Today more than 2 million species are in existence.

Kinds of extinction

A species becomes extinct when none of its kind remains on Earth. But, according to scientists, not all extinctions are alike. Researchers have distinguished several different types of extinction.

Some groups of organisms simply die out and leave no descendants. One of these groups is a type of flat shellfish called trilobites, which became extinct about 240 million years ago. Some species become extinct over many generations, but leave descendant species that may differ only slightly from the parent species. In other cases, mass extinctions have occurred, in which great numbers of unrelated species of animals have died out over a relatively short period of time. Mass extinction, which has occurred five or six times during geological history, has led to the rise of new animal groups that dominated the Earth for millions of years. For example, after the mass extinction of dinosaurs approximately 65 million years ago, mammals became dominant.

Extinction explained

Extinction is a normal part of nature's balancing act. In order for new species to appear, it seems as though the same number of species must disappear.

Most extinct organisms died out because of natural changes in their environment, such as the cooling of the climate, the loss of their food source, or the destruction of their habitat. For example, a species of plant that has adapted to life in wet, swampy areas might die out if the climate in the area became drier. According to the theory of evolution, this plant, unable to adapt to its new environment, is therefore unfit to survive. No longer able to reproduce itself, the species dies out. However, scientists often disagree about the specific cause of an extinction. For instance, they offer many theories about the disappearance of dinosaurs.

But while extinction has been a necessary part of nature over the ages, many species have died out in recent years due to unnatural—and preventable—events. Plants and animals are disappearing from the face of the Earth today at such an alarming rate that some scientists believe a mass extinction may be in progress. Why is this happening? The answer is expressed in a quote from the comic strip "Pogo" by Walt Kelly—"We have met the enemy and he is us."

Human responsibility

The greatest threat to the survival of wild species is the destruction of their habitat. When people want more space for settlement, farming, or industry, they often damage wildlife habitats. Rain forests are cut down; swamps and marshes are drained. Poor farming practices also destroy land, and the spread of cities and industries paves over wildlife habitats. Pollution poisons the air and the water, the plants and the animals.

Wildlife trade is another practice that has put species at risk. Capturing wild animals for pets, zoos, and research and killing them for their fur or other body parts has wiped out some species and endangered many others. And while many animals are protected by law today, they are still hunted illegally by poachers. Also, a number of species are close to extinction as a result of overhunting and overfishing.

Struggle to save the species

Over the last 200 years, about 100 species of animals have become extinct. The dodo, great auk, Labrador duck, moa, and passenger pigeon are among the birds that have disappeared. Mammals that are now extinct include Steller's sea cow and a form of zebra called a quagga. But people can learn from their mistakes and work to ensure that they don't repeat them.

Endangered species are living things at risk of extinction. Thousands of species of animals and plants are now endangered, and the list grows longer every year. Today's endangered animals include blue whales, some kinds of crocodiles, orangutans, snow leopards, rhinoceroses, tigers, and whooping cranes. Endangered plants include running buffalo clover, Santa Cruz cypress, snakeroot, and many species of cactus. But while the word *extinction* means that a species is gone forever, *endangered* tells us there is still hope. These living things—and all the others—have a chance to survive if each of us makes an effort for conservation.

A number of methods are used to conserve wildlife. We can help by ensuring that their environment provides enough food, water, and shelter. This method, called habitat management, involves soil conservation, good forestry practices, and water management. To save wildlife habitats, people and governments must control pollution and set aside areas in which wild animals and plants can find refuge. An animal threatened by overhunting can be protected by law. If a species can no longer survive in its natural environment, its young may be raised in captivity and then released into a protected area. A

The Indonesian komodo dragon, which grows to be 10 feet (3 meters) long, is an endangered land reptile.

species threatened by disease may be helped by sanitation measures in its habitat. Rare plants can be kept in botanical gardens.

A success story

The effort to save the American buffalo—often called bison—is one success story. Great herds of these animals once roamed over North America between the Appalachian Mountains on the east and the Rockies on the west. Many Native Americans depended on the bison. In 1850, about 20 million of these magnificent animals dominated the Western Plains. Then in the late 1800's, white American hunters slaughtered millions of bison. This mass killing deprived the Native Americans of their main source of food and almost wiped out the bison.

By 1889, only 541 bison could be found in the United States. This near extinction spurred efforts to save the species. Game laws and other protective measures allowed the surviving animals to live and multiply. As a result, about 15,000 bison now live on game preserves in the United States.

10 Cells: Life's Building Blocks

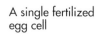

A single fertilized egg cell

The cell is the basic unit of life. All living things are made up of cells—from the ameba with just one cell to the human being with billions. Until about 300 years ago, people wondered how a human being could develop from a single egg cell. Some people thought this cell contained a homunculus—a tiny, completely formed human being. Not until the mid-1600's, when scientists invented the high-powered microscope, could cells be observed. Using such a microscope to look at a piece of cork, the English scientist Robert Hooke was the first to describe plant cells in 1655.

The structure of the cell

The more than 2 million species of plants and animals that live on Earth differ greatly in shape, in size, and in the way they live. But all organisms have one thing in common—they are made up of cells.

Some unicellular organisms lead independent lives, while others live in groups. In plants and animals, the cells are "specialists" with specific work to do. Nerve cells, muscle cells, and other specialized cells group together to form tissues, such as nerve tissue or muscle tissue. Different kinds of tissues form organs, such as the eyes, heart, and lungs. Organs, in turn, form organ systems, such as the circulatory system, which in mammals consists of the heart, lungs, veins, and arteries. Together, all these organ systems form organisms—from dogs to pea plants to human beings.

While all cells are different, they also have much in common. Whether a cell is that of a unicellular organism or just one of many in a multicellular organism, it is alive. It breathes, takes in food, and gets rid of wastes. It also grows, reproduces, and, in time, dies.

The cell is enclosed in an extremely thin (0.00001-millimeter) covering called the *cell membrane,* or *plasma membrane.* This membrane, however, is more like a gate than a solid barrier. Equipped with tiny pores, it regulates everything that enters and leaves the cell, selecting which nutrients, gases, and liquids will pass into the cell, and which will be kept out.

Inside, the cell has two main regions: the nuclear region and the cytoplasmic region. Within the cytoplasmic region are bodies called organelles.

Animal cell

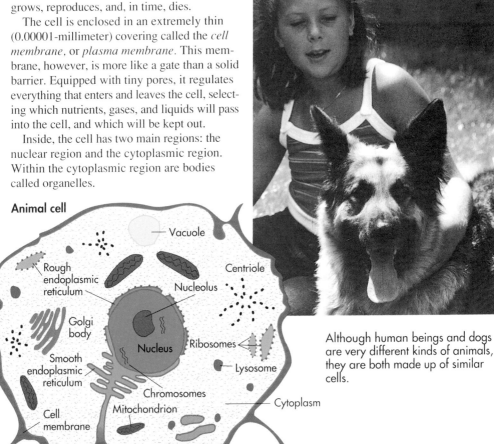

Vacuole
Rough endoplasmic reticulum
Centriole
Nucleolus
Golgi body
Nucleus
Ribosomes
Smooth endoplasmic reticulum
Lysosome
Chromosomes
Cytoplasm
Cell membrane
Mitochondrion

Although human beings and dogs are very different kinds of animals, they are both made up of similar cells.

The nucleus

The nucleus, which controls the cell's activities, is separated from the cytoplasm by the nuclear membrane. This membrane has many pores that allow the movement of molecules between the nucleus and the cytoplasm. Inside the nucleus of most cells are two important types of structures: chromosomes and nucleoli.

CHROMOSOMES play a chief role in cell reproduction because they carry the genes, which are the basic units of heredity. At a certain period in the cell's life, a material called *chromatin* shortens and thickens and forms chromosomes. Chromosomes are composed chiefly of two kinds of organic molecules—*deoxyribonucleic acid* (DNA) and certain proteins. DNA is the substance that carries hereditary instructions and directs the production of RNA. Lined up along the chromosomes' DNA are the genes. *Genes,* each of which is a section of a DNA molecule, determine the thousands of particular characteristics that living things inherit from their parents—such as hair color, eye color, and height.

DNA directs the production of proteins, which make up most of the cell's structures, and certain protein molecules, called enzymes, which speed up many of the cell's functions. The kinds of proteins the cell makes help determine the nature of the cell and, therefore, of the organism itself.

NUCLEOLI are small structures that form in certain regions of specific chromosomes and help in the formation of ribosomes, the centers of protein production. Each nucleus may contain one or more nucleoli, though some cells have none at all.

The cytoplasm

The cytoplasm, which makes up all the material inside the cell except the nucleus, consists of water, carbohydrates, proteins, and lipids, and small amounts of salt, vitamins, and minerals. Many of the cell's activities occur in the cytoplasm, including the manufacture of proteins.

Located throughout the cytoplasm of many cells are tiny structures called *organelles.* The organelles include mitochondria, lysosomes, the endoplasmic reticulum, centrioles, and the Golgi apparatus. Like the organs of the human body, each organelle performs a specific activity vital to maintaining the life of the cell.

MITOCHONDRIA are the cell's powerhouses. They produce a chemical called ATP that supplies almost all the energy the cell needs to live and do its work. A cell may contain hundreds of mitochondria.

LYSOSOMES contain a number of different enzymes that can break down many substances. For example, lysosomes help some cells break down harmful bacteria.

ENDOPLASMIC RETICULUM is a network of elaborate folded membrane systems in the cytoplasm. The surfaces of membranes involved in the manufac-

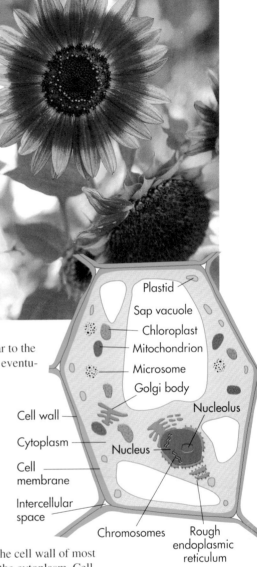

Cells that make up a sunflower plant, *right*, differ from those of animals. A plant cell, *below*, contains chloroplasts rich with chlorophyll, rigid cell walls that make plant stems stiff, and vacuoles that help plants function.

ture of fat molecules are smooth. Other membranes are bordered by *ribosomes*—tiny structures that contain large amounts of RNA, a close chemical relative of DNA. Ribosomes are the cell's protein-manufacturing units. The proteins the cell needs to grow, repair itself, and perform hundreds of chemical operations are made on the ribosomes.

CENTRIOLES lie near the nucleus and are important in cell reproduction.

GOLGI BODIES, found near the cell's surface, are similar to the smooth endoplasmic reticulum. Golgi bodies store and eventually release various products from the cell.

Plant cells

While plant cells and animal cells have a lot in common, plant cells have some special structures. These include chloroplasts, a cell wall, and vacuoles.

Chloroplasts, found in the cytoplasm, are organelles that contain a green substance called chlorophyll. In photosynthesis, chlorophyll uses the energy of light rays from the sun to produce energy-rich sugars. All life depends on these sugars. (See "Photosynthesis" in Chapter 11.)

A *cell wall* surrounds the membrane in plant cells. The cell wall of most plants contains *cellulose*, a substance manufactured in the cytoplasm. Cellulose makes plant stems stiff.

Vacuoles are fluid-filled sacs that are found in some animal cells, and often make up a large part of the plant cell. There are several kinds of vacuoles, each with a different function. Some are active in the cell's metabolism, while others serve as storage.

Plastid
Sap vacuole
Chloroplast
Mitochondrion
Microsome
Golgi body
Cell wall
Cytoplasm
Cell membrane
Intercellular space
Nucleus
Nucleolus
Chromosomes
Rough endoplasmic reticulum

Plant cell

How cells make energy

Green plants trap some of the energy from the sun and use it in photosynthesis to build up the sugars and starches that form the bulk of their tissues. During photosynthesis, plants take minerals and water from the soil and carbon dioxide from the air. In return, they release oxygen—a waste product of their metabolism—into the air.

Animals cannot use such simple chemicals to build up the complex substances that form their bodies. Instead, they must eat and digest food—

plants and animals that eat plants—and reorganize the products of digestion to form tissues. But in order to get energy from their food, animals need oxygen, which plants release into the air. Carbon dioxide, which plants need, is a waste product of an animal's metabolic processes.

Thus nature maintains the balance. Plants and animals complement each other. Each depends on and uses the other's wastes, which are constantly being recycled.

How do cells produce energy? Energy production in animal cells is discussed here. Energy production in plants—a process called photosynthesis—is discussed in the next chapter.

Metabolism

Cells are almost always active. Metabolism is the name for the biochemical process that underlies all cell activity. It has two phases: constructive metabolism, or anabolism, and destructive metabolism, or catabolism. In *anabolism*, cells synthesize complex organic molecules from smaller units. In *catabolism*, the breaking down of large molecules into smaller units releases energy that the cell may use to build other large units. Thousands of these reactions are going on in the cell all the time.

Cellular respiration in animal cells

Cellular respiration is a process in which the products of digestion are broken down into simpler raw materials and energy. This energy is stored in a substance called *adenosine triphosphate* (ATP). Most of an animal's ener-

A cell produces energy through a process called cellular respiration. In digestion, food is broken down into amino acids, fatty acids, and simple sugars. The blood then carries these substances to the cells, where they eventually are oxidized to produce ATP. Carbon dioxide and water leave animals' bodies as waste.

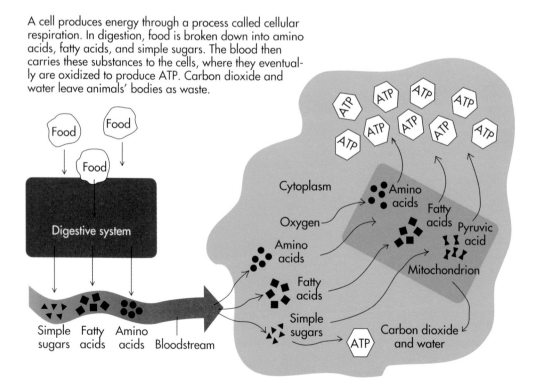

gy is produced in the mitochondria, the "power plants" of the cell, where ATP then supplies energy for all the cell's functions.

ATP production is an extremely complex process. It begins with the digestion of food, which consists, among other things, of proteins, fats, and carbohydrates. In digestion, proteins are broken down into amino acids, fats into fatty acids, and carbohydrates into simple sugars, such as glucose. The blood carries these substances to all the cells in the body.

ATP consists of adenosine (a compound of adenine and the sugar ribose) and three phosphate groups. Chemical bonds—forces that hold atoms together—link the phosphate groups. In building ATP, one phosphate group bonds to adenosine to form *adenosine monophosphate.* Then a second phosphate group is attached by another high-energy bond to form ADP, or adenosine diphosphate. Finally, a third phosphate group is attached by an even higher-energy bond. Now, the substance is ATP. Whenever this last high-energy bond is broken, energy is released, and ATP then loses a phosphate group to revert to ADP.

ATP is ready energy, available for immediate use to make proteins or form chemical bonds in macromolecules such as carbohydrates and lipids, which then store some of the energy. Alternatively, the energy released in other reactions can be used to change ADP back to ATP.

The production of ATP from ADP involves a complex sequence of reactions. Since the breakdown of ATP releases energy, the formation of ATP involves the input of the same amount of energy. That energy is produced by the gradual oxidation of molecules, including sugars, fatty acids, and amino acids. Eventually, these molecules are oxidized to carbon dioxide and water, which leave animals' bodies through excretion and expiration.

● **oxidation:** *the loss of an electron, often through the addition of oxygen or the subtraction of hydrogen.*

Cellular respiration involves two major processes: glycolysis and the Krebs cycle. A system called the hydrogen carrier system occurs along with cellular respiration.

THE GLYCOLYSIS PROCESS. The breakdown of glucose, a six-carbon sugar, in a process called glycolysis marks the start of many metabolic pathways. This process eventually produces raw materials for other synthetic pathways and the ATP to complete the chemical reactions in cells. The name glycolysis

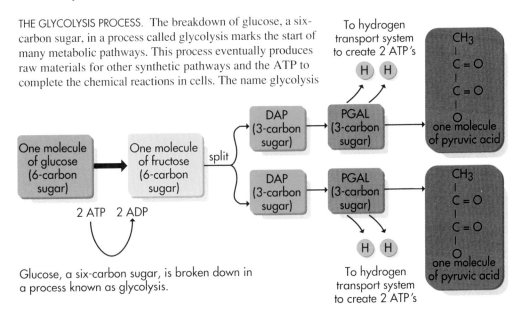

Glucose, a six-carbon sugar, is broken down in a process known as glycolysis.

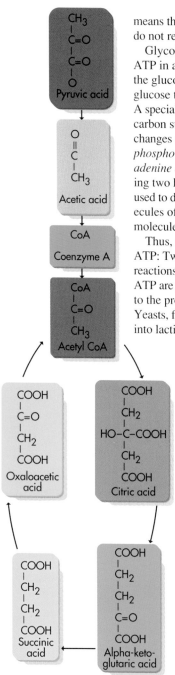

means the breakdown, or splitting (lysis), of sugar (glucose). These reactions do not require oxygen, so they are also called *anaerobic metabolism.*

Glycolysis begins with the activation of glucose with two molecules of ATP in a two-step process. Each ATP molecule adds a phosphate group to the glucose molecule to create a modified form of glucose. This modified glucose then changes into another kind of six-carbon sugar called *fructose.* A special enzyme splits the fructose molecule into two molecules of a three-carbon sugar called *dihydroxyacetone phosphate* (DAP). Another enzyme changes each DAP molecule into another form of three-carbon sugar called *phospho-glyceraldehyde* (PGAL). A hydrogen carrier called *nicotinamide-adenine dinucleotide* (NAD) then oxidizes the PGAL molecules by removing two hydrogen atoms from each, and energy is released. This energy is used to drive other reactions during glycolysis for the formation of four molecules of ATP. The PGAL molecules have now been converted into two molecules of a three-carbon compound called *pyruvic acid.*

Thus, at the completion of glycolysis, the net gain is two molecules of ATP: Two molecules of ATP are used to activate the glucose and begin the reactions, four hydrogen atoms are eventually removed, four molecules of ATP are generated, and pyruvic acid is synthesized. Pyruvic acid contributes to the production of a number of important compounds within organisms. Yeasts, for instance, convert pyruvic acid into alcohol. Mammals convert it into lactic acid, fatty acids, and other compounds.

THE KREBS CYCLE is one of a number of pathways that pyruvic acid can take following glycolysis. The Krebs cycle occurs only in cells with mitochondria in the presence of oxygen. In these reactions, carbon dioxide and positive hydrogen ions and their electrons are removed from molecules to combine with oxygen and form water. In this process, 36 molecules of ATP are generated. This series of reactions was named after a German biochemist who worked in England named Sir Hans Krebs, who worked out the series of reactions. The Krebs cycle is also called the *tricarboxylic acid cycle* or the *citric acid cycle.*

In the first step of the Krebs cycle, pyruvic acid produced by glycolysis is converted to a two-carbon molecule called *acetic acid* by the removal of a carbon dioxide molecule. Acetic acid then can combine with a substance called *coenzyme A* (CoA), forming *acetyl coenzyme A* (acetyl CoA). Acetyl CoA reacts with a four-carbon molecule called *oxaloacetic acid* and forms a six-carbon molecule—*citric acid.* Citric acid is converted to a five-carbon molecule—*alpha-ketoglutaric acid*—by the removal of carbon dioxide and two hydrogens and their electrons. The alpha-ketoglutaric acid is converted to a different kind of four-carbon molecule called *succinic acid.* This step yields more ATP and water. In one additional step, the succinic acid is converted to oxaloacetic acid. The oxaloacetic acid then joins with another acetyl CoA molecule to form a new citric acid molecule. This citric acid follows the same steps as those listed above, continuing the cycle.

Pyruvic acid is converted into carbon dioxide and water in a series of chemical reactions called the Krebs cycle.

THE HYDROGEN TRANSPORT SYSTEM is a series of coupled reactions that results in the production of water. It occurs along with glycolysis and the Krebs cycle. The hydrogen transport system uses a series of enzymes and coenzymes, sometimes called *cytochromes,* to transfer hydrogen ions and their electrons to a final hydrogen ion acceptor—oxygen. The hydrogen ions and their electrons combine with the oxygen, forming water as a by-product.

The energy released in the hydrogen transport system is used to form the bonds between ADP and a phosphate group to generate ATP, a source of stored energy for an organism. For every two hydrogen ions and their electrons that go through the Krebs cycle and the hydrogen transport system, three molecules of ATP are produced. In this way, a glucose molecule with 12 hydrogen atoms is able to generate 36 ATP molecules. Together with the two ATP's produced during glycolysis, the final production of ATP is 38 molecules.

Cell reproduction

Every living thing is made up of one or more cells, and each of these cells was produced by an already existing cell. New cells are formed by growth and reproduction, creating two cells where there once was only one. Unicellular organisms begin and complete their lives as a single cell.

Many-celled organisms like plants and animals begin life as a single cell. However, after the single cell grows to a certain size, it divides and forms two cells. These two cells grow and divide, forming four cells. These cells grow and divide over and over again in the process of replication called mitosis. Inside each cell, DNA molecules carry all the information the organism needs to grow and develop and form all an organism's specialized body structures.

● **replication:** *the process of making a duplicate copy.*

The structure of DNA

The DNA molecule is described as a *double helix.* It looks like a twisted rope ladder. The "ladder" is in two parts, split down the middle of its "rungs." The DNA ladder is formed by joining the half-rungs.

The two sides of the DNA ladder are composed of alternating phosphate molecules and a sugar called *deoxyribose.* The rungs of the ladder are made up of four compounds called *nucleic bases.* These bases—adenine, cytosine, guanine, and thymine (A, C, G, and T)— are attached to the sugar units that make up the ladder's sides. Each rung consists of two bases: A-T, T-A, C-G, or G-C. The bases' chemical makeup makes no other pairing possible.

Bacteria and other simple organisms usually have only one molecule of DNA. But most plant and animal cells have many more than that to carry all the information their bodies need.

Chromosomes and genes

Each molecule of DNA is protected by special proteins that form a chromosome. All organisms have a specific number of chromosomes in each of their cells. Dog cells have 78 chromosomes, pea plant cells have 14, and human beings have 46.

Chromosomes are divided into sections called *genes*—the carriers of hereditary information. This information is coded in the sequence of bases along the DNA molecule. There is a separate gene for each structure and each characteristic of an individual. Genes line up on chromosomes like beads on a necklace. And just as we can see where each bead is on a necklace, scientists have been able to identify where different genes are located on chromosomes.

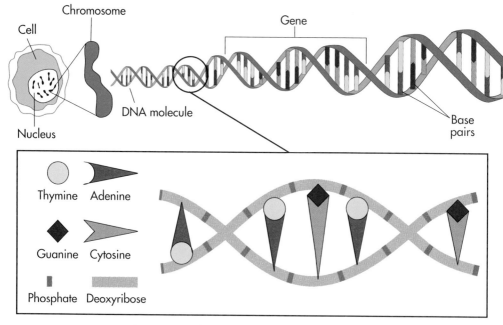

Chromosomes, located in the cell nucleus, *top left,* are divided into sections called genes. Genes are made up of DNA, which is shaped like a twisted ladder, *top right.* Hereditary information is coded in a sequence of bases located on the rungs of the DNA ladder. Each rung of DNA consists of two matching bases, *above right.* The sides are sugar and phosphate.

Mitosis

The process by which most cells divide is called mitosis. In mitosis, a cell divides into two identical cells, called *daughter cells.* Each daughter cell then doubles in size and also becomes capable of dividing. In order to be identical, each daughter cell must have a copy of the DNA carried by the genes on the chromosomes. The cell must make a copy of its chromosomes before it can divide.

Mitosis takes place in four stages: prophase, metaphase, anaphase, and telophase. Between mitoses, the cell is in interphase. Scientists once referred to interphase as a "resting stage," but they have since discovered that the cell is quite active during interphase. At this stage, many of the cell's structures double prior to the next mitotic division.

Near the end of interphase, the chromosomes double by way of replication. In this process, a special enzyme unwinds a DNA molecule. As the DNA unwinds, the strands split down the middle of the rungs and separate. New DNA strands begin to form next to the open strands. Special enzymes hold the new strands to the old strands by lining up adenine next to thymine (A-T) and guanine next to cytosine (G-C). Replication continues until all the DNA has been copied.

PROPHASE. During prophase, the first stage of mitosis, the chromosomes begin to condense into threads that become progressively shorter and thicker. As a result of replication, each chromosome consists of two identical structures called chromatids. The chromatids are joined together by a ring-like structure called a *centromere*.

The *centrioles*—the two bundles of rods outside the cell's nucleus—doubled prior to mitosis, just as the chromosomes did. As prophase progresses, each pair of centrioles begins to move apart and long fibers appear in the cell. The centrioles move to opposite sides of the cell and form structures called *poles*. The long fibers extend across the cell between these two poles, forming a *spindle*. Toward the end of prophase, the nuclear membrane and nucleolus or nucleoli of the cell dissolve.

METAPHASE. In metaphase, the chromatids move to the middle of the spindle, called the *equator*. Still joined, the chromatids line up on opposite sides of the equator. Each chromatid is attached to a spindle fiber.

Mitosis

Nucleus   Chromosomes   Spindle   Chromatids   Spindle   Chromosome

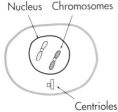   

Centrioles   Centrioles   Centrioles

1. An animal cell with two chromosomes is about to divide. Before it does, the chromosomes and centrioles duplicate.

2. The centrioles move to opposite sides of the cell, forming a spindle across it. The duplicated sister chromatids go to the spindle's middle.

3. The sister chromatids now separate. The members of each pair move to opposite sides of the cell, and each becomes a new chromosome.

4. The cell splits in two. Each new daughter cell receives identical chromosomes. They are exact duplicates of those of the parent cell.

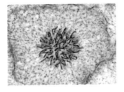   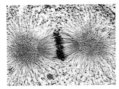   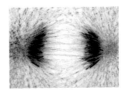   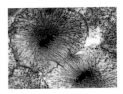

ANAPHASE. When anaphase begins, the centromeres separate, and each chromatid becomes a new chromosome. Now free, the chromosomes separate and move to the opposite poles.

TELOPHASE. In telophase, the final stage, the cell splits at the equator. This results in the ultimate goal of mitosis—two new identical cells. Each new cell has a full set of chromosomes and contains the same hereditary information as the original cell.

Mitosis in plant cells is somewhat different from mitosis in animal cells. For example, cells in multicellular plants do not have centrioles, but they form a spindle similar to that formed in animal cells.

Meiosis

Human beings and many other organisms reproduce sexually. A new individual can be produced only if a male sex cell, called a *sperm,* unites with a female sex cell, called an egg. Sex cells are produced in special reproductive tissues or organs called ovaries in females and testes in males. At first, new sex cells are produced by mitosis. But before a sex cell matures, it goes through another kind of cell division called meiosis.

While mitosis involves a single division of cells, meiosis consists of two separate divisions. During interphase in meiosis, as in mitosis, the genetic material is replicated. Then in prophase, the chromosomes, which now consist of two joined chromatids, line up side by side in pairs with other closely related chromosomes. In metaphase, each pair of doubled chromosomes

Meiosis

Nucleus   Chromosomes   Spindle   Chromosomes   Chromatids   Nucleus

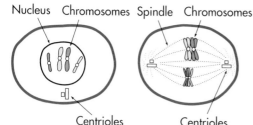
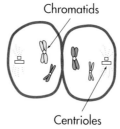
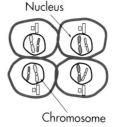

Centrioles   Centrioles   Centrioles   Chromosome

1. A cell with four chromosomes is about to undergo meiosis. In preparation, the chromosomes duplicate. The similar ones then pair up.

2. The doubled pairs of chromosomes move to the middle of the spindle. The doubled members separate and go to opposite sides of the cell.

3. The first division of meiosis occurs. Each of the new cells receives one member of each original pair. Each member consists of two chromatids.

4. The sister chromatids in the two cells separate. The cells divide. The four resulting cells thus get one chromosome from each pair.

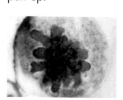
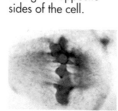
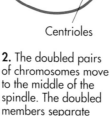

moves to the equator, and during telophase, the paired chromosomes separate. One chromosome, still consisting of two chromatids, migrates toward one pole; the other chromosome moves toward the opposite pole. Then the cell divides along the equator. Each daughter cell thus receives one chromosome, made up of two chromatids, from each original pair. These new cells then divide once more.

The goal of the second division—a process that resembles the first division—is to supply each new daughter cell with one of each of the chromatids. Thus meiosis produces four sex cells, each of which contains half the number of chromosomes found in all the other cells of the organism.

How proteins are made

Proteins are composed of one or more long, folded polypeptide chains. These polypeptide chains are in turn composed of small chemical units called amino acids. All amino acids contain carbon, hydrogen, oxygen, and nitrogen, and some also contain sulfur. Twenty different amino acids are involved in protein production, but any number of proteins may be linked in any order to form a polypeptide chain. Some polypeptide chains contain only 10 amino acids, while others contain more than 100. Each different arrangement of amino acids forms a different polypeptide chain. Thus, the number of different chains and the number of different proteins that can be formed is seemingly endless.

Proteins—complex, three-dimensional substances—form all the structures of living organisms and all the enzymes that control their functions. Cell membranes, organelles, and cytoplasm are all made up of proteins. Enzymes; antibodies, which help the human body fight disease; and hormones, the substances that regulate chemical activities throughout your body, are proteins.

In order to produce proteins, hereditary information is coded in the sequence of the bases along the DNA molecule. The code directs the production of amino acids, which—linked together in polypeptide chains—are the basic components of all proteins.

Transcription

Transcription, a process vital to protein production, is very similar to replication in cell reproduction. In transcription, a strand of DNA codes the building of a partial copy of itself. The code controls protein production, but the DNA does not leave the nucleus to help make proteins. DNA's close chemical relative—*ribonucleic acid (RNA)*—does this work.

RNA is manufactured in the nucleus of the cell and is present in both the nucleus and the cytoplasm. RNA resembles DNA in chemical structure, but there are two major differences. The sugar in RNA is ribose instead of deoxyribose, and RNA contains the base uracil (U) instead of thymine. Like thymine, uracil will pair only with adenine.

We can learn how proteins are made by following the production of a protein consisting of only one polypeptide chain. The first step takes place in the nucleus, where the two sides of the DNA double helix split apart. A molecule of a type of RNA, called *messenger RNA (mRNA)*, then forms

How proteins are made

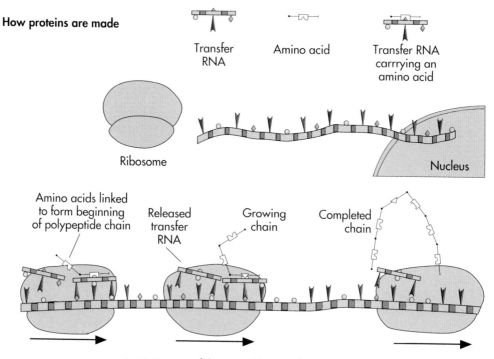

An RNA copy of the DNA blueprint for a particular protein is made in the nucleus. This messenger RNA then goes to a ribosome in the cytoplasm, where it lines up amino acids in the proper order. Transfer RNA collects amino acids in the cytoplasm. Each kind of transfer RNA carries a specific amino acid. The amino acids link together, and the transfer RNA is released. As the ribosome moves down the messenger RNA, a polypeptide chain forms. The final segment of messenger RNA signals that the chain is complete.

from free nucleotides that are floating in the nucleus. The nucleotides pair with the bases of the section of DNA coded for the protein under construction. In this way, mRNA makes a copy of the DNA blueprint for the polypeptide chain.

Next, the mRNA leaves the nucleus and enters the cytoplasm. Once there, it acts as a template, or pattern, for the building of amino acids into proteins. The mRNA then travels to the cell's centers of protein production—the ribosomes. A ribosome moves along the mRNA, "reading" the information coded on it. The mRNA acts as a guide, lining up the amino acids in the exact order called for by the DNA of the genes. The amino acids are then linked together one by one to form a new polypeptide chain.

Translation

The amino acids needed to make proteins are spread throughout the cytoplasm. Individual amino acid units must be picked up and brought to the template in the right order. This work, called translation, is done by another type of RNA—*transfer RNA (tRNA)*. Transfer RNA collects the appropriate amino acids in the cytoplasm and brings them to the mRNA in the ribosome. There is at least one tRNA molecule for each kind of amino acid. The specific tRNA and the correct amino acid are brought together with the help of ATP—adenosine triphosphate, an energy-supplying compound formed in the cell—and a special enzyme.

At any one time, the ribosome covers two coding segments of mRNA, called codons. Each of these codons, which consist of a sequence of three bases, specifies one amino acid. The correct tRNA, with its amino acid attached, lines up on the first codon of the mRNA template. After a second tRNA and its amino acid have lined up on the other codon, the two amino acids are linked. The first tRNA is then set free to collect more amino acids. The second tRNA holds the growing polypeptide chain to the ribosome. The ribosome then moves one codon further down the mRNA, while the appropriate tRNA, with its attached amino acid, lines up on this codon. The amino acid is joined to the first two amino acids, and the second tRNA is then set free. The ribosome moves one position further, covering the next codon on the mRNA template.

This process continues until the ribosome has passed over the entire length of the mRNA, codon by codon. The last codon on the mRNA signals that the chain is complete. The finished polypeptide chain is then released. In this single polypeptide chain, the protein is complete.

In most proteins consisting of more than one polypeptide chain, the chains are manufactured separately and combine to make the protein. The finished protein then begins to do its particular job. Some proteins are used inside the cell. Other proteins, such as hormones and enzymes, are released from the cell to do their work.

Genetics

All animals begin life as a single cell—the result of joining a sperm cell with an egg cell. If everything has gone right, that new cell contains all the chromosomes the animal will ever need. Half of these chromosomes come from one parent and half come from the other parent.

Chromosomes are important to the cell's development and function in a number of ways. We can better understand the process by discussing how a human being develops. Like any other animal, humans begin life as a single cell. When humans begin to develop, this single cell divides by mitosis. The resulting cells continue to divide until all the millions of cells that make up the human body are present. Inside the nucleus of each of those cells is a copy of a complete set of 46 chromosomes—23 from each parent.

Early in the development of a human being, the cells begin to *differentiate*, or specialize in various categories, such as muscle cells, skin cells, and nerve cells. The different cells then group into tissues that form organs, such as the heart, lungs, and liver. Scientists do not completely understand the process of differentiation, but they think certain protein molecules called enzymes may cause cells to specialize—meaning that different kinds of cells develop as a result of the action of different kinds of enzymes.

The genetic code

The message of mRNA is called the genetic code. The genetic code is used to convert the sequence of DNA into the sequence of amino acids in proteins. The code lies in the order of the bases in the DNA molecule. This order of bases is passed on from one generation to the next, and from one generation of an organism to the next. The order of the bases determines, for example, that a giraffe gives birth to a giraffe, not an elephant. And it is this order that determines the color of our eyes, the shape of our ears, and all our other traits.

As we have seen, the order of the 4 bases arranged in triplets determines the order of the 20 amino acids when the cell produces specific proteins. The instructions for making specific proteins are carried by specific genes and each gene contains a certain number of bases in a certain order.

How can the order of only 4 bases determine the order of 20 amino acids in a protein chain? The answer lies in the triplet code. In other words, a group of three bases in a certain order forms the codon for a specific amino acid. Each codon is given a three-letter name made up of an abbreviation of the names of its bases. For example, the codon for the amino acid tryptophan is UGG, which stands for Uracil-Guanine-Guanine.

A total of 64 three-letter codons can be formed from the 4 letters of the DNA bases. Because there are only 20 amino acids—and not 64—there is more than one codon for most amino acids. Three of the codons, UAA, UAG, and UGA, act as signals for the release of the polypeptide chain from the ribosome and do not code for any amino acid.

Identical twin Olympic skiers Phil, *right,* and Steve Mahre look so much alike because they share the same genetic makeup.

Heredity

Most offspring produced by sexual reproduction look a lot like their parents—but not exactly like them. Similarities and differences among parents and their offspring are a result of heredity. Inheritance is a complex process in which characteristics—which may or may not show themselves in the offspring—are passed on.

Among the chromosomes contained in every organism's cells are thousands to millions of genes, each of which controls one or more characteristics and all of which are responsible for what a new individual is—and will become. Except for genes on the sex chromosomes in males (see next section), genes occur in pairs. Each pair of genes is contained in a pair of chromosomes—one from the mother and one from the father—with one copy of a gene in each chromosome. Each chromosome carries about 1,000 genes. Some traits are determined by a single pair of genes. Others are determined by several pairs. For example, about six pairs of genes influence skin color and each skin-color gene causes a slight darkening of the skin. People with extremely dark skin may have up to six pairs of skin-color genes. From tens

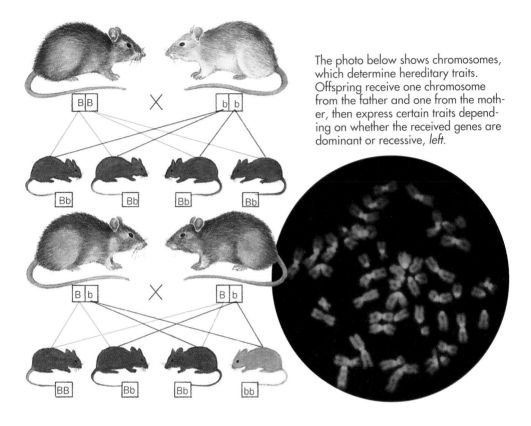

The photo below shows chromosomes, which determine hereditary traits. Offspring receive one chromosome from the father and one from the mother, then express certain traits depending on whether the received genes are dominant or recessive, *left.*

to hundreds of gene pairs influence traits such as height, weight, and intelligence.

A gene is positioned on a chromosome at its gene locus, a location that corresponds with the position of the gene's "partner" on the other chromosome of that homologous pair. Each gene is an *allele,* and a pair of alleles controls or modifies a single characteristic in a normal body cell. The only exception to this is in a gamete, or sex cell, where only one of each pair of alleles is carried. A gene is called *homozygous* when its two alleles are identical, and *heterozygous* when they are different.

The two alleles in a pair may differ in the effects they produce. In some cases, one allele has such a strong effect that it overpowers the action of the other. A heterozygous gene contains one *dominant* allele and one *recessive* allele. A homozygous gene contains either two recessive or two dominant alleles. Dominant alleles always prevail, that is, the trait they code for appears in the offspring. A recessive trait shows itself only when they are homozygous—that is when an individual has two recessive alleles for that trait. For example, in humans, the gene for brown eyes is dominant (B), and the gene for blue eyes is recessive (b). Only offspring that have received one gene for blue eyes from their father (b) and one gene for blue eyes from their mother (b) will have blue eyes (bb). Offspring that receive one gene for blue eyes from their father (b) and one gene for brown eyes (B) from their mother have brown eyes (Bb).

● **homologous:**
matching or corresponding.

Each person has a maximum of two alleles of any gene, but some genes exist in more than two forms. Such genes are said to have multiple alleles. For example, three alleles are involved in determining blood type—an A allele, a B allele, and an O allele. A person who has two of the same allele has the corresponding blood type—A, B, or O. Both A and B are dominant over O. Thus, a person who inherits one A allele and one O allele will have type A blood, and a person who inherits one B allele and one O allele will have type B blood. A person with one A allele and one B allele has type AB blood.

Sex chromosomes

Two of the chromosomes an animal receives from its parents determine its gender—male or female. Sex chromosomes are called either X or Y chromosomes. Females have two X chromosomes in each of their cells. Males have one X and one Y chromosome in each cell. Males always receive their Y chromosome from their father and their X chromosome from their mother. Females get one X chromosome from each parent.

When an immature sex cell in a female goes through meiosis, the X chromosomes pair with each other and separate just like the other chromosomes. Each egg cell thus receives a single X chromosome. However, when an immature sex cell in a male undergoes meiosis, the X and Y chromosomes pair with each other and separate. As a result, half of the sperm cells have an X chromosome, and the other half have a Y chromosome.

If a sperm cell containing an X chromosome fertilizes an egg cell, the fertilized egg will have two X chromosomes and will therefore develop into a female. If a sperm cell containing a Y chromosome fertilizes the egg cell, the fertilized egg will have one X chromosome and one Y chromosome and will develop into a male.

Sex chromosomes determine the gender of a fertilized egg. All female sex cells carry X chromosomes. Half of all male sex cells carry X chromosomes; the rest carry Y chromosomes.

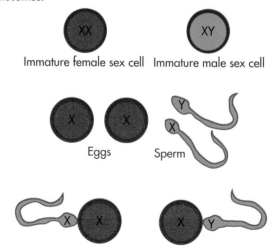

Immature female sex cell   Immature male sex cell

Eggs   Sperm

Genetic Engineering: Helping Mother Nature

Imagine a world where fruits and vegetables are always fresh, delicious, and filled with megavitamins; where parents can be assured of giving birth to babies with no birth defects; and where people can live without the fear of life-threatening disease. Does all this sound like science fiction? Believe it or not, it's more like modern science.

The above scenario could become reality in our lifetime, thanks to genetic engineering. This technique involves the manipulation of genes to achieve a particular goal. In other words, scientists can give an organism and its offspring different traits than nature intended by changing the organism's genes.

The idea behind genetic engineering is not new. For years, breeders of plants and animals have used breeding methods to produce the most desirable combinations of genes. These forerunners of today's "genetic engineers" have produced most of the popular varieties of flowers, vegetables, grains, cows, horses, dogs, and cats. In the 1970's and the 1980's, scientists took "breeding" to the cel-

lular level—the source of physical traits—when they learned how to isolate individual genes and reintroduce them into cells and living organisms. Such techniques alter the heredity of the cells or organisms.

Isolating genes

As we know, genes are located on chromosomes. Each chromosome contains a single molecule of DNA, and a molecule of DNA may contain thousands of genes. Within its chemical structure, DNA stores the information that determines thousands of an organism's characteristics.

To isolate a specific gene, scientists use a technique called gene splicing. In this procedure, a gene-sized fragment of DNA is isolated from one organism and joined to a DNA molecule from another organism or from the same organism. Gene-sized DNA fragments are isolated by *restriction enzymes*, which react chemically with a specific base sequence in the DNA molecule and break the molecule at that point, called a cleavage site.

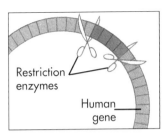

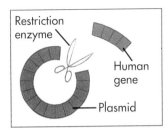

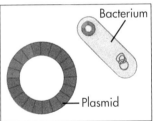

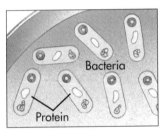

Scientists create genetically identical cells in a process called cloning. A genetic engineer uses a restriction enzyme to snip out a human gene that codes for a particular protein, *top left*. The restriction enzyme opens a DNA molecule called a plasmid, *top right*. The engineer joins a fragment of DNA to the plasmid, *bottom left*. Transformation occurs, and the transformed cells multiply, cloning the new genetic information, *bottom right*.

After a gene has been isolated, an enzyme called ligase is used to splice the gene to another DNA fragment. The hybrid molecule formed—called *recombinant DNA*—is then inserted back into a cell where it replicates as the cell divides by mitosis. Thus, the number of recombinant DNA molecules increases rapidly.

Cloning around

Some bacteria contain small, circular DNA molecules called plasmids. Plasmids are found in the bacterial cell outside the cell's chromosomes. A genetic engineer uses a restriction enzyme to isolate and split a plasmid at a cleavage site. Using ligase to form a hybrid circular molecule of DNA, the engineer then can join a fragment of DNA from any source to the plasmid. When hybrid DNA plasmids are mixed with specially prepared bacterial cells, a few of the cells take up the plasmid that contains the hybrid molecule in a process called *transformation*. The genetic engineer then places a mixture of bacterial cells on a special culture medium so that the "transformed" cells are widely separated. Each of the transformed cells carrying the newly added genetic information grows overnight into a colony of millions of cells. This colony represents a *clone*—a group of genetically identical cells.

Genetic engineering at work

Scientists who study genetic engineering believe that the fruits of their labor can—and will—affect our lives in several important ways. Already they have found helpful uses for genetic engineering in a number of areas.

In medicine, scientists can now produce large quantities of the hormone insulin in bacterial "factories" by splicing the insulin gene from human cells to plasmids from cells of *Escherichia coli (E. coli)* bacteria. This manufactured insulin has saved the lives of millions of diabetes patients. Many other illnesses that are caused by the failure of certain body cells to make specific proteins may be treatable using proteins manufactured through the techniques of genetic engineering. Many people suffer from diseases caused by inherited genetic defects. Using recombinant DNA techniques, scientists have tested DNA isolated from the cells of unborn babies to find out whether the babies have a genetic disease. Doctors eventually may be able to prevent such diseases by treating babies before they are born.

Researchers have also investigated methods of gene therapy in an effort to cure people of diseases. Such methods involve inserting genes from a healthy individual or organism into a patient's cells outside the body and then returning the altered cells into the patient's body.

In industry, scientists have used genetically engineered microbes to improve the efficiency of food production. For example, rennin, an enzyme used in making cheese, is produced naturally in the stomachs of calves. Gene-splicing can manufacture rennin at a lower cost. Genetic engineering may also help control pollution. Researchers are working to develop microorganisms that chemically break down garbage, toxic substances, and other wastes.

Agricultural specialists have used genetic engineering to make food production more efficient. Genetic engineers have learned how to obtain large amounts of growth hormone found in cows from genetically engineered bacteria. When treated with this hormone, dairy cows increase their milk production, and beef cattle have leaner meat. Genetic engineers have also created types of corn that are more nutritious and resistant to chemicals used to kill weeds. In addition, farmers have used products made with genetically altered bacteria to protect crops from insects and frost.

What the future holds

In spite of these successes, genetic engineers say they have barely scraped the surface. Scientists are now working on the Human Genome Project, a $3-billion effort to isolate and identify each of the more than 100,000 genes that exist on the human genome—the strand of DNA in the nucleus of each human cell. Scientists hope to complete this project in about 20 years. If they succeed, they will know the order of all the base codes in DNA, giving them the ability to read nature's blueprint for the creation of a human being.

The knowledge that flows from this work will have a powerful impact on medicine and other sciences, industry, agriculture, law, and the environment. For example, doctors will be able to take a blood sample from a newborn infant, extract DNA from the blood, and insert the DNA into a machine that can analyze some 100 genes. Doctors will then know if an infant is predisposed to any number of common diseases. Based on the genetic profile, the machine will dispense medical advice. The genetic profile might show that the individual has a tendency toward skin cancer, for example, and the machine will therefore advise that the person avoid overexposure to the sun. In addition, agricultural scientists will produce new and revolutionary plants that will provide disease-resistant fruits; vegetables with a longer shelf life; and low-fat, high-fiber foods. Scientists can devise a means of extracting lead and nitrous oxides from the air along highways.

The pros and cons

Although genetic engineering has already improved our lives in a number of ways, many people feel it has serious drawbacks. Some oppose genetic engineering because they fear that harmful, uncontrollable bacteria might be accidentally produced. Others worry about possible environmental damage by the deliberate introduction of organisms whose heredity has been altered. And many people question the morality of manipulating the genetic material of living creatures.

With the awesome potential of genetic engineering at our doorstep, we must develop an ethical and moral code to match—and control—its potential in the coming century.

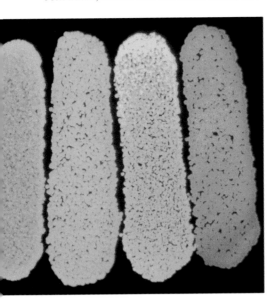

Gene-splicing can be used to make an organism express traits of another organism. When researchers splice genes of a bioluminescent (light-producing) Jamaican beetle called the kittyboo into colonies of bacteria, the bacteria glow, *left.*

11 The Plant World

Desert mallow

Plants are the oldest living things on Earth. Without plants, the Earth would be lifeless. The oxygen that humans breathe comes from plants, and the food we eat comes from plants or from animals that eat plants.

Plants differ from other living organisms in a number of ways. Plants generally cannot move around. The cells—the building blocks of life—in plants and animals are different. One important difference is that some plant cells contain the green pigment chlorophyll. Chlorophyll enables most plants to make their own food from air, sunlight, and water in a process called photosynthesis.

Parts of a plant

All plants consist of various kinds of cells, each with a particular job. Together these cells form the different parts, or tissues, of the plant.

Plants are made up of several different types of tissues. All plants, except bryophytes—mosses, liverworts, and hornworts—have vascular tissue, which carries water, minerals, and other nutrients throughout the plant. This tissue is made up of two specialized tissues called xylem and phloem. *Xylem* tissue, which is tough and woody, consists of cells that carry water and minerals from the roots to the leaves. *Phloem* tissue is made up of cells that carry food produced in the leaves by photosynthesis to other parts of the plant. Plants that have these tissues are called *vascular* plants. Bryophytes, which lack xylem and phloem, are called *nonvascular* plants.

Plants have several important parts. Flowering plants, the most common type of plant, have four main parts: roots, stems, leaves, and flowers. The roots, stems, and leaves are the *vegetative* parts of the plant. The flowers are the *reproductive* parts.

ROOTS generally grow underground. They anchor the plant and absorb essential water and minerals from the soil. The roots of some plants also store food. Many popular vegetables, such as beets, carrots, radishes, and sweet potatoes, come from plants with storage-type roots.

Plants have two main kinds of root systems—fibrous and taproot. A plant with a *fibrous* root system, such as grass, has many slender roots of about the same size that spread out in all directions. Plants with *taproot* systems, such as carrots and radishes, have one root that is larger than the rest and grows straight down.

The root of a plant is one of the first parts to grow. First, a *primary root* develops from the plant's seed and quickly sprouts branches, called *secondary roots*. A *root cap* at the tip of each root protects the tip as it pushes

Fibrous roots, *left,* anchor a tree in place and nourish it by absorbing water and minerals from the soil.

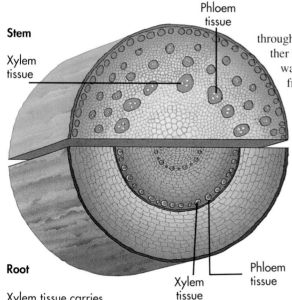

Stem

Xylem
tissue

Phloem
tissue

Root

Xylem
tissue

Phloem
tissue

Xylem tissue carries water and minerals from a plant's roots, *bottom*, to the stem, *top*, and leaves. Phloem tissue carries sugar from the leaves to the root for use or storage.

through the soil. Threadlike *root hair*s grow farther back on the root and absorb most of the water and minerals that the plant takes in from the soil.

STEMS differ greatly among various species of plants. They make up the largest parts of some kinds of plants. For example, the trunk, branches, and twigs of trees are all stems. Other plants, such as cabbage and lettuce, have such short stems and large leaves that they appear to have no stems at all. The stems of some plants, including potatoes, grow partly underground.

Most stems grow upright and support the plant's leaves and reproductive organs so that they can receive sunlight. *Aerial stems* grow aboveground, and *subterranean stems* grow underground. Aerial stems are either woody or herbaceous. Plants with *woody stems*, such as trees and shrubs, are rigid because they contain large amounts of xylem tissue. Most *herbaceous stems* are soft and green because they contain very little xylem tissue.

In almost all plants, the stem grows in length from the end, called the *apex*. The cells that form this growth area are called the *apical meristem*. The apical meristem produces a column of new cells behind itself, and these cells develop into the specialized tissues of the stem and leaves. The apical meristem and the cluster of developing leaves that surround it form a *bud*. Buds may grow on various locations on the stem, and may develop into branches, leaves, or flowers. A *terminal bud* forms at the end of a branch. A *lateral bud* develops at a point where a leaf joins the stem—an area called the *node*. The buds of many plants remain inactive during the winter and then resume their growth in the spring.

LEAVES use photosynthesis to make most of the food needed by most kinds of plants. In photosynthesis, the chlorophyll in the leaves absorbs light energy from sunlight. This energy is used to combine water and minerals from the soil with carbon dioxide from the air. The food formed by this process is used for growth and repair, or stored in special areas in the stems or roots.

Leaves differ greatly in size and shape. Most plants have broad, flat leaves. Many of these leaves have smooth edges, but others have toothed or wavy edges. Grass and certain other plants have long, slender leaves with smooth edges. A few kinds of leaves, including the needles of pine trees and the spines of cactuses, are rounded and have sharp ends.

The leaves of most plants are arranged in a definite pattern. Many leaves grow in an *alternate* pattern, in which only one leaf forms at each node. On plants with the simplest kind of alternate pattern, a leaf appears first on one side of the stem and then on the other side. On plants with a more complex alternate pattern, the nodes are spaced in a spiral around the stem and the leaves seem to encircle the stem as they grow up the plant. If two leaves grow from opposite sides of the same node, the plant has an *opposite* arrangement of leaves. If three or more leaves grow equally spaced around a single node, the plant has a *whorled* arrangement of leaves.

Leaves begin as small bumps next to the apical meristem and most develop two main parts—the blade and the petiole. The *blade* is the flat part of the leaf. The *petiole* is the thin leafstalk that grows between the base of the blade and the stem. The petiole carries water and food to and from the blade. The leaves of some plants also have *stipules*—leaflike structures that grow where the petiole joins the stem.

A network of veins distributes water to the leaf's food-producing areas. These veins also help support the leaf and hold its surface up to the sun. The outer layer of cells on a plant, including the upper and lower surfaces of a leaf, are called the *epidermis*. The epidermis has tiny openings called *stomata*, through which carbon dioxide, oxygen, water vapor, and other gases pass into and out of the leaf. Epidermal cells secrete a fatty, water-repellent substance called *cutin*, which forms a waxy layer called the cuticle on the leaves and other parts of the plant aboveground. The cuticle protects the plant and keeps it from losing too much water to the air.

Leaves vary greatly in appearance. Compare long, narrow oat leaves, *top right,* to the needlelike leaves of a pine, *bottom right.* Most plants have broad, flat leaves, such as those of the kudzu vine, *below.*

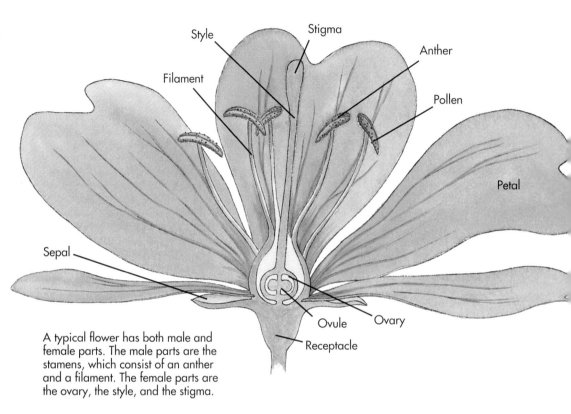

A typical flower has both male and female parts. The male parts are the stamens, which consist of an anther and a filament. The female parts are the ovary, the style, and the stigma.

FLOWERS contain the reproductive parts of flowering plants. They develop from buds on a stem. Some plants produce only one flower, some have many large clusters of flowers, and others have many tiny flowers that form a single, flowerlike head.

Most flowers have four main parts: the calyx, the corolla, the stamens, and the pistils. These parts are attached to the stem at a point called the *receptacle.*

The *calyx* consists of small, usually green leaflike structures called *sepals,* which protect the buds of young flowers. The petals are inside the calyx. All the petals of a flower make up the *corolla.*

The stamens and the pistils are the flower's reproductive organs. They are attached to the receptacle inside the sepals and the petals. In many flowers, the stamens and petals are joined together. A *stamen* is a male reproductive organ. A typical stamen has an enlarged part called an *anther* that grows on the end of a long, narrow stalk called the *filament. Pollen grains,* which produce sperm, are made in the anther.

A *pistil* is a female reproductive organ. The pistils of most flowers have three main parts: a stigma, a style, and an ovary. The *stigma* is a flattened structure at the top of the pistil. The *style* is a slender tube in the middle of

The pine seed, *top,* is a naked seed and stores food in the megagametophyte. A corn kernel, *bottom,* is actually an enclosed seed that develops in the ovary of a flowering plant. It stores food in the endosperm.

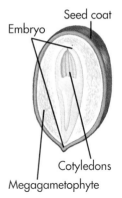

Embryo
Seed coat
Cotyledons
Megagametophyte

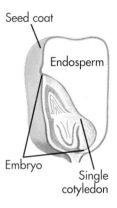

Seed coat
Endosperm
Embryo
Single cotyledon

the pistil. The round *ovary* serves as the pistil's base and contains one or more structures called *ovules.* Egg cells form within the ovules. When sperm cells fertilize the egg cells, the ovules become seeds.

SEEDS vary greatly in size and shape, and the size of a seed has nothing to do with the size of the plant. For example, giant redwood trees grow from seeds that measure only 1/16 inch (1.6 millimeters) long.

The two main types of seeds are *naked* seeds and *enclosed* seeds. Cone-bearing plants have naked, or uncovered, seeds that develop on the upper side of the scales that form their cones. The seeds of flowering plants are enclosed by an ovary that develops into a fruit as the seeds mature. The ovaries of such plants as apples, berries, and grapes develop into a fleshy fruit, but in other plants, including beans and peas, they form a dry fruit. Some plants, such as the raspberry plant, have *aggregate* fruits, in which each tiny section develops from a separate ovary and has its own seed.

The main parts of a seed are the seed coat, the embryo, and the food storage tissue. The *seed coat* is the outer skin that protects the *embryo,* which contains all the parts needed to form a new plant. The embryo also contains one or more *cotyledons,* or embryo leaves, which absorb food from the food storage tissue. In flowering plants, the food storage tissue is called *endosperm.* In some plants, the embryo absorbs the endosperm, and food is stored in the cotyledons. In cone-bearing plants, a tissue called the *megagametophyte* stores the food.

How plants live

Looking at a tree on a nice summer day, you might think that it is not doing much. But appearances can be deceiving. Within the tree—and within all plants—a variety of complex processes necessary for life are occurring.

Photosynthesis

Plants make their food by photosynthesis. Aside from a few bacteria, plants are the only living organisms capable of this incredible feat. The word *photosynthesis* means putting together with light. The plant uses the energy of sunlight to produce organic molecules from water and carbon dioxide.

Most photosynthesis occurs in the leaf blade's *palisade cells* and s*pongy cells.* These cells have *chloroplasts*—small bodies that contain many molecules of the green pigment *chlorophyll.*

An air space filled with carbon dioxide, water vapor, and other gases partly surrounds each palisade and spongy cell. The cells absorb carbon dioxide from the air space, and when light strikes the chloroplasts, photosynthesis begins. The chlorophyll absorbs energy from the light, and this energy splits water drawn from the soil into molecules of hydrogen and oxygen. In a se-

Photosynthesis takes place in chloroplasts of plant leaves, which absorb sunlight. Sunlight splits water molecules into hydrogen and oxygen. Hydrogen then joins with carbon dioxide to produce a simple sugar.

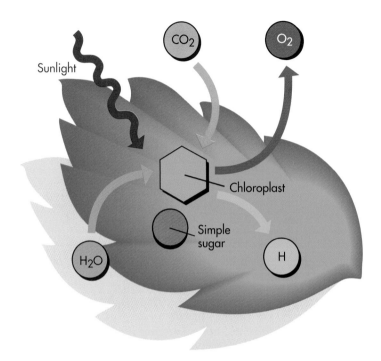

ries of complex chemical reactions, the hydrogen then combines with carbon dioxide to produce a simple sugar. Oxygen from the water molecules is given off in the process, and most of it exits the leaf through the stomata.

Plant respiration

The cells of the leaf's phloem tissue begin to carry the simple sugar produced by photosynthesis to all other parts of the plant, where it is stored for future use. A process called respiration breaks down this stored food and releases energy for the plant. The plant uses this energy for growth, reproduction, and repair.

Respiration takes place in the cell's cytoplasm, principally in the mitochondria. It involves the chemical breakdown of sugar. The major sequence of chemical reactions follows a cyclic path known as the *Krebs cycle,* which is preceded by another metabolic pathway called *glycolysis.* Some of the products resulting from this breakdown combine with oxygen, releasing carbon dioxide, energy, or water. Unlike photosynthesis, which takes place only during daylight, respiration goes on day and night, increasing rapidly with the spring growth of buds and leaves and decreasing as winter approaches. (For more information about respiration, see "Respiration in animal cells" in Chapter 10.)

Water movement

● **hydrostatic:** *supported by liquid under pressure.*

Without water, plant cells could not carry out their work. Water acts as a hydrostatic skeleton that helps support the plant. This explains why most plants wilt when they are deprived of water. In addition, a plant's life processes take place in water. But perhaps water's most important role lies in transporting various materials—dissolved gases, minerals, and nutrients—through the plant's tissues.

Most water enters a plant through its roots. The tiny root hairs absorb moisture and minerals from the soil by a process called *osmosis,* in which water crosses the semipermeable membranes surrounding the cells. In vascular plants, these materials are transported through the xylem tissue of the roots and stems to the leaves. There, water and minerals are used to make food. Water also carries this food through the phloem tissue to other parts of the plant.

Plants give off water through a process called *transpiration.* Most of this water escapes through the stomata on the surfaces of the leaves. Transpiration occurs as the sun warms the water inside the blade of the leaf. This warming changes much of the water into water vapor, which can then escape through the stomata. Transpiration helps cool the inside of the leaf because the escaping vapor has absorbed heat. Some scientists believe that this water loss prevents the leaves from overheating in the sunlight.

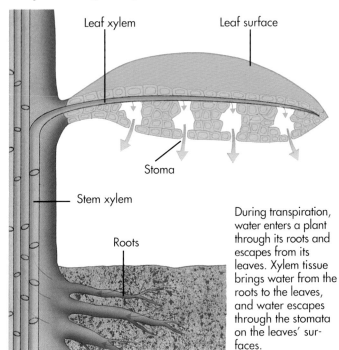

During transpiration, water enters a plant through its roots and escapes from its leaves. Xylem tissue brings water from the roots to the leaves, and water escapes through the stomata on the leaves' surfaces.

Transpiration helps keep water flowing up from the roots. Water forms a continuous column as it flows through the roots, up the stem, and into the leaves. Scientists believe that the molecules of water in this column stick to one another, so that as the molecules at the top of the column are lost through transpiration, the entire column of water is pulled upward. This pulling force is strong enough to draw water to the tops of even the tallest trees. In addition, transpiration provides the plant with a steady supply of minerals from the soil.

How plants grow

The sprouting of a seed is called *germination.* Most seeds have a period of inactivity called *dormancy* before they start to grow. In most areas, this period lasts through the winter. After spring arrives, seeds begin to germinate.

Seeds need three things to grow—a proper temperature, moisture, and oxygen. Most seeds, like most plants, grow best in temperatures between 65 °F. (18 °C) and 85 °F. (29 °C). Seeds get the moisture they need from the ground. The moisture softens the seed coat, allowing the growing parts to break through. Moisture also prepares certain materials in the seed for their

When a seed germinates, it first forms a seedling. The hypocotyl then forms the primary root. The epicotyl grows upward to form the stem. The plumule produces the first leaves.

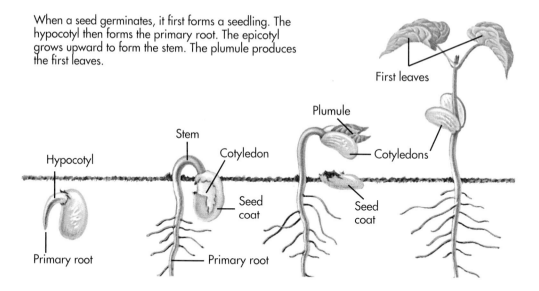

part in seed growth. Seeds need oxygen for the changes that occur inside them during germination.

The embryo of a seed has all the parts needed to produce a new plant. It may have either one or more *cotyledons,* which digest food from the endosperm for the growing seedling. The seed absorbs water, which causes it to swell. The swelling splits the seed coat, and a tiny seedling appears. The lower part of the seedling, called the *hypocotyl,* becomes the primary root that anchors the seedling in the ground and develops a root system. Next, the upper part of the seedling, called the *epicotyl,* begins to grow upward to form the stem. At the tip of the epicotyl is the *plumule*—the bud that produces the first leaves. Once a seedling has developed roots and leaves, it can make its own food.

Most plants grow in length at the tips of their roots and branches. The cells in these areas make up *meristematic tissue.* The cells in this tissue divide and grow rapidly and most of them develop into the various tissues that make up the adult plant. In trees and other plants that increase in thickness, new layers of cells form in the *cambium,* the area between the bark and wood. The new layers of cells made as the cambium grows each year form the woody rings that tell us the age of a tree.

A plant's growth is shaped by hereditary traits, such as a flower's color and general size, that are passed on from generation to generation. Within the nucleus of all plant cells are tiny chromosomes that contain genes, the carriers of genetic information. The chromosomes hold the "instructions" that direct the growth of the plant. As the cells divide and multiply, these "instructions" are passed on to each new cell. (See "Genetics" in Chapter 10.)

Substances made within a plant also affect plant growth. These substances, called hormones, control such activities as the growing of roots and the production of flowers and fruits. Although scientists do not know exactly how all plant hormones work, they do know that hormones called *auxins* affect the growth of buds, leaves, roots, and stems. Other growth hormones, called *gibberellins,* speed seed germination and make plants grow larger and blossom. Still other hormones called *cytokinins* make plant cells divide.

Environmental factors also influence plant growth. All plants need light, a suitable climate, and an ample supply of water and minerals. But some species grow best in the sun, while others thrive in the shade. Plants also differ in the amount of water they need and in the temperatures in which they can survive. Such environmental factors affect the plant's rate of growth, size, and reproductive success.

The length of the periods of daylight and darkness may affect a plant's growth. Some plants bloom only when the photoperiod, or period of daylight, is long. Such plants are called *long-day plants.* On the other hand, some plants are *short-day plants* that bloom only when the dark period is long. Still other plants are not affected at all by the length of the photoperiod. Such plants are called *dayneutral plants.*

Plant responses

Plants are affected in several other ways by their environment. For example, a plant may display a bending movement called tropism in response to such stimuli as light, gravity, water, and touch. A plant may have either a positive or a negative tropism, depending on whether the plant bends toward or away from the stimulus. Tropisms are named according to the stimuli that cause them.

Heredity, hormones, and environmental factors affect a plant's rate of growth. After a tree is cut down, the variations in annual growth rates are recorded by the growth rings in its trunk.

PHOTOTROPISM is bending caused by light. Because light is a green plant's only source of energy, it has strong influence on plant response. A plant exhibits *positive phototropism* when its stems and leaves grow toward light. Roots, on the other hand, display *negative phototropism* and grow away from light.

GEOTROPISM is bending caused by gravity. Roots demonstrate *positive geotropism.* Even if a seed or bulb is planted upside down, its roots grow downward—toward the source of gravity. The stem of the same bulb shows *negative geotropism* by growing upward—away from the source of gravity.

HYDROTROPISM is bending caused by water. This form of tropism occurs mainly in roots and is almost always positive.

Thigmotropism caus-
es the open leaves of
the sensitive *Mimosa
pudica* plant, *top,* to
close when touched,
bottom.

THIGMOTROPISM is bending caused by touch. In some plants, a change in pressure within certain cells enables the plant to respond to contact. After the stimulus has been removed, the branches and leaves return to their original position.

Plant classification

The classification of plants provides a system by which scientists can identify them. But plant classification means more than just assigning a name to each of the plant kingdom's more than 260,000 species. It also involves grouping plants in categories of ever-increasing size—a process known as scientific classification.

Scientists classify plants by grouping them according to similarities in their overall appearance, their internal structure, and the form of their reproductive organs. The basic unit of classification is the species. Members of a species look so similar as to be more or less identical, and they can interbreed. As discussed in Chapter 9, there are seven chief classification groups—from species to kingdom.

Most scientists use the same basic framework for classification. Not all of them agree on how individual plants fit into this scheme, however, and so classifications often differ in details. The system used here divides the plant kingdom into five basic groups—seed plants, ferns, lycophytes, horsetails, and bryophytes.

Seed plants

Seed plants, also called *spermatophytes,* consist of a wide variety of plants that bear seeds to reproduce. Most scientists divide seed plants into two main groups—angiosperms and gymnosperms.

ANGIOSPERMS are flowering plants. They make up almost 90 percent of the more than 260,000 kinds of plants. Angiosperms have seeds that are enclosed in a protected seed case, and they produce flowers and fruits. Some scientists divide angiosperms into two smaller groups. Plants in one group, called *monocotyledons* or *monocots,* grow from seeds that contain one cotyledon. Plants in the other group, called *dicotyledons* or *dicots,* have two cotyledons.

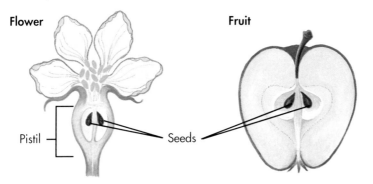

Flower **Fruit**

Pistil — Seeds

Angiosperms are flowering plants whose seeds are enclosed in a protected seed case. The flower and fruit of an angiosperm, *left,* contain the plant's seeds.

Monocots and dicots grow throughout the world. Monocots range from small flowers to large trees. They include orchids and many other popular garden plants. Monocots also include the grasses and cereals whose grains serve as staple foods in many countries. Dicots include many of the most abundant wood-producing plants, such as oak, teak, and all other hardwoods. In addition, dicots provide much of the food eaten by people and domestic animals, such as cabbage, potatoes, tomatoes, apples, pears, cucumbers, beans, peas, and other fruits and vegetables.

GYMNOSPERMS include a wide variety of trees and shrubs that produce naked seeds. Most gymnosperms bear their seeds in cones. They do not produce flowers. This group consists of such plants as conifers, cycads, ginkgoes, and gnetophytes.

Conifers, such as pines, firs, and balsams, are the best-known gymnosperms. Most conifers are *evergreens*—they shed old leaves and grow new leaves continuously, so their needlelike leaves stay green throughout the year. The seeds of evergreens grow on the upper side of the scales that make up their cones.

Cycads and ginkgoes have lived on earth for millions of years. Large numbers of these plants once grew over wide regions. Most cycads look much like palm trees. They have unbranched trunks topped by crowns of long leaves. But unlike palm trees, they bear their seeds in large cones. The only kind of ginkgo that still survives is an ornamental tree with flat, fan-shaped leaves.

Gnetophytes are an unusual group of gymnosperms. They have many features that resemble those of flowering plants, including flowerlike cones.

Ferns

Ferns grow chiefly in moist, wooded areas, and they vary widely in size and form. Fern leaves, called fronds, are made up of many tiny leaflets and may be quite large. The fronds are the only parts of most ferns that grow aboveground. They develop from underground stems. They are tightly coiled when they first appear, and they unwind as they grow.

Lycophytes

Lycophytes, which include club mosses and quillworts, have leaves with a single, central vein. They were among the first plants to grow on land.

Club mosses grow in tropical and temperate regions, and they often form a "carpet" on the forest floor. They have tiny needlelike or scalelike leaves that usually grow in a spiral pattern. They are not true mosses. Quillworts have short stems and long, quill-like leaves. They grow chiefly in moist soils around lakes and streams.

Stag's horn club moss, *right,* is a type of lycophyte.

Because of its coarse stem, the horsetail, *left,* was once used to polish metal.

Horsetails

Horsetails are unusual plants with hollow, jointed stems and tiny, black leaves. Their green stems capture the sunlight for photosynthesis. In some horsetails, the branches grow in whorls, or circles, around the main stem, and the plant resembles a horse's tail. Tiny amounts of minerals are present in the stem, particularly silica. Silica makes the stem very coarse, like sandpaper. Horsetails grow to a height of about 2 to 3 feet (60 to 90 centimeters).

● **silica:** *silicon dioxide (SiO_2), a common mineral. Quartz is a form of silica.*

Bryophytes

Bryophytes are a group made up of liverworts, mosses, and hornworts. They live in almost all parts of the world, from the Arctic to tropical forests, and they grow in such moist, shady places as forests and ravines. Bryophytes are among the most primitive land plants. They are the only types of plants that lack vascular tissue.

Most liverworts, mosses, and hornworts grow less than 8 inches (20 centimeters) tall. None of these plants have true roots. Instead, they have hairy rootlike growths called *rhizoids* that attach them to the ground—or to a substrate such as tree bark—and absorb water and minerals.

Bryophytes are important ecologically because they can survive in inhospitable conditions and are often among the first species to colonize land laid waste by fire or earthquake. Once established, bryophyte colonies help prevent soil erosion and promote the retention of moisture.

● **substrate:** *the medium or matter on which an organism grows.*

Liverworts are bryophytes that absorb water and minerals through hairy growths called rhizoids, which resemble roots.

P*lant reproduction*

Plants create more of their own kind by either sexual reproduction or asexual reproduction. In *sexual reproduction,* a male sperm cell joins with a female egg cell to produce a new plant. Both the egg and sperm cell contain genes, which determine many of the plant's characteristics. The new plant thus inherits genes from both parent plants and has traits that may be different from either parent. *Asexual reproduction* can occur in many ways. It often involves the division of one plant into two or more parts that become new plants. These plants inherit genes from only one parent and thus have exactly the same characteristics as that parent plant. This type of asexual reproduction is called *vegetative propagation.*

If plants reproduced by asexual means only, evolution and adaptations could not occur as rapidly because most new plants would have exactly the same genetic makeup as their parents. Sexual reproduction makes change and adaptation more likely.

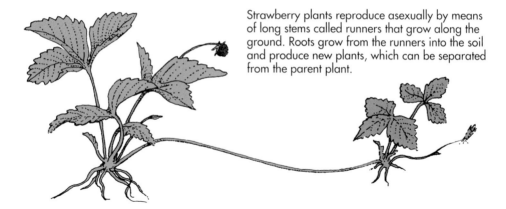

Strawberry plants reproduce asexually by means of long stems called runners that grow along the ground. Roots grow from the runners into the soil and produce new plants, which can be separated from the parent plant.

Sexual reproduction

Sexual reproduction in plants occurs as a complex cycle called *alternation of generations.* It involves two distinct generations or phases. During one phase, the plant is called a *gametophyte,* or gamete-bearing plant. The gametophyte, which is barely visible in most species of plants, produces gametes, or sperm and egg cells. It may produce either sperm cells or egg cells, or both, depending on the species of the plant. When the sperm and egg cells unite, the fertilized egg develops into the second phase. In this phase, the plant is called a *sporophyte.* Sporophytes, or spore-bearing plants, produce tiny structures called spores through a process of cell division called meiosis. (See "Meiosis" in Chapter 10.) The spores form in closed capsulelike structures called *sporangia.* Gametophytes then develop from the spores, and the cycle begins again.

In seed plants, which include flowering plants and cone-bearing plants, alternation of generations involves a series of complicated steps. Among these plants, only the sporophyte generation can be seen by the unaided eye.

Spores are produced in both the male and female reproductive organs and grow into gametophytes. The gametophytes remain inside the plant's reproductive organs.

In flowering plants, the flower is the part designed for sexual reproduction. As discussed earlier, a plant's stamens are its male reproductive organs. Each stamen has an enlarged tip called an anther. The pistil is the plant's female reproductive organ and the ovary, which forms the round base of the pistil, contains the ovules. The anthers consist of tiny structures called *microsporangia,* and the ovules contain structures called *megasporangia.* Cell divisions in the microsporangia and the megasporangia result in the production of spores.

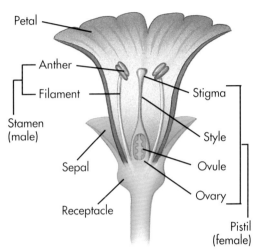

The flower is the organ of sexual reproduction in plants, containing both male and female reproductive organs.

In most species of flowering plants, one spore in each ovule grows into a microscopic female gametophyte, which produces one egg cell. In the anther, the spores—called pollen grains—contain microscopic male gametophytes. Each pollen grain produces two sperm cells.

POLLINATION. For fertilization to occur, a pollen grain must be transferred from the anther to the pistil in a process called pollination. If pollen from a flower reaches the pistil of the same flower, or a pistil of another flower on the same plant, the fertilization process is called *self-pollination.* When pollen from a flower reaches a pistil of another plant, the process is called *cross-pollination.*

In cross-pollinated plants, the pollen grains are carried from flower to flower by birds, insects, or other animals, or by the wind. Many cross-pollinated plants have features that attract these animals, such as large flowers, a sweet scent, and sweet nectar. As birds and insects move from flower to flower in search of food, they carry pollen on their bodies. Most grasses, trees, and shrubs have small, inconspicuous flowers, and the wind carries their pollen.

If a pollen grain reaches the pistil of a plant of the same species, a *pollen tube* grows down through the stigma and the style to an ovule in the ovary. In the ovule, one of the two sperm cells from the pollen grain unites with the egg cell. A sporophyte embryo then begins to form. The second sperm cell unites with two structures called *polar nuclei* and starts to form the nutrient tissue that makes up the endosperm. A seed coat then forms around the embryo and endosperm.

In conifers, the reproductive parts are contained in the cones. A conifer has two kinds of cones. Of the two, the pollen, or male, cone is smaller, softer, and simpler in structure. Seed, or female, cones are larger and harder than male cones.

A pollen cone has many tiny sporangia that produce pollen grains. Each of the scales that make up a seed cone has two ovules on its surface and every ovule produces a spore that develops into a female gametophyte. This tiny plant produces egg cells.

Bees—along with wind, birds, animals, and other insects—assist in cross-pollination by carrying pollen grains from the anther of one flower to the pistil of another.

The wind carries pollen grains from the pollen cone to the seed cone. A pollen grain sticks to an adhesive substance near an ovule, and usually enters the pollen chamber of the ovule through an opening called the *micropyle*. The pollen grain then begins to form a pollen tube. Two sperm cells develop in the tube, and after the pollen tube reaches the egg cell, one of the sperm cells fertilizes the egg. The second sperm cell disintegrates. The fertilized egg develops into a sporophyte embryo, and the ovule containing the embryo becomes a seed. The seed falls to the ground and, if conditions are favorable, a new sporophyte begins to grow.

Fern spores grow in clusters called sori that develop on the underside of the plant's leaves, *above.* Ripened spores fall to the ground and grow into tiny gametophytes.

REPRODUCTION BY SPORES. In ferns and mosses, the sporophyte and gametophyte generations consist of two greatly different plants. Among ferns, the sporophytes have leaves and are much larger than the gametophytes. Clusters of sporangia called *sori* form on the edges or underside of each leaf, and spores develop in the sporangia. After the spores ripen, they fall to the ground and grow into barely visible, heart-shaped gametophytes. A fern gametophyte produces both male and female sex cells. If enough moisture is present, a sperm cell swims to an egg cell and unites with it. The fertilized egg then grows into an adult sporophyte.

Among mosses, a sporophyte consists of a long, erect stalk with a podlike spore-producing container at the end. The sporophyte extends from the top of a soft, leafy, green gametophyte on which it depends for food and water. The gametophyte is the part of the plant community recognized as moss.

Vegetative propagation

Plants can spread without sexual reproduction. Through vegetative propagation, part of a plant may grow into a complete new plant. Vegetative propagation can occur because the pieces of the plant form the missing parts through a process called *regeneration.* Any part of a plant—the root, stem, leaf, or flower—may be propagated into a new plant. A new plant may even grow from a single cell.

Propagation occurs most often in plants with stems that run horizontally just above or below the ground. The strawberry plant, for example, sends out long, thin stems called *runners* that grow along the surface of the soil. At points where they touch the ground, the runners send out roots that produce *plantlets*—new leaves and stems—that are actually part of the parent plant. New plants form only when the plantlets are separated from the parent plant.

Many nuisance plants, such as crabgrass and dandelions, are able to spread rapidly by vegetative propagation. These plants are sometimes difficult to kill because they often can regrow their lost parts by regeneration.

Farmers and gardeners use vegetative propagation to grow crops. They use three methods—cuttage, grafting, and layering.

CUTTAGE involves the use of *cuttings*—parts of plants—taken from growing plants. Most cuttings are stems. When placed in water or moist soil, cuttings usually develop roots and then grow into complete plants.

GRAFTING also uses plant cuttings. But instead of placing the cutting in water or soil, it is *grafted,* or attached, to another plant, called the *stock.* The stock provides the root system and lower part of the new plant. The cutting forms the upper part.

LAYERING is a method of growing roots for a new plant. In *mound layering,* soil piled up around the base of a plant causes roots to sprout from the branch, which is then cut off and planted. In *air layering,* a cut about 3 inches (8 centimeters) long is made about halfway through a branch. A type of moss called *sphagnum moss* is placed in the cut to keep it moist, and this portion of the branch is wrapped in a waterproof covering. After new roots sprout around the cut, the branch is cut off and planted.

Grafting is a technique used to reproduce trees and bushes. The process of fitting two twigs together also is used to create hardier plants and to repair injuries to branches and stems.

Where plants live

A plant, like any other organism, must be adapted to its surroundings in order to survive. Most plants live in areas that have warm temperatures at least part of the year, plentiful rainfall, and rich soil. But some plants can live under extreme conditions.

Not all types of plants grow in all parts of the world. Through long periods of time, small changes have taken place in various kinds of plants. These changes have enabled the plants to survive in a particular environment.

Many elements make up a plant's environment. One of the most important is the weather—sunlight, temperature, and precipitation. A plant's environment also includes the soil it grows in, and the other plants and animals that live in the same area. All these elements form what scientists call a *natural community.*

Although no two natural communities are exactly alike, many resemble one another more than they differ. Scientists divide the world into *biomes*—natural communities of plants, animals, and other organisms. Major land biomes include the tundra; forests, including taiga, deciduous forests, and tropical rain forests; chaparrals; grasslands; savannas; and deserts. In addition, plants live in aquatic, or water, regions that are not classified as a specific biome.

Tundra

There are two types of tundra community: arctic and alpine. Cold and treeless, the *arctic tundra* surrounds the Arctic Ocean near the North Pole and stretches across the northern parts of North America, Europe, and Asia. The land in these regions is frozen most of the year, and the annual precipitation is a sparse 6 to 10 inches (15 to 25 centimeters). Summers in the arctic tundra last only about 60 days, and summer temperatures average about 45 °F. (7 °C). The top 12 inches (30 centimeters) or so of the land thaws during the summer, creating many marshes, ponds, and swamps.

Blue alpine flowers, *below,* grow rapidly in the short spring season of the tundra, *right.*

Alpine tundras are found on mountains at elevations that are too high and cold for trees to grow.

Mosses, grasses, low shrubs, and grasslike plants called *sedges* make up the tundra plant community. These plants tend to grow close to the ground, where they are sheltered from cold winds. In winter, snow may cover these low growing plants, conserving their heat and shielding them against wind and dehydration. Instead of growing upward, tundra plants spread out. Their roots tend to spread out just beneath the surface of the soil because they cannot penetrate the frozen ground.

Forests

Forests cover almost one-third of the Earth's land. They consist mainly of trees, but many other kinds of plants also live in forests. Some scientists divide forests into three major groups: taiga, deciduous forests, and tropical rain forests.

White twinflowers, *bottom*, are one of the few plants that can survive in the sandy topsoil of the coniferous forest, *top*.

TAIGA forests are made up mainly of coniferous (cone-bearing) evergreen trees, such as cedars, spruces, pines, and firs. During winter, when the ground is frozen, tree roots are unable to obtain water from the soil. Although precipitation may reach 10 to 39 inches (25 to 99 centimeters) a year, most of it falls as snow. The only trees that grow in these conditions are *xerophytic*, or drought-resistant, a feature achieved chiefly by the form of their leaves. The leaves of most conifers are tough, leathery, and evergreen, with a waxy cuticle that reduces water loss caused by evaporation. Their toughness prevents the leaves from collapsing or wilting due to lack of water. In addition, the leaves of most coniferous trees are needle-shaped and resistant to frost.

Evergreens do not need to use up energy producing new green leaves each spring, and the year-round growth of their leaves provides a means of conserving nutrients. They can photosynthesize whenever it is warm enough, and in the brief summer months they can concentrate their energy on reproduction. The trees themselves tend to be shaped like a cone, which enables them to shed snow that might otherwise accumulate and break the branches. The snow covering that remains helps insulate the trees from the cold and reduces water loss.

Few plants can survive on the floor of a coniferous forest due to the thick layers of old needles that build up beneath the trees. As the needles decay, acids are slowly released into the soil, dissolving minerals and carrying them into the deeper layers of the soil. As a result, the topsoil is often quite sandy and unable to support many types of plants. However, some less highly evolved plants can survive in this environment. Fungi and bacteria feed on the decaying needles. In fact, the trees depend on the fungi, which take carbohydrates from the tree and in return provide the tree with minerals. However, some herbaceous plants, such as wood sorrel, western sword fern, and piper bellflower, thrive on the floor of coniferous forests.

Many simple plants known as *epiphytes* live on the trees of coniferous forests. They feed on nutrients carried from the air by rain. Epiphytes include mosses, ferns, and lichens.

The deciduous forest bursts with color as chlorophyll breaks down in the leaves of deciduous trees, revealing secondary colors such as red, yellow, and orange.

DECIDUOUS FORESTS cover large areas of the Earth that have heavy rainfall in spring and summer. In general, they are found on the edges of continents. In the interior of such continents as Asia and North America, the hot, dry summers and very cold winters allow only grasslands to develop.

Deciduous trees include elms, oaks, dogwood, maple, and hickory. One of the most striking characteristics of trees in temperate deciduous forests is the loss of their leaves in winter and the growth of new leaves in spring. During the long summer days, when light and water are plentiful, photosynthesis can occur for many hours. In winter, however, the water supply is low, especially when the ground is frozen, and photosynthesis is reduced because light levels decrease. Deciduous trees have broad, flat leaves that are thin and often fairly large. These leaves, which maximize photosynthesis at the expense of low control over water loss, are shed in winter in an effort to reduce water loss.

When the soil temperature drops below about 39 °F. (4 °C), the roots of deciduous trees can no longer draw up water. As a result, the chlorophyll in the leaves breaks down, and they lose their green color, revealing secondary colors such as red, yellow, orange, and purple. Before these leaves fall, however, important nutrient elements are drawn in from the leaves into the branches. Then a thin layer of cork grows across the base of the leafstalk, and the leaf falls off. In this way, the loss of important nutrients is minimized. The fallen leaves decompose to form *humus,* which provides nutrients for the tree roots in the next growing season.

In the rich earth of the temperate deciduous forest floor, many small herbaceous plants grow. These plants include bloodroot, Solomon's-seal, Jack-in-the-pulpit, bellwort, wild hyacinth, Dutchman's-breeches, wild geranium, and painted trillium.

Temperate evergreen forests are found in both cool and warm temperate regions and include both broad-leaved trees and coniferous trees. Evergreen broad-leaved trees in warm temperate areas do not need to shed their leaves because temperatures are warm enough so that the roots can constantly absorb water. In addition, leaves of these trees have waxy surfaces and small stomata that limit transpiration and thus avoid excessive water loss.

Other warm temperate regions are also inhabited by various coniferous species. The high humidity in these areas ensures a rich understory growth of mosses, ferns, and lichens.

● **understory:** *the layer of trees underneath the canopy in a forest.*

TROPICAL RAIN FORESTS are the richest biomes on Earth in terms of number of plant species living there. A single acre may support 100 different tree species and a corresponding wealth of microorganisms and animals. Tropical rain forests are found in regions that have warm, wet weather the year around, including Central America and the northern parts of South America, central and western Africa, Southeast Asia, and the Pacific Islands.

Most trees in tropical rain forests are broad-leaved trees that never completely lose their leaves. Because of the warm, wet weather, they lose a few leaves at a time throughout the year. The trees grow so close together that little sunlight reaches the ground, so the only plants on the forest floor are ferns and other plants that can survive under such conditions. But many plants, including orchids and vines, grow high on the trees.

The heavy rains that occur in tropical rain forests wash much of the nutrients and organic material out of the soil. As a result, the soil contains a very small amount of nutrients and organic matter. However, the lush growth in these forests is maintained because fresh nutrients from the decay of fallen leaves are continually being released into the soil.

Exotic flowers such as the bird of paradise, *right,* grow in the warm, wet climate of tropical rain forests.

Thick, low growths of wildflowers, such as California's fire poppies, flourish in a chaparral.

Chaparrals

Chaparrals are thick growths of shrubs and small trees found in regions with hot, dry summers and cool, wet winters.

Such areas are found in the western part of North America, the southern regions of Europe near the Mediterranean Sea, the Middle East, northern Africa, and the southern parts of South America, Africa, and Australia. Sugarbush, California buckwheat, white sage, chamise, black sage, coyote brush, California scrub oak, and deerweed are common plants of the North American chaparral. Mediterranean chaparral plants include cork oak, live oak, aleppo pine, olive, myrtle, and rosemary. In Australia, eucalyptus and acacia are typical chaparral plants.

Fires are common on chaparrals during the dry summer season, but the plants in these areas have adapted to withstand its effects. In fact, fires actually help maintain the plant life. Many chaparral plants are either resistant to fire or able to grow back quickly after they burn. The fires clear the dense vegetation and expose the bare ground, allowing for new growth. Many types of short-lived, small flowers appear only after a fire has occurred, and the heat of the fires stimulates development in the seeds of some plants.

Grasslands

Grasslands are open areas where grasses are the most plentiful plants. Grassland plants include Indian grass, switchgrass, prairie cordgrass, Canada wild rye, and big bluestem. In the United States and Canada, most natural grasslands are used to grow crops.

Plants of the grassland include gray-headed coneflowers, *inset.* But as the name implies, grasses are the area's most plentiful plants.

One of the most important features of grasses is their method of growth, which enables them to survive in their habitat. Grasses have underground stems that continuously produce new leaves and large numbers of shoots. Growth takes place through cell division at the bases of the leaves and stems, rather than at the tips as in most other plants. These underground stems are the means of vegetative reproduction that allow the plant to be closely cropped aboveground by grazing animals, burned by fire, die down in cold weather, and lie dormant in times of drought.

Grasses in the savannas respond to changes in humidity by growing in different areas each season. Herds of wildebeest migrate in search of grass to eat.

Savannas

Savannas are grasslands with widely spaced trees. Some savannas are found in regions that receive little rain. Others are found in tropical regions, such as the Llanos in Venezuela, the Campos in southern Brazil, and the Sudan in Africa. Grasses grow tall and stiff in the dry winters and wet summers of these areas. Drought and fire, caused naturally or by farmers, have reduced the number of plant species in savannas. The species that survive show many adaptations to fire, and it is fire, rather than climate or grazing animals, that determines the stability of the vegetation.

Baobabs, acacias, and palms are typical savanna trees. Many savanna trees have thick, corky, fire-resistant barks that are spongy and filled with water, another adaptation that helps them survive during drought. In addition, trees and shrubs produce a great many seeds, and many of the herbs have underground food storage organs.

Deserts

Deserts cover nearly one-fifth of the Earth's land. A huge desert region that extends across northern Africa and into central Asia includes three of the world's great deserts—the Arabian, the Gobi, and the Sahara.

Some deserts have almost no plant life. Parts of the Gobi and the Sahara, for example, consist chiefly of shifting sand dunes. All deserts receive very little rain and have either rocky or sandy soil. The temperature in most deserts rises above 100 °F. (38 °C) for at least part of the year, and some deserts also have cold periods. In spite of such harsh conditions, many plants have found ways to adapt. These plants can conserve and store water and endure heat. Desert plants of North America include jumping cholla, mesquite, barrel cactus, saguaro, bur sage, organ-pipe cactus, ocotillo, paloverde, prickly pear, desert marigold, brittlebush, and strawberry hedgehog. In southern Africa, cow's horn, big tooth, and African milk barrel are typical desert plants. Sodom's apple and bronzed chenopod grow in the desert of Saudi Arabia.

Desert plants tend to be widely scattered. Because the plants compete for the small amount of water available, they cannot grow close together. Some desert plants obtain water from deep beneath the Earth's surface. The roots of most desert plants extend over large areas, allowing them to capture as much water as possible. Other plants store water in their leaves, roots, or stems. The stem of a barrel cactus, for example, swells with water after a rainfall and shrinks as the water is used up. Other plants survive by reducing their water loss. Because most of this loss occurs through the leaves, some plants shed their leaves in dry periods.

After a rainfall, flowers can spring up in deserts. This colorful change occurs because many desert plants do not grow in dry periods. So after a rainfall, dormant seeds may germinate. These plants quickly sprout, flower, and disperse seeds that will lie dormant until the next growing season.

Some desert plants store water in their leaves, roots, or stems in order to survive the dry climate. Others depend on their roots to capture as much water as possible by extending over large areas. Still others survive in dry conditions by shedding their leaves to reduce water loss.

Aquatic plants, such as cattails, bulrushes, and floating water lilies, have enlarged air spaces in the tissue of their submerged parts that allow oxygen to flow from the stems and leaves to parts below the water.

Aquatic regions

Aquatic regions are bodies of fresh or salt water. Freshwater areas include lakes, rivers, swamps, and marshes, and coastal marshes and oceans are salt-water regions. Most aquatic plants, also called *hydrophytes,* live in places that receive sunlight—near the water surface, in shallow water, or along the shore. Some species float freely on the water surface, and others grow partly underwater.

One of the greatest challenges of living in such an environment is the air-less material in which the plants' roots are lodged. Without air, the roots—and thus the plants—cannot survive. As a result, these plants have adapted in a number of ways to obtain oxygen. The most significant modification is the enlargement of intercellular air spaces in the tissue of the submerged parts of the plants. These air spaces allow oxygen to pass through the plant from the exposed stems and leaves to the submerged parts. These air spaces also help the plants stand erect or stay afloat.

Some aquatic regions are subject to regular flooding. The plants inhabiting these areas grow in zones that correspond to the frequency of flooding, the depth of water, and the length of submergence. Their positions are deter-mined by the degree to which they can cope with the flooding and the salt content of the water. Some plants that live in freshwater ponds are reed grass, black willow, swamp-loosestrife, sphagnum moss, cattails, pickerelweed, water lilies, and wild celery.

Salt-tolerant plants—known as *halophytes*—have difficulty obtaining water because the high salt concentrations in the surrounding water make it difficult to remove any "free" water. As a result, many halophytes have developed thick, leathery, fleshy leaves that store and retain large amounts of water and slow down transpiration. Mangroves, eelgrass, cordgrass, and many types of sedges grow in salt water.

● **intercellular:** *between cells.*

Peculiar Plants

The plant world is filled with the weird and the wonderful. Even scientists are astonished at the complexities of plant adaptation. They range from plants that are confirmed meat-eaters because the soil where they live lacks essential nutrients, to plants that live high aboveground, surviving on the hard work of others, because they lack roots. Thousands of "common" plants lie somewhere in between, and they too have a story to tell.

Meat-eating plants

Meat-eating, or *carnivorous,* plants feed on insects and other small animals in addition to producing food by photosynthesis. Four hundred or more plants are meat-eaters. Scientists believe that these plants made this adaptation in response to living in areas where the soil is deficient in nitrogen. The nutrients absorbed from insects allow these meat-eating plants to thrive in such areas. Most meat-eating plants have some leaves that serve as traps, and many use bright colors and sweet nectar to attract their prey.

Meat-eating plants have one of three types of traps. The leaves of Pitcher plants, such as the monkey cup and cobra plant, are folded to form a tube, or pitcher, that collects water. Sweet substances around the rim of each tube lure insects, and tiny downward pointing hairs keep the struggling victim from escaping. Soon the insect falls into the water, drowns, and is digested by the plant. The cobra plant, named for its resemblance to the snake, has a hooded head and forked "tongue," called a fishtail. The roof of its hood is covered with "windows" that are glasslike in their transparency. These windows illuminate the interior, giving an illusion of freedom, and helping trap food. The tubelike leaves and the "tongue" are covered with nectar that attracts insects. An insect that enters the hooded area rarely gets out.

The obvious way out would seem to be the windowed area, but if insects fly to the roof of the hoods, they slip, lose their footing, and drop into the tube, or pitcher. Once their wings are moistened by the water in the bottom, the insects seldom escape.

The Venus's-flytrap uses a spring-trap mechanism to catch its unlucky prey. The plant has a cluster of small, white blossoms at the top of the flower stalk, rising from a tuft of oddly shaped leaves. The leaves have two parts—a lower bladelike portion and an upper part with two lobes hinged to a rib. The surface of each lobe has three sensitive hairs, and its edges are fringed with sharp bristles. When an insect brushes two of the hairs, or the same hair twice, the two lobes close like a trap with the bristles interlock-

Leaves of the meat-eating Venus's-flytrap spring closed to catch a fly, which the plant digests by secreting a fluid from a gland in its leaf. After the prey is digested, the trap opens again.

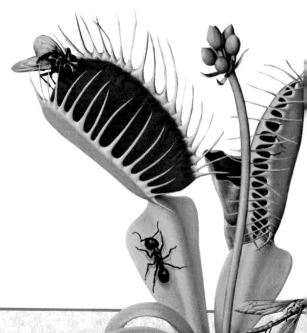

ing. The soft parts of the insect are digested by a fluid secreted by special glands of the leaf. After the plant has digested the food, the trap opens for business again.

The third type of trap is used by the butterwort. Sticky droplets on the leaves' surfaces entrap their prey. The butterwort has a cluster of fleshy leaves that lie close to the ground and produce the sticky substance. When an insect lands on a leaf, the edges curve in and trap it. The insect dies and is digested by the plant.

Unwelcome guests?

Epiphytic and parasitic plants grow on other living plants. Epiphytes, or air plants, include tropical orchids, bromeliads, and some mosses that live in temperate regions. Epiphytic plants are not usually rooted in soil. Instead they live on the stems and branches of other plants. They get water from trapped rain water and moisture in the air and obtain minerals from organic matter on the surface of the plant they live on. Like other green plants, epiphytes produce their food through photosynthesis.

Parasitic plants get all their nutrients from the host plants on which they grow. The parasites produce *haustoria*—rootlike organs that penetrate the stem or roots of the host and grow inward to merge with the host's vascular tissue. In effect, haustoria "steal" water, minerals, and nutrients from the host plant. Because they have no need to produce their own food, parasitic plants lack chlorophyll and have no foliage leaves. Partially parasitic plants, such as mistletoe, get water and minerals from the host plant but have green leaves and stems that enable them to produce food by photosynthesis.

Rafflesia, for example, is a parasitic plant with huge flowers but no leaves or stems. The flowers, which grow on the stems and roots of several vines and shrubs in Malaysia, Sumatra, and other tropical places, are up to 3 feet (91 centimeters) wide—the largest of any known plant. The plant's stamens and pistils grow on separate flowers, so some agent, such as an insect, must pollinate them. The flowers usually have four or five wide, fleshy lobes and have a bad odor.

Other oddities

Another peculiar plant—called the Welwitschia —grows in the sandy deserts of southwestern Africa and looks like a giant, flattened mushroom. Its short, woody trunk rises from a large taproot and may spread 5 to 6 feet (1.5 to 1.8 meters). The plant has a single pair of leathery green leaves that spread over the ground. These leaves may originally be 2 to 3 feet (61 to 91 centimeters) wide and often twice as long. Older plants seem to have many leaves because hot winds and blowing sand have split the two leaves into long ribbons over the years. Welwitschia plants grow slowly and often live an incredible 1,000 to 2,000 years.

And finally there's the bucket orchid, which has a cunning way of getting bees to pollinate. Most flowers simply lure bees with sweet nectar, but not the bucket orchid. It has a much more complex system. The bucket-shaped lobes that give the flower its name contain a heavily scented liquid that is produced by two glands. This liquid attracts male bees. When bees land on the flower's lip, they slip and fall into the bucket. The slippery sides prevent the bee's escape. Eventually the bee finds a narrow tunnel and wriggles through it, covering its body with pollen from the orchid in the process. Once free, the bee finds a second flower and repeats the performance. This time it leaves its cargo of pollen behind, enabling the orchid to produce seed.

12

The Animal World

Nile crocodile

Animals contribute immensely to the diversity of life on planet Earth. More than 1-1/2 million different species of animals live in the world today, and new ones are always being discovered. In fact, scientists believe that the Earth actually may support as many as 50 million different species of animals. Most kinds of animals are smaller than the tip of your finger. Many are so tiny that they can be seen only with a microscope. And animals vary dramatically in complexity: from worms made up of only a few layers of cells to highly intelligent apes, porpoises, and human beings.

Animal classification

We usually can easily distinguish animals from other types of living organisms. For example, most animals move around, while most plants and fungi remain in one place, anchored by roots or rootlike structures. Most animals are made up of many different types of cells. Other organisms such as protists and monerans typically consist of only one cell.

But the scientific study of animals involves more than simply distinguishing among life forms. Scientists also must make distinctions among the different organisms that form each of the five kingdoms discussed in Chapter 9. The organisms of the Animalia kingdom are classified according to their body characteristics—an arrangement that demonstrates how the various kinds of animals are related.

Scientists group animals according to their likenesses and separate them according to their differences. Each group is called a *phylum*. Scientists separate the animals of each phylum according to certain differences. Every phylum is divided into groups called *classes*. These classes are divided into *orders*, orders into *families*, families into *genera*, and genera into *species*. This system makes it possible for scientists to classify every kind of known animal.

Every species has a correct scientific name. In this way, scientists around the world can identify the animal no matter what language the scientist speaks or what the animal may be called locally. In addition, scientific classification allows scientists to group related kinds of animals into larger groups that reflect evolutionary relationships.

For example, the lion's scientific name is *Panthera leo*. The name indicates that the lion belongs to the species *leo* and the genus *Panthera*. This

The lion's scientific name, *Panthera leo*, identifies it as the species *leo* and a member of the genus *Panthera*.

The classification of the lion

Kingdom Animalia	**Order** Carnivora
Phylum Chordata	**Family** Felidae
Subphylum Vertebrata	**Genus** *Panthera*
Class Mammalia	**Species** *leo*

genus also includes the jaguar (*Panthera onca*) and the tiger (*Panthera tigris*). All these animals belong to the cat family, Felidae, which, in turn, belongs to the order of flesh-eating animals called Carnivora. This order also includes other animals with similar features, such as sharp teeth.

But as a member of the order Carnivora, the lion bears no close resemblance to the anteater, for instance, which belongs to a different order—Edentata, meaning "toothless." However, since both animals have mammalian characteristics, they are members of the class Mammalia. All mammals have a vertebral column and are therefore placed in the subphylum Vertebrata, along with fish, amphibians, reptiles, and birds. All are placed in the phylum Chordata along with their apparently dissimilar relatives the lancelets and sea squirts, which have a stiffening rod of cartilage called a *notochord* along the back.

● **lancelets:** *small, limbless marine animal regarded as a link between the vertebrates and the invertebrates.*

To simplify our study, we can divide animals into two main groups: animals without backbones, or invertebrates, and animals with backbones, or vertebrates.

Invertebrates

More than 95 percent of the Earth's million or so existing animal species are invertebrates—they have no backbone. Many invertebrates are very small and not easily seen by the human eye, but they can be found in almost every habitat imaginable—from forests to grasslands, from oceans to ponds, and from deserts to your own backyard. Many species live in water. Insects and spiders are the only major groups of invertebrates that live on dry land.

There are about 30 invertebrate phyla, and new groups are continually being discovered. Of these phyla, 8 are particularly important because they represent more than 90 percent of all living invertebrates. They range from very simple organisms to fairly complex ones. They are: (1) Porifera (sponges), (2) Cnidaria (jellyfish and their relatives), (3) Platyhelminthes (flatworms and their relatives), (4) Nematoda (roundworms), (5) Mollusca (snails, squids, and clams), (6) Annelida (earthworms, ragworms, and leeches), (7) Arthropoda (insects, spiders, and decapods), and (8) Echinodermata (starfish and sea urchins).

PORIFERA contains about 5,000 species of sponges, which are among the oldest kinds of animals and represent the simplest level of multicellular animals. Sponges do not have heads, arms, or internal organs. They attach themselves to rocks, plants, and other objects, and most live in shallow waters, though some live on the ocean floor. Sponges range in size from less than 1 inch (2.5 centimeters) to more than 4 feet (1.2 meters) long. Sponges are made up of several cell types, each of which performs an independent and specific function. This feature makes regeneration easy— if a sponge is fragmented, the cells simply organize themselves into a new sponge. The simplest sponges are tubular with an external layer of cells called *epithelial* cells. The name *Porifera* means "pore-bearer," and sponge bodies are full of openings through which water constantly flows. The internal surface is covered with flagellated *collar cells*, which maintain this water current through the sponge. Each of these cells has a delicate tissue, or collar, that acts as a net to trap food particles. Water is drawn in through small pore cells in the walls of the sponge, and ejected from the *osculum*, its large mouth. Sponges reproduce both sexually and asexually. In sexual reproduction, a new sponge develops from the joining of two sex cells. In asexual reproduction, a new sponge is formed by methods that do not involve sex cells. Sponges range in color from bright yellow, orange, and purple to gray and brown.

● **flagellated:** *having a long whiplike tail or part.*

The vase sponge, *top,* belongs to the phylum Porifera. The red sea anemone, *bottom,* is a cnidarian.

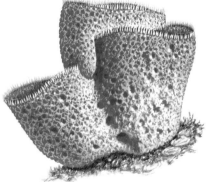

CNIDARIA includes about 9,000 species of such animals as corals, jellyfish, hydras, and sea anemones, which—like porifera—are some of the simplest types of the multicellular animals. Cnidarians have two layers of cells that surround a tubular body cavity, with a single opening at one end forming a mouth. They also have a middle layer made of a stiff, jelly-like material that helps support the animal. In many species, this jelly layer is thin, but in jellyfish it is thick enough to fill most of the body. Most cnidarians live in salt water. The two basic forms of cnidarians—medusas and polyps—are radially symmetrical, with no definite front or back side. A *medusa*, or jellyfish, has a bell- or umbrella-shaped body, while a *polyp* is shaped like a hollow cylinder. These two basic forms alternate in the life cycle of some cnidarians. Special polyp buds break free to form medusas, the medusas produce eggs and sperm that unite and develop into polyps, and the cycle continues. One form is usually dominant, however, and in some species the other form is omitted altogether.

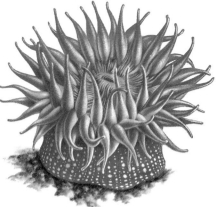

PLATYHELMINTHES, or flatworms, fall into four classes— Turbellaria, Trematoda (flukes), Monogeneans, and Cestoda (tapeworms). Most turbellarians live freely, usually in sand

and mud on the bottom of bodies of water. A few species live on land in moist soil. The other three groups are parasites that live in a wide variety of host organisms. There are about 13,000 species of flatworms. They have three layers of body cells—a layer of *mesodermal* cells lies between the *ectodermal*, or external, layer and the *endodermal* layer, which lines the digestive cavity. Most flatworms lack a circulatory system and an excretory system, and so the epidermal cells on the surface of their bodies carry out these functions. Because these animals are so flattened, they do not require a specialized breathing system—oxygen reaches the inner cells by diffusion. The mesoderm contains the complicated reproductive organs, which are made up of different types of cells. This differentiation represents a higher level of organization than is found in the cnidarians, which have tissues but not organs. Most flatworms measure less than 1 inch (2.5 centimeters) long. However, tapeworms, the largest flatworms, grow up to 100 feet (30 meters) long. Almost all flatworms are hermaphroditic—they have both male and female reproductive organs.

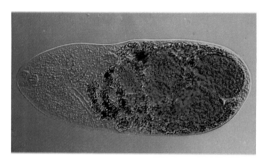

The intestinal fluke, *above*, a trematode, is a parasite that lives inside the bodies of animals. Nematodes, *below*, live in almost all environments.

NEMATODA, or roundworms, include some of the most numerous of the many-celled animals. Their unsegmented bodies usually have a digestive tube with a mouth at one end and an anus at the other. The gut is surrounded by the *pseudocoelom*—a fluid-filled cavity that acts as a hydrostatic skeleton. Roundworms are an extremely abundant and varied group. They live freely in almost all environments, though some of the approximately 12,000 known species are parasitic. Nearly all vertebrates and many invertebrates can be hosts to parasitic roundworms. Hookworms, lungworms, pinworms, trichinae, and filariae live as parasites and often cause disease in human beings and in such animals as dogs, sheep, and horses.

● **hydrostatic:** *made of fluid under pressure.*

Viewed from the end or cut crosswise, nematodes are round, hence their common name. Their bodies are usually pointed at the ends and covered in a thick protein layer called the *cuticle*, which the animal sheds periodically as it grows. Most nematodes are so small they can be seen only through a microscope, while others grow to more than 36 inches (91 centimeters) long. Most males are smaller than females. The intestine of these organisms runs from the mouth to the anus and is enclosed by longitudinal muscles. Roundworms move like snakes by contracting these muscles. They have separate sexes and give birth to larvae that resemble the adult.

Nematode

ANNELIDA, or segmented worms, are the most highly developed worms. The three major groups of annelids include: polychaete worms, the largest group, which dwell mainly in salt water and along shorelines; earthworms, which live mainly in fresh water and on land; and leeches,

which are found in salt water, fresh water, and on land. Annelids' bodies are divided into many segments, giving them a ringed appearance.

Annelids, such as the earthworm, *above,* are characterized by their segmented bodies.

In some annelids, each segment of the body—apart from the head and the last segment—is identical, and the external and internal organs are repeated in each segment. In others, some segments are specialized for particular functions. Like nematodes, annelids have a space in the body surrounding the gut. This space, called a *coelom,* is formed in a different way than the pseudocoelom of the nematodes during annelids' development.

Many polychaetes have tentacles, or feelers, on their heads and a pair of leglike projections called *parapodia* on each body segment. The parapodia are used in crawling and have many *setae*—bristles that help them grip the surface on which they are moving. Many of these worms live among algae or burrow in mud or sand. Some eat small plants and animals, while others feed on plant and animal remains. Earthworms, which have a few setae but no parapodia, eat decaying plant matter. Leeches, the smallest group of segmented worms, have a flat body with a sucker at each end. Most leeches live in water and eat the blood of fish and other water creatures.

ECHINODERMATA, or the "spiny-skins," is a group that consists of about 6,000 species of starfish, sea urchins, sea lilies, sea cucumbers, and brittle stars. This phylum is the only major phylum made up entirely of sea animals. The five distinct groups have the same radial structure, often consisting of 5 or 10 arms that extend outward from a single mouth. They are all slow-moving or fixed to one spot and unable to move around. The description "spiny-skins" refers to the hard, limy plates that form as part of the internal skeleton, which is covered with spines in some species. These spines are particularly prominent in sea urchins.

● **radial:** *arranged in rays that extend from a central point.*

Echinoderms are the only animals that have many *tube feet*—tiny tubelike structures that project from the body in rows. An internal system of water canals connects the tube feet. Echinoderms use their tube feet for moving, feeding, breathing, and sensing. The outer tip of each tube often forms a suction disk for gripping rocky surfaces. Within the body, a tiny bulb attached to the tube foot forces water into it to make it lengthen. A typical starfish has about 1,200 tube feet covering its underside. Echino-

Echinoderms, such as sea urchins, *above*, have hard shells and tiny tube-feet, which they use to move, feed, breathe, and sense their surroundings.

derms lay eggs that develop into larvae with bilateral symmetry—two similar halves. The larvae swim freely and sink to the ocean bottom where they change into the adult, radial form.

MOLLUSCA is one of the largest and most varied phyla, with about 50,000 species. The three largest classes are the Gastropoda, which consists of snails, slugs, and limpets; Bivalvia, which includes oysters, mussels, and clams; and Cephalopoda, which is made up of squids, cuttlefish, and octopuses. The animals in these classes look very different from one another, but they all have the same basic anatomy. Most mollusks have a hard shell enclosing a soft body. The *visceral mass*, or main bulk of the body, contains the internal organs. All mollusks have a skinlike organ called a *mantle*—a fleshy extension of the body wall—that hangs down on each side of the visceral mass. In mollusks with outside shells, the mantle releases liquid shell materials and adds them to the shell as the mollusk grows. In mollusks with no outside shell, such as cuttlefish and squids, the mantle provides a tough cover for the body organs. Gastropods have a wide range of beautifully shaped and patterned shells. Octopuses, which belong to the cephalopod class, are one of the largest and most intelligent types of invertebrates.

This snail, like other gastropods, has a beautifully patterned shell that encloses its soft body.

Mollusks live in most parts of the world, from the deepest oceans to high mountains and deserts. Wherever they live, mollusks must keep their bodies moist to stay alive. Most land mollusks live in damp places such as under leaves or in soil.

ARTHROPODA includes crustaceans, spiders, and insects, as well as many smaller groups. The arthropods are the most successful invertebrates, comprising more than three-fourths of all the Earth's species. The insect class, which includes cockroaches, beetles, flies, ants, bees, and butterflies, is the largest group of arthropods. Other important classes include crustaceans (crabs, lobsters, shrimps, and barnacles), arachnids (mites, ticks, spiders, and scorpions), chilopods (centipedes), and diplopods (millipedes).

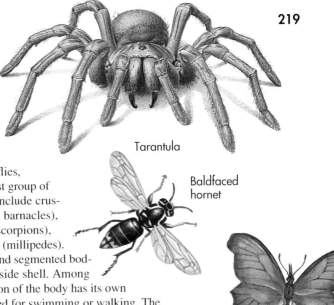

Tarantula

Baldfaced hornet

Australian beak

All arthropods have jointed limbs and segmented bodies covered by an *exoskeleton,* or outside shell. Among some primitive arthropods, each section of the body has its own pair of legs. Most of these legs are used for swimming or walking. The exoskeleton contains a stiff, horny material called *chitin* that acts as a framework supporting the limbs. This framework has allowed arthropods to develop limbs that can move rapidly and other special body features, including wings for flight. Certain arthropods, such as flies and moths, have thin, weak shells. Others, including crabs and lobsters, have thick, strong shells. Nearly all arthropods have a type of heart and circulatory system, and most of them have a well-organized nervous system. Some arthropods have simple eyes, some have compound eyes, and some—including many insects—have eyes of both types.

Scientists have described and classified more than 1,000,000 species of insects—including at least 300,000 beetles—and thousands more have yet to be identified. The success of this group is due partly to its tremendous adaptability and huge variation in life styles. Insects live in almost every habitat, from steamy tropical jungles to cold polar regions. Their ability to fly has enabled them to spread to new habitats and to escape from land-dwelling predators. It also has provided greater access to food and to more favorable living conditions.

All insects have six legs arranged in three pairs. Their bodies are divided into three parts—a head, a thorax, and an abdomen—and most have two pairs of wings. In other ways, insects' body shapes vary tremendously, usually demonstrating adaptation to their particular environment.

Just as insects live in every possible habitat on land, crustaceans dominate the rivers and seas. They come in all shapes and sizes. Most live in salt water, but some inhabit fresh water and a few live on land. Crustaceans have several pairs of legs but no fixed number. Their bodies are segmented into head, thorax, and abdomen and covered by a hard, crustlike *carapace.*

● **compound eyes:** *eyes made up of tiny six-sided lenses.*

● **thorax:** *part of the body between the neck and the abdomen.*

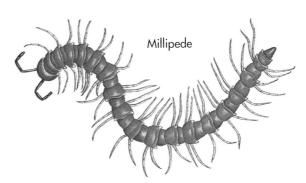

Millipede

Spiders and their relatives, known as arachnids, are the second largest group of arthropods after insects. Most have eight legs and two body parts—a head and an abdomen. Arachnids are biters. They have fangs that help them catch their prey, and many also use their fangs to inject venom into their victims.

Centipedes and millipedes are distinguished by their numerous pairs of legs. The major difference between the two is that centipedes have one pair of legs on each segment, while millipedes have two pairs.

Vertebrates

Animals with backbones, called vertebrates, make up only a tiny fraction of all known creatures—about 40,000 species. However, vertebrates exert an influence out of all proportion to their numbers because they are generally larger than invertebrates and in many cases more mobile. Vertebrates owe their size and mobility to a strong internal body framework that is jointed to provide flexibility and held in place by strong connective tissues called *ligaments.*

Vertebrates are actually part of a larger group, the phylum Chordata, or chordates. Chordates have a rodlike, flexible cord called a *notochord* that acts as an internal support for a series of muscles or muscle segments called *myotomes.* Above the notochord lies a hollow nerve tube that usually is folded at the anterior end to form the brain. Below the notochord lies the digestive tract. At some time in their lives, all chordates are equipped with paired gill slits and a tail.

● **anterior:** *positioned toward the front; fore.*

All vertebrates are bilaterally symmetrical—the left and right sides of the body are alike. The body usually is divided into a head and a trunk, and the more advanced land vertebrates have a neck. In mammals, which have milk glands for feeding their young, the trunk is divided into a thorax and abdomen. Vertebrates never have more than two pairs of limbs. Most vertebrates have a spinal column made up of bones called *vertebrae.* But some, such as the shark, have vertebrae made of cartilage or waxy tissue.

Vertebrates may be divided into eight classes: (1) Myxini (hagfish), (2) Cephalaspidomorphi (lampreys), (3) Chondrichthyes (sharks and other cartilaginous fish), (4) Osteichthyes (bony fish), (5) Amphibia (frogs, salamanders, and other amphibians), (6) Reptilia (reptiles), (7) Aves (birds), and (8) Mammalia (mammals).

MYXINI AND CEPHALASPIDOMORPHI, known as hagfish and lampreys respectively, are the most primitive of all fish. Hagfish live only in the ocean, while lampreys live in both salt water and fresh water. Lampreys and hagfish have slimy, scaleless bodies shaped somewhat like the bodies of eels, though they are not closely related to eels. Like sharks, lampreys and hagfish have a skeleton made of cartilage. But unlike all other fish, they lack jaws. A lamprey's mouth consists mainly of a round sucking organ and a toothed tongue. Certain types of lampreys use this sucking organ to attach

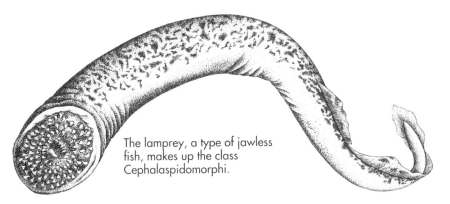

The lamprey, a type of jawless fish, makes up the class Cephalaspidomorphi.

themselves to other fish. Once attached, they cut into their victim with their toothed tongue and feed on its blood. A hagfish has a round mouth surrounded by six short *barbels*, or tentacles. Its tongue has sharp, horny teeth that it uses to bore into dead or dying fish and eat their flesh. Hagfish produce large amounts of slime.

CHONDRICHTHYES includes sharks and other *cartilaginous* fish—fish that have a skeleton of cartilage—such as rays and chimeras. Almost all of these animals live in salt water. Many cartilaginous fish are meat-eaters and have rows of teeth for tearing off chunks of flesh.

Sharks and rays are the most important members of the group, making up about 760 species. Most sharks have torpedo-shaped bodies. Most rays are shaped somewhat like pancakes with a large, winglike fin extending outward from each side of the flattened head and body. However, the angel shark has a flattened body, and the sawfish and a few other rays are torpedo-shaped, so the best way to tell a shark from a ray is by the position of the gill slits. In sharks and rays, gill slits are slotlike openings in the skin that lead from the gills. A shark's gill slits are on the sides of its head just behind the eyes. A ray's gill slits are underneath its side fins.

Chimeras, or ratfish, are medium-sized fish that live near the ocean floor. They have large eyes and long, slender, pointed tails. Several species have long, pointed snouts.

Fish that have a skeleton of cartilage rather than bone, including the great white shark, *right*, belong to the class Chondrichthyes.

OSTEICHTHYES, or bony fish, is the largest vertebrate class. As the name suggests, at least part of the skeleton of these fish is formed from bone, though cartilage is often present. Bony fish can be distinguished readily from cartilaginous fish by the presence of a bony gill cover, or *operculum*. In addition, the mouth is usually at the front of the head rather than on the underside, as it is in cartilaginous fish. Bony fish can be divided into two main groups according to the composition of their skeletons. The skeletons of modern bony fish are composed largely of bone; the skeletons of primitive bony fish are partly bone and partly cartilage. Bony fish have an air sac, which functions as a lung in the more primitive forms and as a swim bladder in the modern forms. A swim bladder makes buoyancy control possible.

● **buoyancy:** *the power to float.*

Many millions of years ago, the few existing species of fish with bony skeletons were greatly outnumbered by sharks and the ancestors of certain present-day bony fish. These early bony fish looked much alike and lived in only a few parts of the world, but they were better able to survive environmental changes than other fish, and so they became the most numerous, varied, and widespread of all fish. Modern bony fish, called *teleosts*, include about 20,860 species—95 percent of all fish. Such well-known groups as bass, catfish, cod, guppies, herring, minnows, perch, trout, and tuna are teleosts. Other teleosts include sturgeons, paddlefish, gars, and bowfins. Each group consists of a number of species.

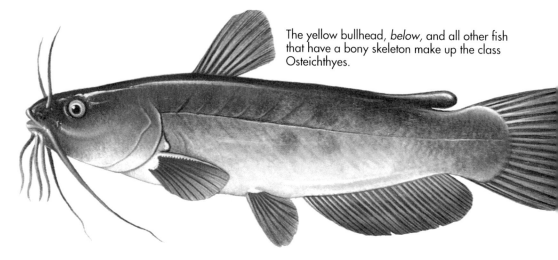

The yellow bullhead, *below,* and all other fish that have a bony skeleton make up the class Osteichthyes.

Primitive bony fish include about 15 species of bichirs, coelacanths, and lungfish—odd-looking relatives of fish that lived many millions of years ago. All the primitive bony fish except the coelacanths live in fresh water. Bichirs have a pair of lungs, so they can survive in oxygen-poor swamps. Lungfish have *choanae*, which are nostrils that connect the mouth cavity to the outside air—a construction that is very similar to the nasal cavities of modern air-breathing amphibians. Coelacanths and lungfish have paired fins with bony supports and muscle in their bases, from which the weight-bearing limbs of land vertebrates may have developed.

The bullfrog is an amphibian.

AMPHIBIA consists of about 4,000 species of amphibians—frogs, toads, salamanders, newts, and caecilians. An amphibian is an animal with scale-less skin that—with a few exceptions—lives part of its life in water and part on land. Most amphibians hatch from eggs laid in water or moist ground and begin life as water-dwelling larvae. Through a gradual process called *metamorphosis*, the larvae change into adults, which look very different from the larvae. Most adult amphibians spend their lives on land, but almost all of them return to water to find mates and produce young. Amphibians are cold-blooded and generally live in moist habitats near ponds, lakes, or streams. Most are meat-eaters that feed on insects.

Frogs and toads have four legs and no tail. Their long hind legs are used for jumping. Frogs generally have longer legs and smoother skin than toads. Most of the more than 3,500 species of frogs and toads have adapted to a wide range of habitats and live on every continent. However, frogs are most common in tropical climates.

Salamanders and newts have long tails, and most species have four short, weak legs. A few species are two-legged. Like frogs and toads, salamanders and newts need moisture and insects, worms, or even fish for food. Most live in areas that have seasonal changes in temperature. They are rarely seen, mainly because they prefer places that are dark, cool, and damp. Newts are actually a type of salamander. The animals look very similar, but unlike most salamanders, newts have flattened tails.

Caecilians have no legs and resemble large earthworms. They like warm climates and are found in tropical forests and streams where they burrow in soft mud and soil, looking for small animals such as worms and insects to eat. Like most amphibians, caecilians have smooth, slimy skin that needs to be kept moist.

REPTILIA includes about 6,500 species of reptiles—animals that have dry, scaly skin and breathe by means of lungs. Scientists divide reptiles into four main groups: lizards and snakes, the largest group; tortoises and turtles; crocodilians; and the tuatara. The animals in this class vary greatly in size.

For example, pythons grow more than 30 feet (9 meters) long and leatherback turtles may weigh more than 1 short ton (0.9 metric ton), while some species of lizards measure no more than 2 inches (5 centimeters) long.

Reptiles are cold-blooded. To stay alive, they must avoid extremely high or low temperatures. Most reptiles that are active during the day keep moving from sunny places to shady spots. Many reptiles have long lives—some turtles have lived in captivity for more than 100 years. Although reptiles live on every continent except Antarctica and in all the oceans except those of the polar regions, they are most abundant in the tropics.

Most lizards have four legs, long tails, movable eyelids, and external ear openings. They thrive in regions that have a hot or warm climate. Lizards are common in deserts.

Snakes have tails that vary in length, depending on the species, but they have no legs, eyelids, or ear openings. An unmovable covering of transparent scales protects their eyes. Snakes live mostly in the tropics and in other warm regions. They are meat-eaters and use various methods for catching and killing their prey. Some snakes crush small animals in their jaws. Pythons and boas, on the other hand, kill animals for food by squeezing them until they suffocate. Some snakes use venom to subdue and kill their prey.

The python, *above,* and the green sea turtle, *below,* are both members of the class Reptilia.

Turtles and tortoises are the only reptiles with a shell. Tortoises live on land, while turtles are aquatic. These animals pull their head, legs, and tail into their shell for protection. Tortoises move slowly, as do turtles when on land. Neither tortoises nor turtles have teeth. Instead, they have a horny beak on the upper and lower jaws. Tortoises eat mainly grasses, leaves, fruit, and other plants. Turtles are meat-eaters and feed on fish, mollusks, and crustaceans.

Crocodilians include alligators, caymans, crocodiles, and gavials—some of the largest surviving reptiles on Earth today. All live in or near water and use their long, powerful tails to swim. They have long snouts, strong jaws, and webbed hind feet. All except a few crocodilians live in the fresh waters and lowlands of the tropics. Alligators live in the southeastern United States and in southern China.

There is only one tuatara species. It is almost identical to reptiles that lived at the time of the dinosaurs, and it is often described as a "living fossil." The tuatara is found on several islands off the coast of New Zealand.

AVES consist of about 9,700 species of birds—the only animals with feathers. All birds also have wings, but not all birds can fly. For example, ostriches and penguins are flightless. Birds have conquered every habitat, from polar regions to deserts. Some birds also live successfully on the water, thus conquering three environments—something no other vertebrate class has done. The key to their success lies in their development of feathers and flight and their warm-bloodedness.

All birds hatch from eggs, and among most species the female lays her eggs in a nest. Birds, like most mammals, have two forelimbs and two hindlimbs, but the forelimbs in birds are wings rather than arms or front legs. Unlike most other vertebrates, birds lack teeth. Instead they use their beak to get food and defend themselves.

All birds are members of the Aves class. They hatch from eggs and have feathers and wings.

MAMMALIA includes about 4,500 species. A mammal is a vertebrate that feeds its young on the mother's milk. Mammals include such well-loved animals as cats and dogs and such fascinating animals as anteaters, apes, giraffes, hippopotamuses, and kangaroos. And people, too, are mammals. Mammals are warm-blooded, and most have fur or hair. Species that live in water often have thick layers of blubber, or fat, under the skin to keep out the cold. Mammals live almost everywhere, from tropical regions to arctic regions and from oceans to deserts.

Mammals differ from all or most other animals in five major ways:
- Only mammals feed their young on the mother's milk.
- Most mammals give their young more protection and training than do other animals.
- Only mammals have hair. All mammals have hair at some time in their lives, though in certain whales it is present only before birth.
- Mammals are warm-blooded. Birds are also warm-blooded, but nearly all other animals are not.
- Mammals have a larger, more well-developed brain than do other animals.

Mammals are one of the most diverse groups of animals, varying re-markably in structure, size, and habitat. Scientists generally divide the

Dogs, like all mammals, nurse their young on milk from the mother's body. No other animals feed their young this way.

class Mammalia into three major groups—the monotremes, the marsupials, and the placental mammals—based on differences in the way the animals reproduce and in the development of their young. *Monotremes*, such as the platypus, are the only mammals that lay eggs. *Marsupials* include koalas and kangaroos. Female marsupials have a special pouch called a *marsupium* that contains their mammary glands. Their babies, born blind and at a very early stage in their development, live in the mother's pouch until they are fully grown. In *placental* animals, most of the baby's development takes place within the mother's body in an organ called the *uterus*. Another organ, the *placenta,* attaches the baby to the inner wall of the uterus and provides the baby's nourishment. More than 90 percent of mammals, including humans, whales, and monkeys, are placental.

Animal communities

Plants, animals, and other organisms that live in the same area form a community. Within a community, the members of each species make up a *population*. The size of a population stays fairly stable unless some change, such as a drought, alters the conditions in the community.

As discussed in Chapter 11, a plant and animal community that covers a large geographical area is known as a *biome*. Usually, the same kinds of animals have lived in the same surroundings for thousands of years, and as a result, they have developed bodies and ways of life that help them survive in that particular biome. They can move about easily, find food, and produce more of their own kind. Biomes in which animals live include mountains, grasslands, temperate forests, tropical forests, deserts, polar regions, and oceans.

MOUNTAINS. Mountain ranges include all kinds of climates and animal environments. In the bitter cold of snow-covered mountain peaks, insects and spiders somehow manage to survive. Below the snowfields, such surefooted animals as goats and sheep live on the rocky cliffs and crags. The rabbitlike pika and other small animals also live in the high, rocky areas. Many birds build their nests among the crags, including the Nepalese swift of the Himalayas, which is found at heights of over 20,000 feet (6,100 meters). Almost every mountain level has grass-covered plateaus and slopes, or forested valleys. Grazing animals such as vicuñas and yaks live in the grassy areas. Many mountain animals move from one level to another to find food as the seasons change.

TAIGA, also called *boreal forests,* are found in regions that have an extremely cold winter, such as northern Europe, Asia, and North America. Beavers, mice, porcupines, snowshoe hares, and other small mammals live in the taiga. Larger mammals include bears, caribou, foxes, moose, and wolves. Birds of the taiga include ducks, loons, warblers, and woodpeckers.

An Asian mountain community is home to, *clockwise from top,* the Nepalese swift, Himalayan ibex, snow leopard, and Marco Polo sheep.

The white rhinoceros is well adapted to life on the grasslands of Africa. It uses its square upper lip to nip off the grasses on which it feeds.

GRASSLANDS. Most of the largest animals and many of the swiftest animals live on grasslands, the world's vast stretches of open country. Among the largest grassland animals are the elephant, hippopotamus, and rhinoceros. Fast-running animals of the grasslands include the blackbuck, kudu, ostrich, pronghorn, and zebra. Africa has more kinds of grassland animals than any other continent. Australia's most familiar grassland animal is the kangaroo. Many small grassland animals, including the prairie dog of North America, live in burrows.

TEMPERATE DECIDUOUS FORESTS. Most of the animals in temperate deciduous forests have small bodies that make it easy for them to move through the underbrush. They include the chipmunk, opossum, porcupine, raccoon, skunk, and squirrel. Some large animals, such as bears, boars, deer, and moose, also live there. The shores of the ponds, lakes, and streams of temperate deciduous forests shelter many animals that live both on land and in water, such as the beaver, frog, muskrat, otter, salamander, and turtle. Many birds build nests in temperate deciduous forests, where they feed on the great numbers of insects and worms that live among the plants and in the rich soil.

TROPICAL FORESTS. Animals of the tropical forests live in an environment that stays hot all year around. Anteaters, jaguars, leopards, tapirs, and tigers live in these forests. Tropical forests include lightly wooded areas with moderate rainfall, and huge rain forests—densely wooded places with heavy rainfall. In tropical rain forests, the tops of the trees and vines form a thick overhead covering called a *canopy* that provides a home for climbing

The small bodies of raccoons, *above,* enable them to move easily through the underbrush of the temperate deciduous forests where they live.

animals, such as monkeys and sloths. Gibbons, orangutans, and other apes also are found in tropical rain forests. In addition, brightly colored parrots and numerous other birds nest in the trees. Many birds feed on the large numbers of insects found in tropical rain forests. Snakes, such as the boa constrictor, and spiders, including the tarantula, grow to giant sizes in tropical rain forests.

POLAR REGIONS. Few land animals can survive in the polar regions that have ice and snow all year around, but even the coldest arctic and antarctic waters have great numbers of fish. In the far north, these fish provide food for the polar bears that live on the arctic islands and ice floes. In the Antarctic, penguins and other birds feed on the fish of the southern

Toucans feed mainly on the various small fruits that grow abundantly in tropical forests. But they sometimes use their large bill, which has sawlike edges, for tearing off pieces of larger fruits.

Penguins, with their waterproof feathers and thick layers of insulating fat, are one of the few animal species that can survive in the bitterly cold Antarctic.

polar seas. However, many animals live in the arctic tundra of northern Asia, Canada, and Europe, including grazing animals such as the caribou and musk ox. Other arctic animals are the hare, ermine, fox, grizzly bear, lemming, wolf, and wolverine. Arctic birds include the loon, rock ptarmigan, sandhill crane, snowy owl, and golden plover.

DESERTS. Most desert animals have small bodies that help them escape the scorching daytime heat. Some desert animals dig holes in the ground to avoid the hot sun, while others find shade under brush, rocks, or trees. After sunset, most deserts become quite cool, and the animals emerge in search of food. Some lizards, snakes, and tortoises are well suited to the high daytime temperatures, but even they must seek shade during the hottest times. Most desert animals can live without water for several days. Small desert animals include mice, hares, rabbits, kangaroo rats, and toads. Among the larger desert animals are camels, coyotes, dingoes, and mule deer.

Camels have evolved food-storing humps and the ability to go for long periods without water. These adaptations enable camels to thrive in desert conditions.

OCEANS. Animals live everywhere in the vast ocean waters that cover 70 percent of the Earth's surface. Many small animals, including the shrimp-like copepod, make up the animal part of *plankton*—a mass of organisms that drifts with the ocean currents and tides. Whales, the world's largest animals, also live in the oceans. Other large ocean animals include sea cows, octopuses, sharks, and sting rays. Many kinds of brightly colored fish live close to the reefs in tropical ocean waters. Most fish live near continents, but some, such as flying fish, are found in the open seas. Many animals that have shells, such as marine clams, and spiny animals, such as sea urchins, live on the ocean floor.

Ecosystems

Each animal community that inhabits a biome is a part of what is known as an ecosystem. An ecosystem—the most complex level of organization in nature—is made up of a community and its *abiotic,* or nonliving, environment, including climate, soil, water, air, nutrients, and energy. Scientists categorize the elements that make up an ecosystem into six main parts, based on the flow of energy and nutrients through the system. They include the sun, abiotic substances, primary producers, primary consumers, secondary consumers, and decomposers.

Whales, the largest animals on Earth, live throughout the world's oceans.

Everything that humans and other animals eat—from milk to pasta to meat—is derived from primary producers: the green plants that convert sunlight into food.

To better understand how an ecosystem works, we can study such a system in its simplest form. First, the sun provides the energy that primary producers need to make food. *Primary producers* consist of green plants, such as grass and trees, which produce their food by way of photosynthesis. In order to grow, plants also need *abiotic substances,* such as nutrients and water. *Primary consumers* include mice, rabbits, grasshoppers, and other plant-eating animals. Foxes, skunks, and other *secondary consumers*—or predators—eat animals. *Decomposers,* such as bacteria and fungi, break down dead plants and animals into simple nutrients. The nutrients go back into the soil and are used again by plants.

The series of stages that energy goes through in the form of food is called a *food chain.* In most ecosystems, a variety of producers, consumers, and decomposers form an overlapping network of food chains called a *food web.* Food webs are especially complex in many tropical and oceanic ecosystems.

Animal groups

As we have seen, many different kinds of animals live together in communities. Whether these animals live in groups of their own kind or with other species, each individual benefits from associating with others in the group. In the case of a food chain, the animals benefit by feeding on one another. But animals of the same species—or different species—often can live together harmoniously.

Many animal species live in groups—hives of bees, schools of fish, herds of deer, and flocks of birds, for example. Some groups form simply because food is concentrated in a small area, and individuals congregate there to eat.

The individuals in a flock of starlings or a shoal of sardines do not know one another and have no special roles. Many groups, however, are not just masses of independent individuals. Different individuals may have separate roles, especially among social insects and mammals—the animals that show the most highly developed systems of group living. This *specialization* increases the efficiency of the group's activities.

In most animal groups, a few members become leaders and the others remain followers. The leaders hold their places by fighting or by showing that they are ready to fight. They usually watch for danger while the other members of the group eat or sleep. The leaders also fight to protect the group.

Chickens and some other birds have a *pecking order.* Every member of the flock fights for its place in the pecking order. Each chicken eats or drinks ahead of all the other chickens it can peck, but steps aside for any chicken that can peck it.

Some insects live in colonies. Ants, honey bees, and termites have queens that lay all the eggs and workers that gather food for the colony. Among some ants and termites, certain individuals with powerful jaws serve as soldiers to protect the colony.

Some animals live so closely together that they form what seems to be a single animal. For example, the Portuguese man-of-war, which drifts in the sea, is really a group of many animals. Each animal has a certain job to do, such as catching food, digesting the food, or producing young.

Different species of animals sometimes help each other and even become partners. For example, small fish called anemone fish live among the tentacles of sea anemones in the coral reefs of the Pacific Ocean. The anemone fish acts as a decoy. Larger fish try to catch the anemone fish but get caught by the sea anemones. When a sea anemone swallows a larger fish, the anemone fish take pieces of the victim for themselves.

White birds called cattle egrets live near large animals such as cattle, elephants, or antelope. The large animals stir up insects as they travel across the grassland, and the egrets eat the insects. Egrets often perch on the back of a large animal. If the birds see danger coming, they fly away, thus warning the animal of danger.

Colonies of bees live in hives according to a structured social order.

Animal reproduction

All animals create more of their own kind. Most animals have special body features with which to reproduce, but others accomplish the task without such features. Animals reproduce in two principal ways: asexual reproduction and sexual reproduction. Many of the simplest kinds of animals reproduce asexually most of the time. Most other kinds of animals reproduce only sexually.

Asexual reproduction

Only the more primitive animals, including sponges, jellyfish, flatworms, and sea squirts, reproduce asexually. In asexual reproduction, one parent produces the offspring. It is a less complicated means of reproduction but has the disadvantage of producing offspring that are identical to their parents. There is no shuffling of genetic material between generations, and therefore less variation within the population.

   Two methods of asexual reproduction take place in animals—fragmentation (or regeneration) and budding. Many flatworms can reproduce by *fragmentation,* which involves breaking the body into two or more pieces. When a flatworm reproduces, it usually divides into halves. Each half then forms the body parts it needs and becomes a new individual. Hydras and coral reproduce by *budding.* The animal extends small projections, called *buds,* from its side. Some of the buds develop their own feeding organs and then detach themselves from the parent as separate individuals.

Sexual reproduction

In sexual reproduction, two parents produce the offspring. Most kinds of animals that reproduce only sexually have special cells to produce their young. Female sex cells, formed in an ovary, are called *ova,* or *eggs,* and

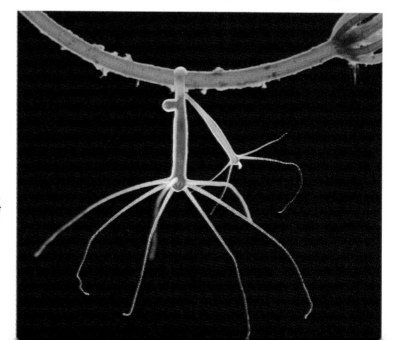

Budding is a form of asexual reproduction. Attached to this parent hydra is an immature offspring. When the offspring is fully mature, it will separate from the parent.

male sex cells, formed in the testicles, are called *sperm*. When a sperm cell unites with an egg cell, a new animal starts to form. The stage of reproduction in which sperm unite with eggs is called *fertilization*.

In most animals, the male and female sex organs are found in different individuals. In some animals, such as hydras, flatworms, earthworms, and snails, however, both male and female sex organs are present in each individual. These animals are called *hermaphrodites*. Tapeworms fertilize themselves, but most hermaphrodites cross-fertilize with other members of their species.

EXTERNAL FERTILIZATION occurs when the female's egg meets the male's sperm outside the female's body. Most fish and amphibians reproduce by external fertilization. In a type of external fertilization called *spawning*, the female usually releases her eggs first, and the male then fertilizes them by covering them with sperm. This method requires exact timing of the release of sex cells from both sexes, or the egg and sperm will not meet. Generally, animals that give their eggs little care, such as some fish, need to produce great numbers of eggs to ensure that enough of them will hatch.

INTERNAL FERTILIZATION. Land animals, including reptiles, birds, insects, and mammals, rely mostly on internal fertilization. A few fish and amphibians also fertilize internally. Usually, when these animals mate, the male deposits his sperm inside the female, where the sperm unite with the egg.

All birds and most reptiles and insects lay their fertilized eggs in shells outside their bodies, and the eggs then develop outside the mother. Some fish reproduce in this way as well. For example, a dogfish reproduces by internal fertilization and produces only a few eggs, which are enclosed in a protective egg purse. Such egg-laying animals are described as *oviparous*.

The hard-shelled eggs of birds contain a fluid in which the embryo floats and develops. Because birds are warm-blooded, the embryos must be kept at body temperature to survive and develop. The temperature is maintained

Most fish reproduce by external fertilization, in which the female lays eggs and the male covers them with sperm.

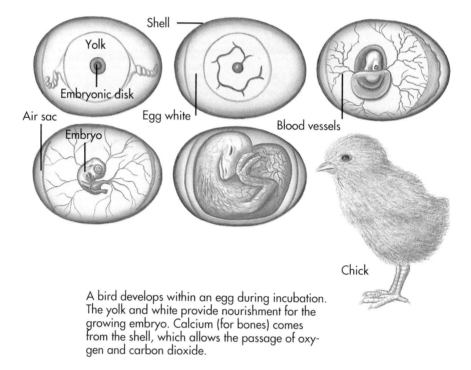

Shell
Yolk
Embryonic disk
Air sac
Egg white
Blood vessels
Embryo
Chick

A bird develops within an egg during incubation. The yolk and white provide nourishment for the growing embryo. Calcium (for bones) comes from the shell, which allows the passage of oxygen and carbon dioxide.

by *incubation,* an activity carried out by one or both parents. Incubation may continue for two to three weeks or more before the young chicks hatch.

Monotremes, such as playpuses and echidnas (spiny anteaters), are the only oviparous mammals. They lay eggs that have a tough, leathery shell.

Some fish, amphibians, insects, and reptiles produce eggs that remain inside the female until the young hatch, but they are not nourished directly by the mother. These animals are described as *ovoviviparous.*

Animals with the most advantageous form of reproduction, however, are *viviparous.* This type of reproduction takes place mainly in placental mammals and ensures that the fertilized egg implants inside the mother's uterus. While the embryo grows inside the mother's uterus, it receives oxygen and nourishment from her body by way of the placenta and remains at a constant temperature. Eventually, the offspring reaches an advanced stage of development and looks like a smaller version of the adult. It is then ready to be born. After birth, young mammals feed on milk from their mother's mammary glands for a period of time that varies depending on the species.

METAMORPHOSIS. Some animals undergo a process called metamorphosis in their development from birth to adulthood. The most highly evolved insects, such as butterflies and bees, develop by *complete metamorphosis.* They hatch from their eggs as *larvae* that do not resemble their parents. A larva spends its life eating and growing. When it is full-grown, it stops eating, and the larva becomes a *pupa.* Inside the pupal case, the adult insect body develops and eventually emerges.

Butterflies reproduce in a process called complete metamorphosis. A caterpillar, the larva of a butterfly, becomes a pupa (1). When the pupa has transformed into an adult butterfly, the pupal shell cracks (2). The adult butterfly is damp and wrinkled when it first emerges (3), but in about an hour it is ready to fly.

1

2

3

Another pattern of development, referred to as *gradual* or *incomplete metamorphosis*, is exhibited by the group of insects that includes dragonflies and grasshoppers. The insects hatch from their eggs as *nymphs,* which resemble the parents, but are wingless, smaller, and sexually immature. Like larvae, nymphs eat all the time. They do not enter a pupal stage, however, but grow and shed their outer skin until they reach adult size. Wings develop along the way. After the last molt, they emerge as adults.

Most amphibians first go through a larval stage, and gradually metamorphose into adult amphibians. In some salamanders, however, the young are born live and do not go through a larval stage.

Animal bodies and behavior

Every kind of animal has special body features and behaviors that allow it to thrive in its environment. An animal uses various parts of its body to move about, eat, reproduce, breathe, and respond to changes in its environment. These special body features are what enable animals to survive in their particular living conditions.

Just as the body features of animals evolve over time, so does their behavior. *Behavior* refers to all of an animal's responses and actions. The general behavior of most animals seems to depend on patterns of reaction called *instincts* and *reflexes*, with which they are born. Such reactions have nothing to do with reasoning—animals do certain things without learning how to do them and without knowing what will happen as a result. For example, after breaking out of its cocoon, a moth flies about and finds its food in the juices of plants without having to learn how to do so. Instincts seem to provide animals with a "guide to life" that directs them to do certain things to stay alive.

The starfish moves by fastening the tube feet of one of its arms to a nearby rock or the seabed. When the tube feet contract, the starfish is pulled forward.

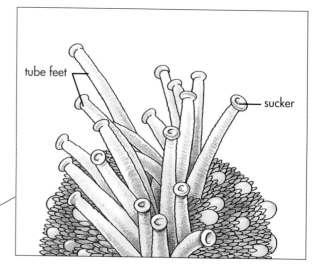

tube feet

sucker

In this section, we will take a closer look at the body features and behaviors that allow animals to survive in their habitats.

Moving around

All animals move about at some time in their lives, but their methods of movement vary widely. Many of the smallest animals live in a fluid medium and travel by means of hairlike extensions of their bodies called *cilia*. For example, the planarian, a type of flatworm that lives in water and damp soil, glides along on cilia located on its undersurface. The youngest corals and sponges also swim freely through the sea by means of cilia. However, these animals soon attach themselves to rocks or other firm objects and stay there for life.

A snail makes its own "roadway" by producing a sticky liquid on the underside of its muscular foot. The rim of its foot skids along on the liquid with a rippling motion, helping the snail get where it wants to go.

Sea urchins, starfish, and some of their relatives move about on *tube feet*—slender, flexible tubes that project from the animal's body in rows. At the end of each tube is a tiny suction disk. The animal holds onto a firm surface by means of these disks and pushes or pulls itself along by moving its tube feet.

Water gives some animals support that they do not get on land. Amphibians, such as frogs and salamanders, can move easily in water, but on land they rest with their underbellies on the ground. Frogs use their back legs to travel in sudden leaps. Salamanders crawl on short legs that extend from their sides. They wriggle their bodies so that the legs catch on the ground and move them along over it.

Alligators, crocodiles, birds, and most mammals have strong legs that usually extend from their undersides. These legs support them and allow them to travel on land. Generally, the swiftest land animals have the longest legs in relation to the size of their bodies. Long-legged animals include antelope, deer, horses, ostriches, rheas, and zebras.

Insects use their six legs in a way that gives them excellent balance, standing on one set of three legs while moving the other set. Flies and some other insects can walk upside down because each insect leg has a pair of claws at the end, and sometimes a sticky pad as well. Most kinds of adult insects, with one or two pairs of wings in addition to their six legs, can fly as well as walk. Birds and bats have wings in place of front legs. Bats are the only mammals that have wings.

Whales, dolphins, and porpoises thrust their bodies through the water by pushing their powerful tails up and down. Their front limbs are flippers, used primarily for balancing and turning. Most fish swim by swishing their strong tail fins from side to side, using their other fins chiefly for balance.

A few sea animals have special ways of swimming. Lobsters and crayfish cup their tail fins downward and dart backward. Cuttlefish and squid also travel backward, using a kind of jet propulsion. They draw water into a large body cavity and expel it through a narrow funnel. Scallops move with another jet propulsion method. They take in water between the two parts of their hinged shells and shoot it out in small jets through openings near the shell hinge.

Obtaining food

Every animal must eat in order to survive, and each kind of animal has special body features that enable it to obtain food. Most also have organs for digesting that food.

Many types of water animals—from the simple sponges to the giant blue whale—filter their food from the water. Sponges have *collar cells* that trap food particles from the water that passes through their bodies. Clams use *cilia* to gather tiny food particles from the water. Water currents sweep the food particles into the open shell of the clam, where they become fastened to a film of mucus. The cilia then sweep the mucus to the clam's mouth, and soft, fingerlike organs push the mucus and food into the mouth.

A pileated woodpecker's long, spiky tongue enables it to scoop insects from holes it bores in trees.

Baleen whales, which have no teeth, gulp huge mouthfuls of water that contains the small sea organisms they eat. Horny plates called *baleen* hang in rows from the roof of the whale's mouth. When the whale closes its mouth, its huge tongue presses up, forcing the water out past the baleen. The small animals are trapped in the baleen, and the whale swallows them.

Many animals, such as lions, use their jaws and teeth to seize and chew their food. Cows, horses, and other grazing animals tear grass with their teeth. A bird's beak lacks teeth, but some birds' beaks are perfect for picking up seeds and crushing them. Many kinds of birds, including the flycatcher, robin, swallow, and wren, use their beaks to capture insects. The eagle, hawk, and owl use their hooked beaks to tear apart the bodies of the animals they eat.

Insects and millipedes use their jaws and parts of their mouths to seize and chew their food. Spiders, which have no jaws, use a pair of fangs located in the front of their mouth to inject a paralyzing poison into flies and other prey. The spider then sprays its prey with digestive juices that turn the prey's body tissues into a liquid. The spider then eats the liquid.

Most animals have organs that digest the food they eat. After the food is swallowed, it may be stored for a time in the animal's stomach and then passed into the intestines. Undigested waste material is discharged through the animal's lower intestine.

Some animals, including many birds, earthworms, and insects, store their food in a *crop.* In most birds, food moves from the esophagus or the crop into a stomach with two sections. In the first section, digestive juices are added to the food. In the second part, called the *gizzard,* food is ground into tiny pieces before reaching the animal's intestine.

Cows, sheep, and most other *ruminants,* or cud-chewing animals, have a stomach with four separate compartments. Each compartment plays an important role in digesting food.

Getting oxygen

Most animals have special body features that take in oxygen from their environment. Land animals get their oxygen from the air. Animals that live in water absorb oxygen from the water. Most kinds of animals use some form of breathing to draw in oxygen and give off carbon dioxide, but a few animals, including tapeworms and many other parasites, live where oxygen is not freely present, such as in the host's in-testines. These animals use a special digestive process to get oxygen from their food.

Most vertebrates breathe with gills if they live in water, or with lungs if they live on land. A fish gulps water, ab-sorbs the oxygen it contains, and then expels the water through spaces between its gills.

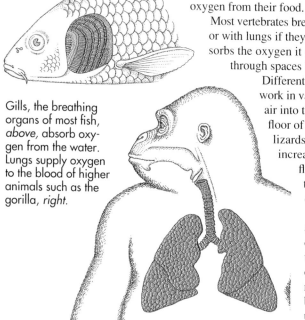

Gills, the breathing organs of most fish, *above,* absorb oxygen from the water. Lungs supply oxygen to the blood of higher animals such as the gorilla, *right.*

Different kinds of land animals have lungs that work in various ways. Frogs, for example, push air into their lungs under pressure, using the floor of their mouth as a pump. Snakes and lizards use muscles between their ribs to increase the volume of their bodies. Air flows into their lungs and occupies the empty space produced by this expansion.

Warm-blooded animals—birds and mammals—have special mus-cles and breathing organs that allow them to take in a large amount of oxygen. Their bodies must produce more energy than those of cold-blooded animals because they are usually more active. In addition, the body of a warm-blooded animal uses a lot of energy to control its temperature, which must stay at the same level whether outside temperatures rise or fall. The body temperature of a cold-blooded animal changes according to the temperature of its surroundings.

Among invertebrates, insects take in oxygen through air tubes called *tracheae*. These tubes extend inward to the body organs from pores on the animal's sides. In some insects, movements of body muscles help pump air in and out of the tubes. Some invertebrates, such as crabs, crayfish, and lobsters, have gills under a thin part of the body wall above the legs.

Some spiders have *book lungs*—one or more pairs of lungs with thin sheets of tissue that look like the pages of a book.

Land snails and some freshwater snails have lungs and must come to the surface of the water to draw air into their lungs through a pore on the side of the body. Other freshwater snails and most saltwater snails have gills and thus get their oxygen from the water.

Many worms, and some other small invertebrates, absorb all the oxygen they need through the surface of their bodies. Earthworms, for example, breathe through their moist skin.

Animal senses

Most kinds of animals have body parts that respond to changes in their environment, such as an odor, a sight, a sound, a taste, or a touch. The simplest kinds of animals react to stimuli with body cells known as *sensory cells,* which are scattered among the outermost cells of the body. Animals with more complex physical structures, especially vertebrates, have highly developed organs for reacting to stimuli. The reactions of these animals depend largely on one or more of the major senses—sight, hearing, smell, taste, and touch.

Some senses are more important to one kind of animal than to another. Most birds, for example, rely on sight to find food, while hearing is vital to bats. If the ears of a bat are covered, the animal crashes into objects when it tries to fly. A keen sense of smell enables dogs to find food, follow trails, and recognize danger, while taste is highly important to many kinds of insects. The butterfly finds its food by tasting the sweetness of flowers with its feet. A cat's long whiskers serve as touch organs, enabling the cat to feel its way through underbrush and avoid bumping into objects.

How animals sense

Touch. Woodcocks and many other birds use the tips of their beaks to locate worms underground.

Smell. Snakes and some lizards use their forked tongues to smell.

Taste. Catfish and other fish taste with their skin by means of cells called taste buds.

Hearing. Bats navigate by producing sounds that bounce off objects.

Sight. A dragonfly's large compound eyes enable it to detect moving objects at great distances.

Animal communication

For many animals, sound is an important means of communication. For example, a male robin hearing the song of another male knows that the singing bird will fight to defend his territory. However, a female robin hearing the same song is encouraged to approach for mating.

Animals use many forms of "language" besides sounds. Some animals communicate by scent. A female moth may signal that she is ready to mate by releasing a certain scent into the breeze. Some male moths, attracted by the scent, can locate a female from nearly 1 mile (1.6 kilometers) away. Male tigers and other members of the cat family mark their territory by urinating. The scent tells other tigers that the area is taken.

A skunk uses its body and its scent to communicate. When threatened, the skunk raises its tail as a warning (1). It gives further warning by raising itself on its front paws (2). If the threat persists, the skunk turns and sprays two jets of foul-smelling fluid from its anal glands (3).

Some animals use their faces and bodies to communicate. A male baboon may threaten another baboon by hunching his shoulders and opening his mouth to show his large, pointed teeth. An angry gorilla may throw leaves into the air and beat its chest with its fists. Honeybees do two kinds of "dances" to tell their neighbors where nectar can be found. If a honeybee finds nectar in flowers near its hive, it returns to the hive and dances in circles. When the bee finds nectar in flowers that are far away, it dances a figure-eight pattern, with an imaginary line between the circles indicating the direction of the nectar in relation to the sun. The other bees in the hive then fly off to find the nectar.

Animals that live in groups need signals that help keep the group together and coordinate their movements. White-tailed deer have light-colored rump patches that are easy for others in the group to follow. Sounds also can be used to maintain contact. Feeding parties of birds twitter to keep in touch as they forage through the trees.

Migration

Many animals move about in groups and travel at certain times. Some travel to avoid cold weather or to find a steady food supply. Others make long trips to favorite feeding places or journey to special places to produce their young. Some animals make round trips at regular times of the year, usually traveling in large groups. The journey of a large group of animals is often referred to as a migration.

In East Africa, millions of wildebeest, or gnu, make a trip each year across the grasslands of the Serengeti plains. Although close to the equator,

Seeking warmth and food, migrating snow geese fly south in the winter, *left*.

the area experiences seasonal changes in rainfall that result in a flush of new grass at different times in different areas. The wildebeest keep on the move to feast on the new grass as it appears.

In Canada, great herds of caribou move up into the arctic tundra in the summer and then travel back south as winter starts. They, too, take advantage of the seasonal growth of food.

Ocean animals that migrate include some kinds of whales. Every summer, these whales go to cold waters to feed, and in winter they swim to warm waters to breed. Salmon are famous for their long migration to breed. Pacific salmon live for years in ocean waters. When the time comes for them to spawn, they may travel hundreds of miles back to the shallow inland brooks and streams where they were born. In these waters, they produce their young and die. Later, the young salmon swim downstream and out to sea.

Many birds make long seasonal migrations. Migrating birds that live in the Northern Hemisphere fly south every year just before winter and return in spring. Some, such as the robin, travel just far enough to find berries and worms for food, while the stork of northern Europe travels much farther to spend the winter in Africa.

Every autumn, monarch butterflies fly from Canada and the northern United States to California, Florida, and as far south as Mexico. They start a return trip the following spring. Many of the older butterflies die on the way north, but the young ones complete the trip.

The woodchuck, *below*, feeds on stored fat as it hibernates.

Hibernation

In lands that turn cold, many animals respond by hibernating, or sleeping through the winter. A hibernating animal finds a protected place, such as a deep hole or cave, and goes to sleep until spring. Many do not eat during their long sleep. They grow fat from feeding in summer, and their bodies use the stored fat as food while they are inactive. Skunks; most bats and frogs; and many burrowing animals, such as prairie dogs and woodchucks, hibernate. Many insects, including bees and certain butterflies, also sleep through the cold seasons. Some animals that live in regions

that get very hot escape heat and dryness in much the same way. They *estivate,* or sleep through the summer. When the water in which they live dries up, African lungfish estivate inside a mud-and-slime cocoon.

Animal defenses

Every animal must have ways to defend itself. An attack on an animal might come from some other animal hunting for food, or from people hunting for sport. An animal can use three basic kinds of behavior to defend itself from a predator—it can hide, it can run, or it can fight back. Some animals use a combination of all three methods. Fighting back is probably the least popular option because there is too much risk of getting hurt or even killed. Even animals equipped with deadly weapons use them as a last resort.

Animal defenses sometimes involve trickery. When attacked, the opossum fools its predator by playing dead, *right.*

Many animals hide when an enemy threatens to attack. Some animals are colored like their surroundings, and others have bodies that resemble parts of plants. Animals with these characteristics seem to disappear merely by remaining motionless. Certain chameleons—a type of lizard—can change color to match their background.

A few animals fool their enemies by appearing to be dead. For example, if an opossum is threatened, its eyes close and its body goes limp. It stays that way even if it is picked up, dropped, turned over, or bitten gently. A dog that would pounce on a live opossum often pays no attention to a "dead" one.

Other animals have a shell or hard covering that they use as armor for protection. Some animals have sharp quills or spines. When an armadillo becomes frightened, it curls up inside its strong, plated shell.

Most animals respond to danger by running away. Sometimes they try to maintain a specific definite distance—the *flight distance*—between themselves and danger. An enemy is tolerated if it is farther away, but once it comes within the flight distance, it triggers instant flight. Some animals can outrun most of their attackers. The antelope, deer, horse, kangaroo, and ostrich have long legs and can cover great distances at high speeds. The rabbit bounds rapidly and also makes long, zigzag jumps. Several small animals, such as prairie dogs, seek refuge in burrows and other places. A squirrel scampers up a tree to escape danger on the ground.

Gnawing trees, gathering twigs, and building dams are skills that young beavers learn quickly.

Learning and intelligence

In addition to instinct, animals can learn ways of coping with their environment and thus modify their behavior to deal with problems that they have encountered before. Some scientists believe the ability to learn is a measure of an animal's intelligence.

An animal's ability to learn and remember is, to a certain extent, dependent upon the life it leads. A worker bee, for example, must be able to learn the position of its hive and of flowers that are good for foraging, but a fly does not need this ability.

Probably the highest form of learning is *insight*—when the answer to a problem arrives in a sudden flash. The term is used to describe the rapid solution of a problem, too fast for a trial-and-error process. An example of this is the immediate construction of a "ladder" by some chimpanzees who want fruit that is out of reach.

Another type of learning is *imprinting,* which is thought to occur when the animal is very young, or at crucial times of an animal's life, such as during the production of offspring. Imprinting occurs in both mammals and birds. Young songbirds, for example, are not able to sing an adult version of the species song if they have never heard it. Instead, they sing a simple version of the song, without any characteristic trills. But a young bird that has heard the adult song during the right period in its early development is able to sing it perfectly at a later stage because it has imprinted the song.

Many scientists say that an animal has high intelligence if it does the following:

• quickly learns to solve certain complicated problems
• plays when it is young
• tries new experiences as an adult.

By these standards, apes and monkeys, ocean mammals, and flesh-eating mammals are generally the most intelligent animals. Other animals are relatively low in intelligence, and invertebrates have very little intelligence. Many animals can learn to do tricks if they are carefully trained, but they learn such tricks largely by imitation. The ability to do tricks is not a sign of intelligence, since even fleas can be trained to do tricks.

Intelligent Animals?

For many years, scientists argued that the one thing that separated humans from all other animals was their intelligence—their ability to think and communicate through language. French scientist René Descartes argued in 1637 that lesser creatures do little more than act by reflex. Charles Darwin, however, asserted that humans were linked by common ancestry to the rest of the animal kingdom. Darwin's controversial theory raised many questions. One of the most compelling is this: If other vertebrates are similar to humans in body features, shouldn't they also share other characteristics, including intelligence?

Attempts to answer this question have resulted in many heated debates. At the beginning of the 1900's, respected Swiss psychiatrist Gustav Wolff said, "An animal can think in a human way and can express human ideas in human language." His statement was based on his observations of Clever Hans, a horse that appeared to show remarkable intelligence. A retired schoolteacher trained the horse to answer simple arithmetic problems by tapping his hoof. But Oskar Pfungst, a German psychologist, found that Hans answered questions based on accidental cues he received from audiences and from his master. For example, his master visibly relaxed when Hans tapped the proper number of times, cueing the horse that it was time to stop tapping.

Ever since Clever Hans, a lot of hard work has gone into trying to answer the question of animal intelligence. In 1972, Penny Patterson, a Stanford University graduate student, began teaching American Sign Language to a gorilla named Koko. Over time, Koko learned more than 500 signs and was able to make statements averaging three to six signs long. Bitter arguments arose among scientists about the meaning of such work. Did Koko's "speech" demonstrate a genuine ability to think symbolically and communicate ideas, or was it largely the result of cueing?

Modern research

Today's evidence of animal intelligence is hard to refute. Take Kanzi, a 12-year-old pygmy chimpanzee, for example. Kanzi has the grammatical abilities of a 2-1/2-year-old child. Trained by Sue Savage-Rumbaugh, this "intelligent" chimp tells researchers what he wants by pointing to geometric symbols printed on a board or pressing symbols on a keyboard that produces the words in English. This research has made it apparent that Kanzi understands spoken language.

Members of the ape family aren't the only animals showing off their intelligence. In 1977, Irene M. Pepperberg began teaching an African grey parrot named Alex to use words and to connect meanings to them. By 1993, Alex could name 71 objects, colors, shapes, materials, and actions. Today, Alex uses language to communicate his wants and needs to his trainers. Research with Alex indicates that some animals—at least African grey parrots—might have some understanding of how to use words to express abstract ideas.

Alex's ability to communicate has made it possible to explore his other mental capabilities as well. He seems able to label objects by their color or shape. And beyond simply labeling them, he is able to understand that given objects share or do not share a particular trait. For example, if he is shown two different shapes of the same color and the trainer asks, "What's same?" Alex answers, "Color."

Then and now

For much of the 1900's, animal psychology was based on "behaviorism." Scientists stud-

Alex, an African grey parrot, has learned to identify objects with an 80 percent rate of accuracy.

ied rats finding their way through mazes and pigeons pecking at colored squares to get food rewards. Animal intelligence was a measure of how quickly and consistently animals could solve problems posed by humans. Behaviorists believed that animals learned by remembering the behaviors that brought success. They were "conditioned," not "taught." In its most extreme form, behaviorism dismissed the very idea that animals are capable of thought.

It is now understood that much learning, even though it is based on conditioning, is specialized for carrying out tasks the animals are likely to encounter. Animals are innately equipped to recognize when they should learn, what cues they should respond to, how to store the new information, and how to refer to it in the future. This perspective allows scientists to see that, like all behaviors, intelligence is shaped by natural selection. Animals tend to learn only things that are significant to their life style. For this reason, although animals tend to think only about their immediate world—food, predators, and social companions—their thinking may in fact be intelligent because it provides the knowledge that they need.

The versatility with which animals overcome the challenges they face often suggests that they are indeed intelligent—that they think about what are doing. Chimpanzees, for example, make sticks suitable for probing into termite nests so that they can catch and eat the termites. Behaviorists, however, still argue that no matter how skillful or ingenious its behavior, there is no way of telling whether an animal is conscious of what it is doing.

Future research

Unfortunately, it is impossible to know precisely what goes on in another creature's mind and to what extent it truly understands language. And since the lives of animals are so different from ours, we can't reasonably apply human standards to them. In the past, scientists have defined the concept of intelligence according to human values. But what is important to animals may be different from what matters to humans. When studying animals, scientists must test them in situations that have meaning for their lives—not humans'. They can no longer judge animals' intelligence simply by how much it resembles their own.

Animal Groups

This chart shows the breakdown of the major groups in the kingdom Animalia discussed in this book.

Invertebrates (animals without a backbone)

Rank	*Features and common name(s)*
Phylum Porifera	Skeleton of spiky fibers; body full of holes; mobile only before adult stage; all aquatic. Sponges.
Phylum Cnidaria	Circular body, with single opening surrounded by tentacles; soft-bodied; two layers of cells separated by jellylike substance; aquatic. Jellyfish.
Phylum Platyhelminthes	Nonsegmented worms; soft-bodied and flat; regeneration possible; found in water or damp soil, or as parasites in other animals. Flatworms.
Phylum Nematoda	Nonsegmented worms; rounded body, tapering at both ends; found in all habitats. Roundworms.
Phylum Mollusca	Most soft-bodied with shells; muscular foot; terrestrial or aquatic. Snails, squids, clams.
Phylum Annelida	Segmented worms; tubular body; most bristled; terrestrial or aquatic. Earthworms, lugworms, leeches.
Phylum Echinodermata	Five-rayed body structure; skeleton of bonelike plates; many tiny tube feet; aquatic. Starfish and sea urchins.
Phylum Arthropoda	Jointed limbs; hard exoskeleton; found in all habitats. Insects, spiders, decapods.
Class Insecta	Body divided in three parts; three pairs of legs; usually two pairs of wings; mostly terrestrial, some aquatic. Silverfish, dragonflies, cockroaches, termites, earwigs, grasshoppers, bugs, beetles, flies, fleas, butterflies, moths.
Class Merostomata	Horseshoe-shaped body, six pairs of legs, tail spine; aquatic. Most species extinct. Horseshoe crabs, king crabs.
Class Arachnida	Body usually divided in two parts; four pairs of legs, fangs; mostly terrestrial. Spiders, scorpions, harvestmen, mites, ticks.
Class Chilopoda	Segmented body, long and flattened; many legs, one pair per segment; fast running; long feelers on head; poison fangs; terrestrial. Centipedes.
Class Diplopoda	Segmented body, long and rounded; many legs, two pairs per segment; slow running; short feelers on head; terrestrial. Millipedes.
Class Crustacea	Body divided into head, thorax, and abdomen; hard, jointed "armor" on body; several pairs of legs; two pairs of feelers; nearly all aquatic. Water fleas, barnacles, pill bugs, crabs, shrimps.

Vertebrates (animals with a backbone)

Rank	*Features and common name(s)*
Class Myxini	Simple skeleton of cartilage; jawless mouth with tentacles; eellike shape; many pairs of gills for breathing; aquatic. Hagfish.
Class Cephalaspidomorphi	Simple skeleton of cartilage; jawless sucking mouth; eellike shape; many pairs of gills for breathing; aquatic. Lampreys.

Class Chondrichthyes	Skeleton of cartilage; rough skin with toothed scales; paired fins; jaws; gill slits for breathing; meat-eating; aquatic. Cartilaginous fish, including sharks, rays, skates, chimaeras.
Class Osteichthyes	Skeleton of bone; smooth skin; paired fins; single pair of gills covered by opercula; aquatic. Bony fish, including lungfish, bichirs, sturgeons, herrings, anchovies, eels, salmon, pike, carps, catfish, cod, flying fish, perch, mackerel, puffers.
Class Amphibia	Skin not waterproof; jellylike eggs; aquatic larvae (tadpoles); breathe through skin, gills, or lungs; terrestrial and aquatic. Caecilians, salamanders, frogs, toads.
Class Reptilia	Dry, scaly skin; most lay large, leathery eggs; no larval stage; breathe through lungs; mostly terrestrial. Include the animals in the orders that follow.
Order Chelonia	Turtles, tortoises.
Order Squamata	Snakes, lizards, worm-lizards.
Order Rhyncocephalia	Tuatara.
Order Crocodylia	Crocodiles, alligators.
Class Aves	Body covered by feathers; lay large eggs covered by shells; two legs with scaly feet; front limbs are wings; beak, but no teeth; breathe through lungs; warm-blooded. The common name for this class is "birds," and it includes ostriches, kiwis, emus, penguins, loons, albatrosses, pelicans, herons, storks, ibises, ducks, geese, cranes, gulls, terns, parrots, pigeons, doves, cockatoos, cuckoos, owls, kingfishers, woodpeckers, toucans.
Class Mammalia	Body covered by fur or hair; young feed on mother's milk; have jaws, usually with teeth; usually have four limbs; breathe through lungs; warm-blooded; mostly terrestrial. Mammals include the following orders of animals.
Order Monotremata	Echidnas, platypuses.
Order Marsupialia	Opossums, kangaroos, wallabies, koalas, wombats.
Order Insectivora	Shrews, hedgehogs, moles.
Order Chiroptera	Bats.
Order Edentata	Anteaters, sloths, armadillos.
Order Lagomorpha	Pikas, rabbits, hares.
Order Macroscelidea	Elephant shrews.
Order Carnivora	Cats, dogs, bears, mongooses, raccoons, pandas, weasels, hyenas.
Order Cetacea	Whales, dolphins, porpoises.
Order Pinnipedia	Seals, sea lions, walruses.
Order Sirenia	Dugongs, manatees.
Order Pholidota	Pangolins.
Order Scandentia	Tree shrews.
Order Dermoptera	Flying lemurs.
Order Rodentia	Beavers, squirrels, gophers, rats, mice, porcupines, chinchillas.
Order Artiodactyla	Pigs, hippopotamuses, camels, deer, giraffes, sheep, goats, gazelles.
Order Perissodactyla	Horses, zebras, tapirs, rhinoceroses.
Order Proboscidea	Elephants.
Order Hyracoidea	Hyraxes.
Order Tubulidentata	Aardvarks.
Order Primates	Lemurs, monkeys, apes, human beings.

13

Other **O**rganisms

A euglena is a one-celled organism in the kingdom Protista.

When we think of living things, we usually think of animals (Animalia) and plants (Plantae). But there are certain organisms with characteristics that are neither exactly plantlike nor animallike. For this reason, in the past scientists disagreed about how to classify these organisms: Some placed them in the kingdom Plantae, and others in Animalia. Today, most scientists agree that these organisms should be classified in their own separate kingdoms—Monera, Protista, and Fungi. The species included in these kingdoms are vital to the diversity of all life forms, though many are so tiny that they cannot be seen without a microscope.

Monera

The kingdom Monera consists of cyanobacteria, sometimes called blue-green algae, and bacteria. Monerans, or *prokaryotes*, are primitive unicellular (one-celled) organisms that live alone or in clusters called *colonies*. Individual organisms can be seen only with a microscope, but some colonies are visible with the unaided eye.

Unlike all other living cells, monerans do not have a nucleus surrounded by a membrane. They do, however, have a nuclear area that contains DNA. Monerans also lack typical organelles, the structures that perform life-sustaining functions in other cells. (See "The structure of the cell" in Chapter 10.)

Monerans live throughout the world, even in areas where no other life can survive. For example, cyanobacteria live in the water of hot springs as well as in frozen wastelands. Free-living bacteria are found throughout the Earth's soil and water, while parasitic species live within nearly all multicellular plants and animals.

Most scientists agree that monerans are among the oldest types of organisms, and they believe that cyanobacteria helped pave the way for life on the surface of the Earth when the world was young. At that time, cyanobacteria lived in the bottoms of pools and lakes, where water protected them from the sun's lethal ultraviolet rays. Over time, they multiplied and spread, and new groups appeared. The oxygen they produced during photosynthesis bubbled up through the water and into the air. As the oxygen accumulated, it prevented more and more harmful ultraviolet light from reaching the Earth's surface.

Cyanobacteria

Although they are similar to algae in that they carry on photosynthesis, the 2,000 species of cyanobacteria are grouped with bacteria because they share some structural features. For example, both cyanobacteria and bacteria lack nuclear membranes, and their DNA is not arranged into chromosomes. In addition, cyanobacteria cells differ from those of other algae. All other algae belong to the Protista kingdom.

There are three kinds of cyanobacteria: *unicellular, filamentous* (made of filaments), and *colonial* (living in groups of cells). They are often surrounded by jelly, and these jellylike blobs can become quite large, though the algae themselves are tiny.

Some kinds of cyanobacteria form a slippery, dark coating on the rocky shores of rivers, lakes, and oceans. Others live in soil, forming a slimy layer on wet ground. Lakes with large numbers of cyanobacteria often look greenish or bluish-green. A few species of cyanobacteria may poison fish or animals that drink water containing these organisms. Many species can take nitrogen from the air and convert it to compounds called nitrates, contributing to the fertility of soil and water. Most cyanobacteria reproduce only by cell division.

Bacteria

Bacteria are simple, unicellular organisms that rank among the smallest living things. They can survive in almost any environment, and there are

A bacterium has up to three protective layers. All bacteria are surrounded by a cell membrane, and most have a cell wall. Some species are further enclosed by a slimy layer called a capsule. These layers surround the cytoplasm, which contains the nucleoid. Whiplike flagella help the bacterium move.

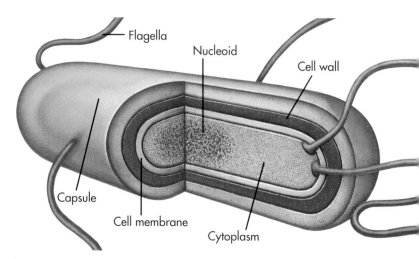

Flagella

Nucleoid

Cell wall

Capsule

Cell membrane

Cytoplasm

thousands of species. Air, water, and the upper layers of soil contain many bacteria. In addition, these organisms live in the digestive and respiratory systems as well as on the skin of human beings and other animals. A group of bacteria called *archaebacteria* include species that live in environments in which no other organism can survive, such as hot sulfur springs, on the bottom of the ocean near boiling volcanic vents, and in extremely salty water such as that in the Dead Sea.

Most bacteria cannot photosynthesize because they lack chlorophyll, and so they must use other biochemical means to obtain energy. Some manufacture their energy supplies from chemicals in their immediate environment. Most kinds of bacteria, however, feed on other organisms. Some feed on dead organisms, while others are *parasites* and get their food from a host organism. These parasitic bacteria include the disease-causing types.

Nearly all bacteria have a tough protective layer called a *cell wall*. The cell wall gives the bacterium its shape and enables it to live in a wide range of environments. All bacteria have a *cell membrane* that allows small molecules of food to enter the cell through its pores but prevents large molecules from passing through. The cytoplasm lies within the cell membrane.

Bacteria, like the cells of all other living things, contain DNA. In a bacterium, the DNA forms an area of the cytoplasm called the *nucleoid*. In all other organisms except cyanobacteria, the DNA is in the nucleus.

Scientists generally identify bacteria by shape. Spherical bacteria are called *cocci*, rod-shaped bacteria are *bacilli*, and bacteria that look like bent rods are *vibrios*. There are also two types of spiral-shaped bacteria—*spirilla* and *spirochetes*.

Certain bacteria, called *aerobes*, require oxygen to live, but others, known as *anaerobes*, can survive without it. Some anaerobes can exist either with or without oxygen. Other anaerobes cannot live with even a trace of oxygen in their environment.

Some bacteria protect themselves against a lack of food, oxygen, or water by forming a new, thicker membrane inside the original one. The material surrounding the new membrane dies, and the remaining organism, called a *bacterial spore*, becomes inactive. Bacterial spores may live for decades because they can resist extreme temperatures and other harsh conditions. If conditions improve, the spores change back into active bacteria.

Large numbers of bacteria live in the human body. Some cause disease, but most do not harm their host, and many are actually helpful. For example, the bacteria that live in the intestines of human beings and other animals help digest food and destroy harmful organisms. In addition, intestinal bacteria also produce some vitamins needed by the body.

Diseases caused by bacteria include cholera, gonorrhea, leprosy, pneumonia, syphilis, tuberculosis, typhoid fever, and whooping cough. Harmful bacteria can prevent the body from functioning properly by destroying healthy cells. Bacteria also can cause disease in other animals and in plants.

Bacteria in soil and water play a vital role in recycling carbon, nitrogen, sulfur, and other chemical elements used by living things. Many help decompose dead organisms and animal wastes into chemical elements, thereby restoring essential mineral elements to the ecosystem and preventing waste accumulation and pollution.

● **decompose:** *to become separated into its parts; decay.*

Protista

The kingdom Protista consists chiefly of unicellular organisms, such as protozoans and certain algae. These organisms have a well-defined nucleus and typical organelles. Most protists reproduce by mitosis, though some reproduce sexually.

Algae

The species of algae that are not cyanobacteria fall into the Protista kingdom. Unlike cyanobacteria, these algae have at least one nucleus and spe-

Green algae can take the form of leafy seaweed, *below,* or single-celled species that can color an entire lake.

● **pigments:** *natural substances coloring the tissues of an animal or plant.*

cialized parts called *chloroplasts* that contain chlorophyll and other pigments. They generally are grouped according to the color of their pigments—brown, green, or red. Diatoms, often grouped with golden-brown algae, are another type of Protista algae. Some algae are microscopic and unicellular, and others are large and contain many cells. Large marine algae are called *seaweeds.*

RED ALGAE include about 4,000 species, most of which live in subtropical seas, where they sometimes grow with corals. A few species live in fresh water. Some red algae have blue as well as green and red pigments. Certain species are the source of *agar*—a gelatinlike substance used in laboratories to grow bacteria. Red seaweeds may be smooth to the touch, or stiff and rough with a chalky layer. Some dwell on rocks and larger seaweeds, while others grow into branched fronds.

BROWN ALGAE include about 1,500 species, almost all of which live in the ocean. There are no unicellular species. Brown algae are an important part of the vegetation of cooler coastlines, and they thrive along the shores of temperate zones. Some kinds of brown algae, called *kelps,* grow up to 200 feet (61 meters) long. *Algin,* a gummy substance obtained from kelp, is used in cosmetics, ice cream, mayonnaise, and other products. Some brown algae are used as fertilizers.

GREEN ALGAE include about 7,000 species, ranging in size from unicellular organisms to medium-sized green seaweeds. Although the largest green algae grow in oceans, most species are microscopic and live in freshwater lakes, ponds, and streams. Large quantities of green algae may cover an entire lake. Some scientists are experimenting with growing green algae for food.

DIATOMS include more than 12,000 species of microscopic unicellular organisms that live in oceans; in freshwater lakes, rivers, and streams; and on moist soil. Diatoms are probably best known as part of the mass of drifting organisms in oceans called *plankton.*

● **silica:** *a hard, white or colorless mineral.*

Diatoms differ from other algae in that their cells are enclosed in a hard shell made of silica. The shell, called the *frustule,* consists of two parts that fit one inside the other, like a box and its lid. When diatoms die, their hard shells remain intact and eventually sink to the bottom of the sea. Over thousands of years, the layer of diatom shells may become very deep. On land, the accumulation of diatom shells from ancient seabeds is mined as *diatomaceous earth,* or *diatomite.* This substance has many uses, from polishing powder to a filler in paints and rubber and plastic products.

Protozoa

Protozoans are one-celled organisms that may have plantlike or animallike characteristics. Most of the more than 30,000 kinds of protozoans are so small that they can be seen only through a microscope. They live in moist places, including salt water, fresh water, soil, plants, and animals.

The structure of protozoans ranges from extremely simple to fairly complex. Some protozoans contain chlorophyll, which allows them to manufacture their own food.

Based on how they move about, protozoans are divided into four groups: flagellates, sarcodines, apicomplexans, and ciliates.

FLAGELLATES move by whipping one or more hairlike projections called *flagella*. Flagellates are usually oval in shape, and many contain chlorophyll. The green *euglena*, shaped much like a submarine, is common in fresh water. The *volvox*—a green ball of flagellates that live together—moves about when the flagella of its individual members are whipped in the water. The *trypanosomes*, the protozoans that cause African sleeping sickness, are also flagellates.

SARCODINES move by extending fingerlike *pseudopods*, or false feet. A sarcodine forms these structures by pushing out its membrane. Sarcodines also use pseudopods to capture food. This group includes the *ameba*, one of the simplest protozoans. An ameba is a shapeless mass that obtains energy by wrapping itself around food particles. Some amebas are parasites that live in the bodies of human beings and animals. Others cause disease.

APICOMPLEXANS, also known as *sporozoans,* move by gliding. They live as parasites. The malarial parasite is a well-known apicomplexan.

CILIATES are the most complex of the protozoans. All of them have fine hairlike projections called *cilia* that help them move about to capture food. The *stentors*, which are shaped like a horn or trumpet, rank among the largest of all protozoans. The *vorticella*, another kind of ciliate, looks like a funnel with a long tube. The vorticella draws food into its body by creating a little whirlpool around the top of the funnel.

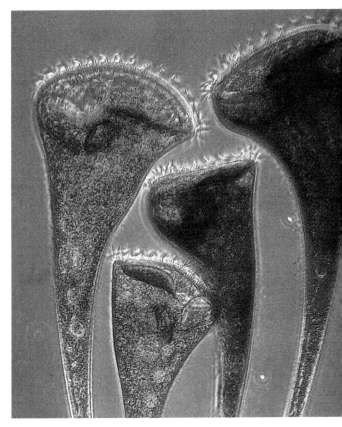

Ciliates are protozoans characterized by hairlike cilia. The stentor, *above,* is a large ciliate.

Fungi

Molds are a type of fungi. A colony of the green mold *penicillium, right,* looks like a spoked wheel.

● **chitin:** *a horny substance that forms the shell of some crustaceans, insects, and fungi.*

The kingdom Fungi consists of a wide variety of organisms that share certain characteristics. All fungi lack chlorophyll and, therefore, cannot make their own food through photosynthesis. Instead, they feed on decaying matter or living organisms. Furthermore, most fungi reproduce by forming spores, and they usually have cell walls that contain chitin or cellulose. Scientists believe that there are more than 100,000 species of fungi. Yeasts and other unicellular fungi are too small to be seen without a microscope, but most types can be seen with the unaided eye. Mildews, molds, mushrooms, plant rusts, and slime molds are among the most common fungi.

STRUCTURE. Except for yeasts and other unicellular fungi, the main part of a fungus consists of thousands of threadlike cells called *hyphae.* These tiny, branching cells form a tangled mass called a *mycelium.* In many species of fungi, the mycelium grows beneath the surface of the material on which the organism is feeding. For example, the mycelium of a mushroom often grows just beneath the surface of the soil. The umbrella-shaped growth known as a mushroom is actually the *fruiting body* of the fungus. The fruiting body produces the fungus's reproductive cells, which develop into new hyphae.

Some bread molds and microscopic species of fungi bear reproductive cells in tiny structures called *sporangia.* In black bread mold, the sporangia form at the tips of upright hyphae called *sporangiophores,* while other hyphae, or *stolons,* spread over the surface of the bread. The stolons are anchored by rootlike structures known as *rhizoids.* Groups of sporangia usually form above the rhizoids.

REPRODUCTION. Fungi reproduce by means of *spores.* Spores serve the same function as the seeds of plants, but they are smaller and simpler. The spores of most fungi are scattered by the wind or transported by water or by animals. However, mushrooms and some other fungi discharge their spores forcefully. A spore that lands in a suitable location starts to grow and eventually produces a new mycelium.

Yeasts can reproduce by forming spores, but many species reproduce by *budding.* This process produces a large number of yeast cells rapidly. When a yeast buds, a bulge forms on the cell. A cell wall then forms, separating the bud from the original yeast cell. The bud then develops into a new cell.

HOW FUNGI LIVE. Fungi live almost everywhere on land and in water. Some are parasites, feeding on living plants and animals, and others, called *saprophytes,* live on decaying matter. Some species of fungi live with other organisms in ways that are mutually beneficial—a fungus and an algae may live together to form a *lichen,* for example. The fungus in the lichen gets all its food from the algae and in return the fungus protects the algae from dehydration and overexposure to the sun's ultraviolet light.

Fungi get their nutrients from the animals, plants, or decaying matter on which they live by discharging enzymes that break down complex carbohydrates and proteins into simple compounds that the hyphae can absorb.

IMPORTANCE OF FUNGI. Fungi break down complex animal and plant matter into simple compounds. This decomposition enriches the soil and makes essential substances available to plants. In addition, decomposition returns carbon dioxide to the atmosphere, where green plants can capture and reuse it during photosynthesis.

Fungi play a major role in a number of foods. For example, many people consider some mushrooms delicacies, and cheese manufacturers add molds to certain cheeses to ripen them and produce distinctive flavors. Yeast causes the fermentation that produces alcoholic beverages by breaking down sugar into carbon dioxide and alcohol. Baker's yeast causes bread to rise by producing carbon dioxide bubbles from the carbohydrates in the dough. Someday, yeasts may become an important source of food. Some people already eat them as a rich source of protein and B vitamins.

On the medical front, some molds produce important drugs called *antibiotics*. These drugs weaken or destroy bacteria and other organisms that cause diseases. *Penicillium notatum* is one of several green molds that produce penicillin, an antibiotic used in treating many diseases.

Some fungi cause problems. Parasitic fungi such as mildews, rusts, and smuts destroy many crops and other plants. Other fungi cause diseases, such as ringworm and thrush, in animals and people. Some mushrooms are poisonous and can cause serious illness or death if eaten.

Mushrooms and other fungi growing on a dead tree help break down the wood into simple compounds that enrich the soil and nourish plants.

Colossal Organisms

While all species are different, living organisms have one thing in common—the basic building block of life, the cell. From cyanobacteria to protozoa, from daisies to elephants, and from ants to humans, living things depend on the precise operation of their microscopic cells. No matter how small an organism may be—or how huge—all life stems from the cell. This fact becomes even more astonishing when we consider the mind-boggling size of some of the world's largest living organisms.

A humongous fungus

Until recently, a fungus known as *Armillaria ostoyae* was considered the "world's largest living thing." *Armillaria*, a 400- to 1,000-year-old fungus found near Mount Adams in southwestern Washington, grows mostly underground and stretches across three counties, covering 1,500 acres (608 hectares), or 2.5 square miles (6.5 square kilometers). While its weight has yet to be determined, the fungus probably weighs about 825,000 pounds (374,550 kilograms).

This humongous fungus is composed of filaments that grow from the same individual and join together in thick strands called *rhizomorphs*. The fungus begins to spread when it reaches a weak or dying tree. It may lie dormant near a living tree for years, until the tree's resistance weakens. Then the fungus invades the tree's root system, spreading and enlarging its network of rhizomorphs. This spreading helps *Armillaria* achieve its mammoth proportions.

The latest largest organism

The new leader in the "world's largest" contest is a quaking aspen growing just south of the Wasatch Range in Utah. The scientists who discovered this mammoth tree say that while Washington's humongous fungus may cover a wider area, the quaking aspen they have nicknamed Pando—a Latin word meaning "I spread"—is greater in mass. Pando is made up of 47,000 tree trunks, each with leaves and branches. The vast tree covers 106 acres (43 hectares) and weighs more than 13 million pounds (about 5.9 million kilograms), making it at least 15 times heavier than *Armillaria*.

Pando is a single organism made up of thousands of quaking aspens that share a root system and genetic information. Pando reached its size by vegetative propagation, a kind of growth discussed in Chapter 11. The plant sends out horizontal stems or roots that travel either above or below ground. Then they take root and grow into new, connected plants. Individual roots can travel as much as 100 feet (30.5 meters) before sprouting, and each new stem forms its own roots from which more new trees can grow. In this way, each aspen can grow to great dimensions. How far one individual can spread depends on how long it can survive—something scientists have yet to determine.

The other "big tree"

So the quaking aspen may be the world's largest organism—and thus the world's largest tree—but that takes none of the glory from the incredible giant sequoia. The "General Sherman Tree," a giant sequoia in Sequoia National Park in California, also once held the "world's largest" title.

Although only 275 feet (83.8 meters) high, the General Sherman Tree has a volume of 52,500 cubic feet and the base of its trunk has a circumference of 103 feet (31.4 meters). Estimated to be between 2,200 and 2,500 years old, the tree is still growing, and each year it adds a volume of wood equivalent to a tree that is 1 foot (30 centimeters) in diameter and 50 feet (15 meters) tall. The

Although this scene looks like a small forest, these tree trunks—along with about 47,000 more—are actually all part of the same tree: a quaking aspen growing in central Utah.

General Sherman Tree is believed to weigh about 1,385 short tons (1,256 metric tons).

What accounts for the giant sequoias' tremendous size? Their secret is simple: They grow rapidly as long as they live, and they live a long time. Sequoias can survive about 3,000 years, so they have lots of time to grow. Like many other conifers, they begin life on a pine cone as a tiny seed only 1/4 inch (6.3 millimeters) long. The cones may cling to their parent tree for as long as 20 years, but at last they fall and new saplings sprout. A young giant sequoia looks like a pine tree. It has a cone shape, with branches reaching down to the ground. As it grows, its lower branches fall off, and its bark thickens. Considering the trees' size, the roots of the giant sequoias are quite shallow, generally reaching less than 8 feet (2.4 meters) down into the ground, but they can spread out over 3 acres (1.2 hectares). A substance called tannin, manufactured by trees, makes the giant sequoia's wood impenetrable to most insects, and its bark—12 inches (30.5 centimeters)

thick—serves as armor in a fire. Not a single sequoia has been known to die of old age or disease.

The largest animal

If asked to guess the largest animal that has ever lived, you might be tempted to name one of the lumbering, slender-necked dinosaurs that became extinct tens of millions of years ago. But actually, the world's all-time largest animal is alive and well today. It's the blue whale.

Blue whales can grow up to 100 feet (30 meters) long and can weigh more than 150 short tons (135 metric tons)—that's about as much as 1,935 adult humans. Its tongue alone is 10 feet (3 meters) thick and as heavy as a full-grown elephant.

Will scientists ever discover an organism that can take away the title of world's largest living thing? Only time will tell. Perhaps right now an unknown giant lurks under the soil, stretches into the sky, or drifts in the vast oceans.

14

The Human Body

The human body is sometimes called an incredible machine. But the human body is infinitely more amazing than any machine. The body begins as a single cell and in a short time develops into a complex individual, composed of trillions of cells—most smaller than a pinpoint. These cells may be specialized in many ways. Cells performing a similar task form tissue, such as muscular tissue, nerve tissue, and skeletal tissue. Tissues grouped together for common purposes form organs. Cooperating groups of organs, in turn, make up body systems. From one small cell comes a network of systems that work together to form the most intelligent of all animals—the human being.

This sketch of the human body's musculature was drawn by Michelangelo during the 1500's.

The body systems

The human body consists of nearly a dozen major interrelated systems, each designed for a special function. The skeleton provides the framework, muscles are the workhorses, and together these two systems make it possible for the body to move. The fuel and oxygen that keep muscles working travel through miles of tubing in the circulatory system, which in turn depends on the respiratory system to supply the body with oxygen, and the digestive system, where food is broken down into nutrients that can be used as fuel. The urinary system rids the body of wastes, the endocrine system and the nervous system control body activities, and the reproductive system allows for the creation of more human beings. All these systems are protected and held inside the body by the largest organ of all—the skin.

The skeletal system

The human skeleton is made up of about 200 bones linked together to form a strong framework that supports the body and helps protect the internal organs. The brain, for example, is shielded by the skull, the spinal cord by the spinal column, and the heart and lungs by the ribcage. The skeleton also works with the muscles to enable the body to move.

Bones can transmit body weight and help muscles move limbs and other body parts because they are linked at joints. *Diarthrotic joints*—such as hinge joints in the knee and ball-and-socket joints in the shoulder— are freely movable and allow varying degrees of motion. The bones of a diarthrotic joint are held together by bundles of tough, flexible connective tissue called *ligaments*. *Synarthronic joints*, in contrast, allow only limited movement of the bones. For example, the bones of the skull, except for the jawbone, are linked by synarthronic joints.

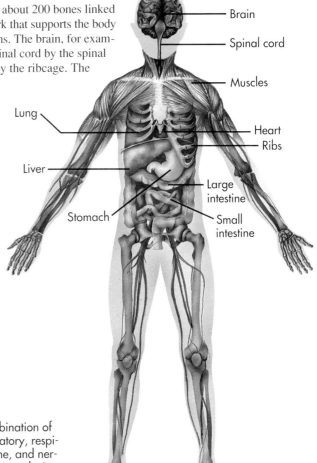

Brain

Spinal cord

Muscles

Lung

Heart

Ribs

Liver

Large intestine

Stomach

Small intestine

The human body maintains a combination of systems—skeletal, muscular, circulatory, respiratory, digestive, urinary, endocrine, and nervous—all made up of organs. The complexity of the human body is such that not all organs can be represented in one diagram.

In addition to its role in support and movement, the skeleton has another crucial task. Bone tissue contains various kinds of cells that help keep the blood healthy. The cells of *bone marrow*—the soft, fatty core of many bones—produce new blood cells and release them into the bloodstream. Two types of bone cells regulate the mineral content of the blood—one kind removes minerals from the blood and deposits them in the bone, and the other dissolves old mineral deposits and releases minerals back into the bloodstream as needed.

The muscular system

More than 600 muscles work together to move the body. They lift limbs, push food through the gut, make the heart beat, and control blood flow. Each muscle consists of special fibers that can contract. When a muscle contracts, it moves the tissue to which it is attached by pulling it.

The energy for the contraction comes from chemical reactions involving fuel and oxygen, which are brought to the muscles through a rich supply of blood vessels.

The muscles of the human body can be divided into three types—skeletal, smooth, and cardiac.

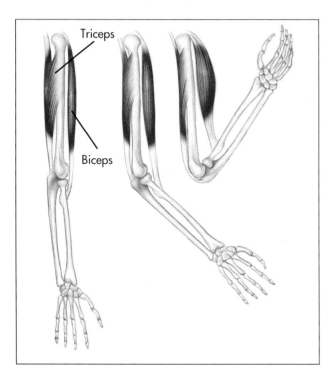

Triceps

Biceps

Muscles move limbs by contracting. The arm straightens when the triceps muscle contracts and bends when the biceps muscle contracts.

SKELETAL MUSCLES are attached to bones and make them move. Groups of skeletal muscles operate the arms, legs, torso, neck, and face. We can move skeletal muscles at will, so they are sometimes referred to as *voluntary muscles*. The fibers that make up skeletal muscles have crossbands called *striations*.

A typical skeletal muscle has both ends connected to bones. One end of each skeletal muscle is attached to a bone that does not move when the muscle contracts. In most cases, the other end of the muscle is attached to another bone, either directly or by cord-like bundles of connective tissue called *tendons*. The second bone moves when the muscle contracts.

Muscles can move the body only by pulling. They cannot push the tissue to which they are attached. Therefore, two sets of muscles control most skeletal movements, such as the raising and lowering of the forearm. One set of muscles pulls the bones in one direction, and the other set pulls the bone in the opposite direction.

SMOOTH MUSCLES are found in most of the body's internal organs. For example, smooth muscles operate in the digestive tract, urinary tract, and blood vessels. Smooth muscle tissue in the walls of the stomach and intestines moves food through the digestive system and controls the width of blood vessels and the size of breathing passages. Unlike skeletal muscles, smooth muscles lack striations. Smooth muscles contract and relax automatically—without our conscious control. Therefore, they are referred to as *involuntary muscles.*

CARDIAC MUSCLE is found only in the heart. This muscle has striations like skeletal muscle, but like smooth muscle, it contracts automatically and rhythmically without tiring. Cardiac muscle also has dark bands called *intercalated discs*, which are found at the ends of the individual cardiac muscle fibers. Cardiac muscle enables the heart to beat an average of 72 times a minute without rest throughout a person's lifetime.

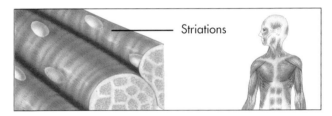

Skeletal muscles

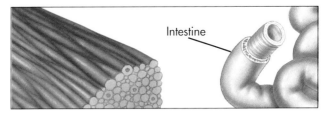

Smooth muscles

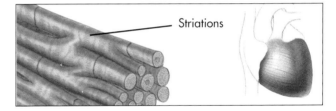

Cardiac muscle

The human body has three kinds of muscles. Skeletal muscles, *top,* are attached to bone and made up of fibers with crossbands called striations. Smooth muscles, *center,* found in most of the internal organs, contract and relax automatically. Cardiac muscle, *bottom,* found only in the heart, contracts rhythmically like smooth muscles and has striations like skeletal muscle.

The circulatory system

The cells of the body cannot survive without a continuous supply of fresh blood. The circulatory system carries that blood to every tissue in the body, delivering oxygen and nutrients from the respiratory and digestive systems, respectively, and removing wastes to be disposed of by the lungs and kidneys. This complex system also transports chemical messengers called hormones and carries disease-fighting substances that help protect the body. It also maintains a constant body temperature, fluid volume, and pH.

The circulatory system consists of the heart, blood vessels, blood, and the lymphatic system. The spleen also is considered part of the circulatory system.

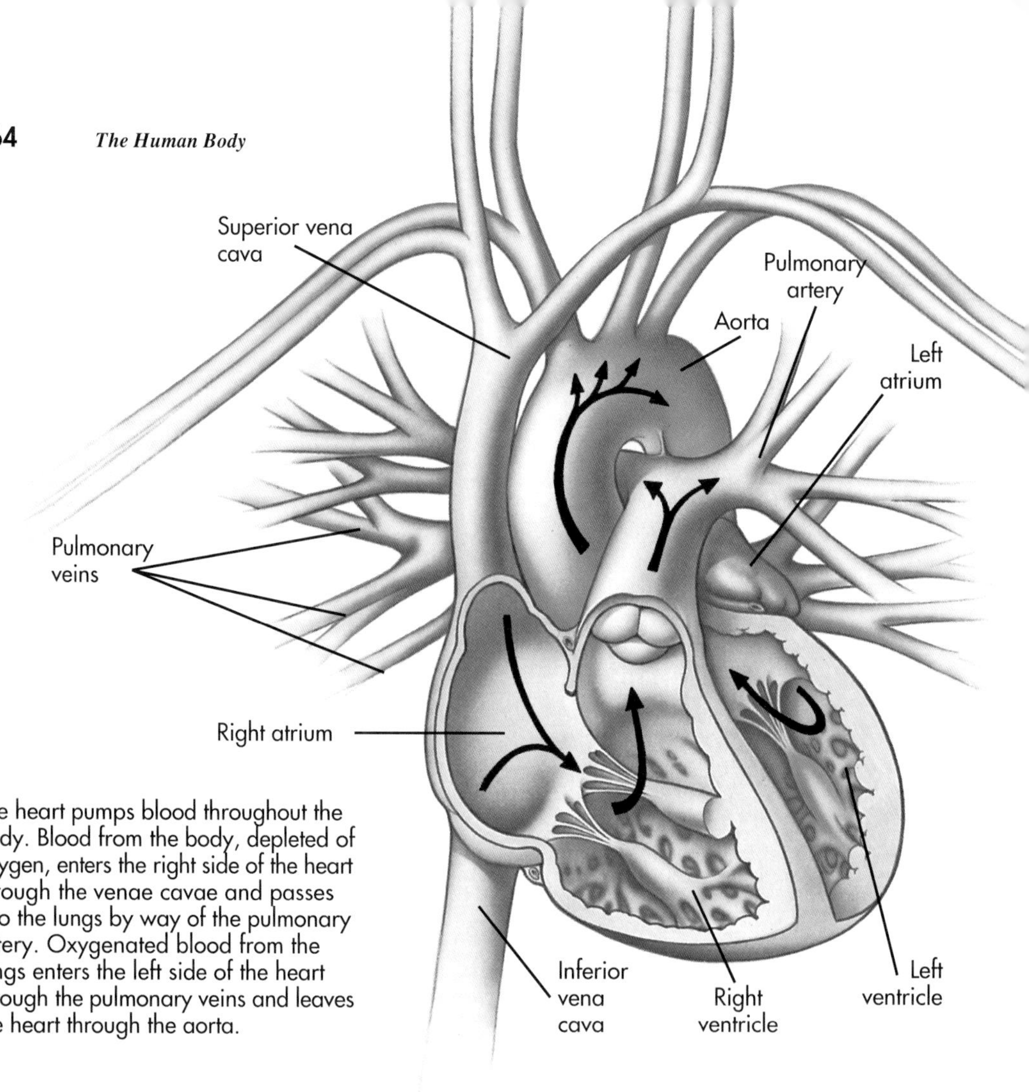

Superior vena cava

Pulmonary artery

Aorta

Left atrium

Pulmonary veins

Right atrium

The heart pumps blood throughout the body. Blood from the body, depleted of oxygen, enters the right side of the heart through the venae cavae and passes into the lungs by way of the pulmonary artery. Oxygenated blood from the lungs enters the left side of the heart through the pulmonary veins and leaves the heart through the aorta.

Inferior vena cava

Right ventricle

Left ventricle

THE HEART is a hollow muscle that pumps blood through the circulatory system by contracting and relaxing rhythmically. The heart actually consists of two pumps that lie side by side. Each side contains an upper chamber called the *atrium* (or *auricle*) and a lower chamber called the *ventricle*. The left side of the heart—the stronger pump—receives oxygen-rich blood from the lungs and sends it to cells throughout the body. The blood, which picks up carbon dioxide and other wastes from the cells, returns to the right side of the heart. This weaker pump moves the blood to the lungs and then back to the left side of the heart. In the lungs, the carbon dioxide is removed from the blood, and oxygen is added.

BLOOD VESSELS can be divided into three types: *arteries*, which carry blood from the heart; *veins*, which carry blood to the heart; and tiny *capillaries*, which connect the arteries and veins.

Blood leaves the left side of the heart through the *aorta*, the largest artery in the body. Several major arteries branch off the aorta, and in turn, divide into smaller and smaller vessels called *arterioles*, which finally empty into the capillaries. Through the thin walls of the capillaries, nutrients in the blood are exchanged for carbon dioxide and other wastes from the cells.

The cells absorb oxygen and nutrients from the blood and give up carbon dioxide and other waste products to it. The blood then begins its journey back to the heart.

From the capillaries, the blood enters small veins called *venules,* which join larger and larger veins. Finally, the blood enters the right side of the heart through the two largest veins: the *superior vena cava,* through which blood from the head and upper body enters the heart, and the *inferior vena cava,* through which blood from the lower trunk and legs enters. The right side of the heart then pumps the blood through the pulmonary arteries to the capillaries surrounding the air sacs in the lungs. The blood returns from the lungs to the left side of the heart through four pulmonary veins. The left side of the heart then pumps the blood out through the aorta, and the blood's journey begins again.

BLOOD is vital to the life of every cell in the body. This complex fluid carries the foods and fuel that provide the energy and materials for repairing damaged cells and building new ones. Blood helps remove worn-out cells and other wastes, as well as harmful foreign substances. In addition, blood brings materials that minimize blood loss and promote healing to wounds, and it delivers heat from the body core to the extremities.

Blood consists of a liquid and three kinds of solid particles called *formed elements.* The liquid—called *plasma*—makes up about 55 percent of the total volume of blood, and it carries many important substances. For example, food that enters the blood from the intestines and liver dissolves in the plasma, which then transports the dissolved food throughout the body. The plasma also carries many of the wastes that the blood picks up from the body tissues.

The formed elements in blood are red blood cells, white blood cells, and platelets. *Red blood cells* transport oxygen from the lungs to the body tissues and carry some of the carbon dioxide away from the tissues. *White blood cells* help protect the body from disease by attacking bacteria, virus-

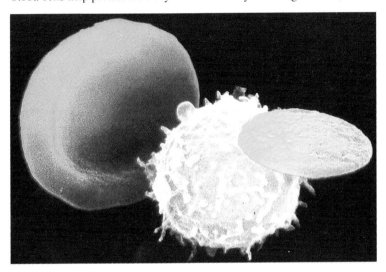

In addition to plasma, blood is composed of red blood cells, *left,* which carry oxygen to the body tissues and carbon dioxide to the lungs; white blood cells, *center,* which help protect the body from infection; and platelets, *right,* which play a part in blood clotting.

es, poisons, and other harmful substances. *Platelets* are disklike structures that, together with various proteins in the plasma, seal wounded blood vessels by forming a clot.

THE LYMPHATIC SYSTEM consists of a network of tubes that circulates a colorless fluid that comes from the blood and eventually returns to it. Water, proteins, and dissolved food leave the blood through the capillary walls. This fluid, which is known as *interstitial fluid*, bathes and nourishes the cells of the body tissues and then drains into tiny, open-ended tubes called *lymphatic vessels,* taking wastes, dead cells, and bacteria with it. At this point, the fluid is known as *lymph.*

As the lymph flows through the small tubes into larger and larger lymphatic vessels, harmful substances are filtered out by white blood cells. These cells are produced by *lymph nodes,* beadlike structures that occur at various pockets along the lymphatic vessels. Eventually, all the lymph flows into either the thoracic duct or the right lymphatic duct. The lymph drains from these ducts into veins near the neck and so rejoins the blood.

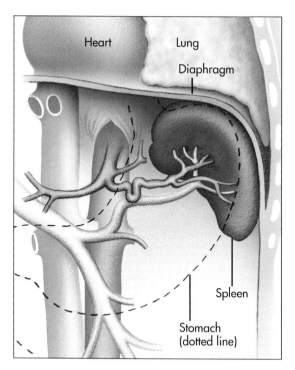

Heart

Lung

Diaphragm

Spleen

Stomach
(dotted line)

The spleen, a spongy organ located behind the stomach, fights infection and filters bacteria, parasites, and damaged cells from the body.

THE SPLEEN is a soft, purplish organ located behind and to the left of the stomach. Scientists do not fully understand the spleen's role, but they know that the spleen helps filter useless substances from the blood. Blood travels through a maze of spongelike spaces called *sinusoids* in the spleen. There, cells called *macrophages* surround and destroy old or damaged blood cells. Macrophages also rid the body of certain parasites and bacteria. The spleen releases special proteins called *antibodies* into the blood, which in turn weaken or kill bacteria, viruses, and other organisms that cause infection. (See the special feature on AIDS at the end of this chapter for more information on macrophages and antibodies.)

The respiratory system

The human body needs oxygen to break down and release the energy in food. During this process, carbon dioxide forms as a waste product. The respiratory system provides the body with oxygen and rids the body of carbon dioxide. The organs involved in respiration include the nose, the pharynx, the trachea, the larynx, and two lungs.

The lungs, *below,* are the chief organs of the respiratory system. With each inhalation, we draw oxygen-rich air into the trachea and through the bronchi and bronchioles, which end at tiny air sacs called alveoli. Cilia, *below right,* microscopic hairlike objects, line airways and sweep invading particles up and out of the bronchial tubes and trachea.

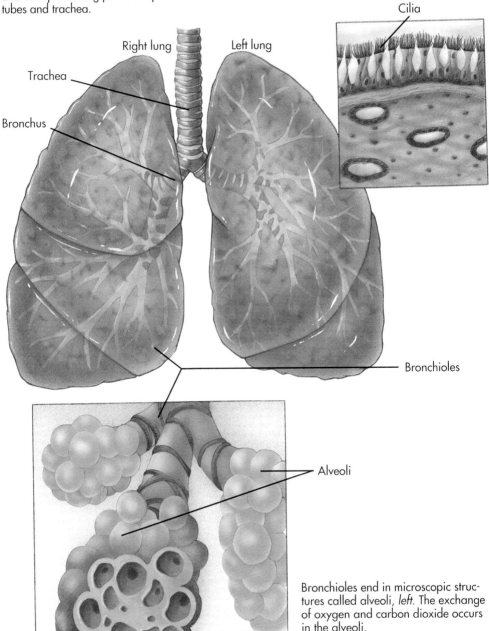

Cilia

Right lung

Left lung

Trachea

Bronchus

Bronchioles

Alveoli

Bronchioles end in microscopic structures called alveoli, *left.* The exchange of oxygen and carbon dioxide occurs in the alveoli.

Breathing involves inhaling and exhaling. When we inhale, the chest cavity expands, and the lungs expand along with it. Air from the atmosphere rushes in to fill the enlarged lungs. When we exhale, the chest cavity shrinks, pushing air out of the lungs. Inhaling and exhaling result chiefly from contractions of the *diaphragm,* a large, dome-shaped muscle that forms the floor of the chest cavity. As the diaphragm contracts, the chest cavity expands, and as the diaphragm relaxes, the chest cavity shrinks. The muscles that move the ribs also play a part in the breathing process.

Air enters the respiratory system through the mouth and nose, where it is warmed and moistened. The air flows from the nostrils to the nasal passages. The nasal passages are lined with coarse hairs and a sticky substance called *mucus.* Together, these hairs and mucus filter dust and dirt from the air.

From the nose and mouth, the air passes through the *pharynx*, the cavity behind the nose and mouth; the *larynx*, or voice box; and the *trachea* or windpipe, which carries the air toward the lungs. The larynx has the *epiglottis*, a piece of cartilage that closes the trachea so that food can't slip down while a person is eating. Before reaching the lungs, the trachea splits into two tubes, or *bronchi*, one of which enters each lung. Within the lungs, each bronchus divides into smaller and smaller tubes, finally branching into extremely tiny tubes called *bronchioles*.

The bronchioles end in hundreds of millions of thin-walled structures called *alveoli*, or air sacs, where the exchange of carbon dioxide and oxygen occurs. Each alveolus is surrounded by a network of capillaries that, like the alveoli, have extremely thin walls. The blood that enters these vessels has a high level of carbon dioxide, which it picked up from the body tissues, and contains little oxygen. The carbon dioxide leaves the blood and moves through the walls of the blood vessels and alveoli into the lungs. Oxygen from the air in the lungs then passes into the blood through the walls of the alveoli and blood vessels. The oxygen-rich blood leaves the lungs and travels to the heart, which pumps it to the cells throughout the body. The carbon dioxide is expelled from the lungs when we exhale.

Respiration takes place 16 to 18 times a minute and is normally controlled unconsciously by the respiratory center, a collection of cells in the brain. After air has been exhaled, carbon dioxide builds up again in the bloodstream. When the carbon dioxide in the blood reaches a certain level, the respiratory center sends a message to the diaphragm and rib muscles that trigger contraction, and inhalation begins. As the lungs expand during inhalation, cells in the lung walls send signals back to the respiratory center. The center responds by instructing the muscles of the ribs and diaphragm to relax so that exhaling occurs.

The digestive system

The digestive system breaks down food into simple substances that the cells can use, and then it absorbs these substances into the bloodstream and eliminates waste matter. The main part of the digestive system is a long tube called the *alimentary canal*. This convoluted muscular tube has two openings—the mouth, which takes in food, and the anus, which releases wastes. Between these two openings lie specialized organs, such as the esophagus, the stomach, and the small and large intestines. Other parts of the digestive system include the gallbladder, liver, pancreas, salivary glands, and teeth.

Digestion begins in the mouth, where the teeth crush food into small pieces. As food is chewed, three pairs of *salivary glands* secrete *saliva* into the mouth, moistening the food and making it easier to swallow. Saliva also contains the first of the system's several digestive enzymes, which break food down into chemicals the body can use.

After the food is swallowed, it enters the *esophagus*, a short, muscular tube that leads to the stomach. Contractions of skeletal and smooth muscle move the food down the esophagus and into the stomach. The *stomach* serves as a sort of "holding tank" in which food remains for several hours. Stomach muscles contract, churning up the food and mixing it with an acid and an enzyme secreted by the stomach wall. This serves to further break down the food and results in a thick liquid called *chyme*.

Chyme passes from the stomach into the *small intestine* at a steady rate. Within the first section of the small intestine, various digestive enzymes complete the breakdown of the food. The small intestine produces some of these enzymes, and the rest are made by the pancreas. The pancreatic enzymes empty into the small intestine through a duct. *Bile*, a liquid made by the liver and stored in the gallbladder, also enters the small intestine through a duct. Although bile contains no digestive enzymes, it aids digestion by emulsifying large molecules of fatty foods.

By the time it leaves the small intestine, the food is completely digested. Special cells lining the wall of the small intestine absorb useful substances from the digested food, and these substances then enter the blood. Some are carried directly to cells throughout the body, and the rest are transported to the liver, where they are either stored or released, as the body requires.

Substances that are not absorbed by the small intestine—generally water, minerals, and wastes—pass to the *large intestine*. The large intestine absorbs most of the water and minerals, which then enter the bloodstream. The waste moves down toward the *rectum,* the end of the large intestine, and leaves the body as *feces.*

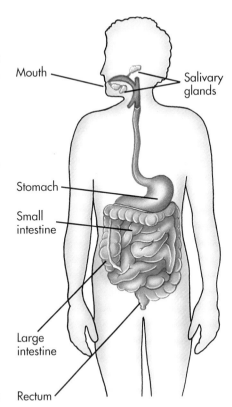

Mouth

Salivary glands

Stomach

Small intestine

Large intestine

Rectum

Digestion begins in the mouth with the action of saliva. Food is completely digested after it passes through the stomach and the small intestine. The waste then moves through the large intestine and rectum before elimination.

The urinary system

The body must have a way to rid itself of wastes. Without an efficient disposal system, poisonous wastes would collect in body tissues. Several body systems work to eliminate unwanted materials, such as carbon dioxide and undigestible food, but the urinary system removes most of the wastes that build up in the blood and flushes them out of the body.

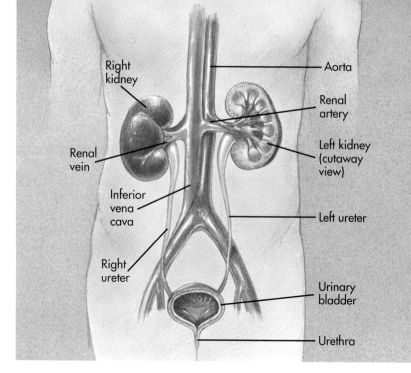

The urinary system, *right*, eliminates harmful wastes from the body. Blood enters the kidneys through the renal artery. The kidneys filter the blood, which then exits through the renal vein. Wastes and water from the blood—in the form of urine—pass through the ureters to the urinary bladder. Urine leaves the body through the urethra.

The main organs of the urinary system are two hard-working *kidneys*. They process about 2.75 pints (1.3 liters) of blood every minute, and all the blood travels throughout the kidneys every five minutes. Remarkably, if one kidney is diseased or damaged, the other one usually compensates.

Each kidney has about a million microscopic filtering units called *nephrons*. As blood passes through a nephron, a complicated network of capillaries and tubes filters out a small amount of water along with urea, sodium chloride, and certain other wastes. This filtered-out material forms a yellowish fluid called *urine*. Two tubes called ureters carry urine from the kidneys to the *urinary bladder*, a hollow storage organ. Urine is eventually squeezed out of the bladder by muscular contractions and leaves the body through a tube known as the *urethra*.

The endocrine system

The endocrine system consists of ductless glands that release chemicals called hormones into the blood. The chief endocrine glands include the anterior pituitary, the posterior pituitary, the thyroid, the parathyroid, the islets of Langerhans in the pancreas, the adrenal glands' cortex (outer) and medulla (inner) regions, the pineal gland, and the gonads—ovaries in females, testes in males. This system plays a major

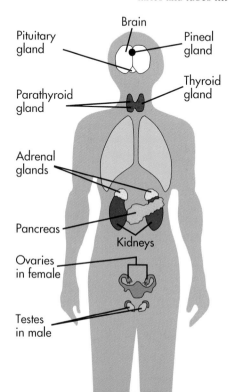

Glands that release hormones into the blood make up the endocrine system, *left*.

role in regulating all aspects of physical life, including growth, reproduction, and the way the body uses food. It also helps prepare the body to deal with stress and emergencies.

The endocrine glands release *hormones* into the blood, which then carries them throughout the body. Hormones act as chemical messengers. After a hormone reaches the organs or tissues it affects, it triggers certain actions. Many hormones have widespread effects. For example, the hormone insulin causes cells throughout the body to take in and use sugar from the bloodstream.

The *pituitary gland,* which lies near the base of the brain, is often called the "master gland" because it releases a number of hormones that regulate the other endocrine glands. However, the pituitary itself is controlled by hormones produced by the *hypothalamus,* a part of the brain that links the nervous and endocrine control systems.

The body also has glands that do not produce hormones. These *exocrine glands* make chemicals that perform specific jobs in the area where they are released. Major exocrine products include digestive juices, mucus, sweat, and tears.

The nervous system

The nervous system regulates and coordinates the activities of all the other systems of the body. Without this complex system, the other systems would not be able to function. The nervous system enables the body to adjust to changes that occur within itself and in its surroundings. The system is made up of countless nerve cells called *neurons*, which form a communications network that extends to every part of the body. The system has two main divisions: the central nervous system, which consists of the brain and spinal cord, and the peripheral nervous system, which includes the sense organs, such as the eyes and ears, and the autonomic nervous system.

The human nervous system has three main parts: the central nervous system; the peripheral nervous system; and the autonomic nervous system, which has two parts—the sympathetic and parasympathetic systems.

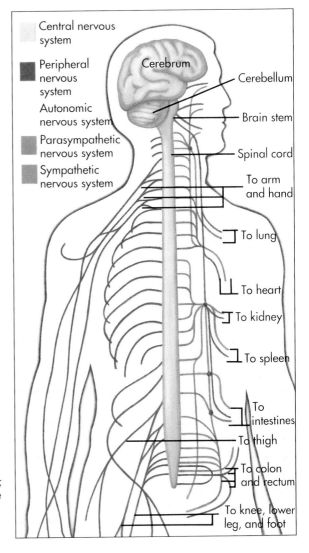

Central nervous system

Peripheral nervous system

Autonomic nervous system

Parasympathetic nervous system

Sympathetic nervous system

Cerebrum

Cerebellum

Brain stem

Spinal cord

To arm and hand

To lung

To heart

To kidney

To spleen

To intestines

To thigh

To colon and rectum

To knee, lower leg, and foot

THE CENTRAL NERVOUS SYSTEM functions as the control center of the nervous system. The central nervous system receives information from the senses, analyzes the information, decides how the body should respond, and then sends instructions that trigger the required actions.

The central nervous system makes some simple decisions within the spinal cord, such as directing the hand to pull away from a hot object. These simple decisions are called *spinal reflexes*. Most of the decisions we make, however, are more complex and therefore involve the brain. The brain is an enormously complicated collection of billions of neurons linked together in precise patterns. These neurons enable the brain to think and remember. Much brain activity occurs at the conscious level—we are aware of decisions made at this level and can voluntarily control them. Other activity occurs at the subconscious level and is beyond our control. This brain activity regulates the smooth muscles of the body.

THE PERIPHERAL NERVOUS SYSTEM connects the central nervous system with every part of the body. The nerves in this system include both sensory neurons, which carry information to the central nervous system, and motor neurons, which relay instructions from the central nervous system.

Sensory neurons run between the sense organs and the central nervous system. The sense organs have special sensory neurons called *receptors* that translate information about the internal or external environment into nerve impulses—electrical signals that nerves can carry.

The body has many kinds of sense receptors. Vision receptors in the eyes change light waves into nerve impulses, and hearing receptors in the ears convert sound waves into nerve impulses. Smell receptors in the nose and taste receptors on the tongue convert chemical information into nerve impulses. Receptors in the skin respond to heat, cold, pressure, and pain, while receptors deep within the body provide information on the chemical and physical conditions of inner body tissues.

Nerve impulses from the sensory receptors travel along sensory neurons to the central nervous system, which analyzes the information and decides what action, if any, is necessary. If a response is required, the central nervous system sends out instructions to the appropriate tissues by way of the *motor neurons* of the peripheral nervous system.

The *autonomic nervous system* is the part of the peripheral nervous system that carries messages from the subconscious level of the brain to the internal organs. It regulates the automatic functions of the body, such as the beating of the heart and the movement of food through the digestive system.

The reproductive system

The organs of the reproductive system enable men and women to have children. Human beings reproduce sexually. A new individual begins to develop after a *sperm*—a sex cell produced by the father—unites with an *ovum,* or egg—a sex cell produced by the mother. The union of ovum and sperm results in fertilization. The fertilized ovum, called a *zygote*, has all the information necessary for the development of a new human being.

The male reproductive system includes two *testicles*, which are glands that produce sperm. The testicles hang between the legs in a pouch called the *scrotum*. The sperm travel through tubes to the *penis*, an organ in front of the scrotum. Sperm leave a man's body through the penis.

Most of the female reproductive system lies inside the woman's body. Deep within the pelvis are two glands called *ovaries*, each containing thousands of ova, though only about 400 ova will mature during a woman's childbearing years. About once a month, one of the ovaries releases an ovum, which then travels down a narrow duct called the *fallopian tube*. The female body has two fallopian tubes leading from the ovaries into the top of the *uterus*—a hollow, muscular organ. The other end of the uterus leads to a canal called the *vagina*, which extends to an opening on the outside of the body, between the legs.

During sexual intercourse, sperm from the penis enter the vagina. They swim from the vagina to the uterus and into the fallopian tubes. If an ovum is present in one of the tubes, a sperm may fertilize it.

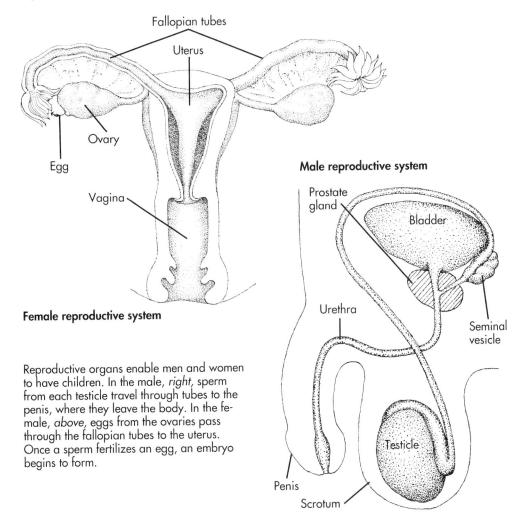

Fallopian tubes

Uterus

Ovary

Egg

Vagina

Female reproductive system

Male reproductive system

Prostate gland

Bladder

Urethra

Seminal vesicle

Penis

Scrotum

Testicle

Reproductive organs enable men and women to have children. In the male, *right*, sperm from each testicle travel through tubes to the penis, where they leave the body. In the female, *above*, eggs from the ovaries pass through the fallopian tubes to the uterus. Once a sperm fertilizes an egg, an embryo begins to form.

The fertilized ovum then continues its journey to the uterus, where it becomes attached to the wall of the organ. The cell divides over and over, forming the beginning of a developing baby. Soon, the formation of a complex organ called the *placenta* enables the developing baby to obtain food and oxygen from the mother's bloodstream.

After about nine months, the baby is ready to be born. Powerful contractions of the uterus push the baby out through the mother's vagina, which widens to allow the baby to pass through.

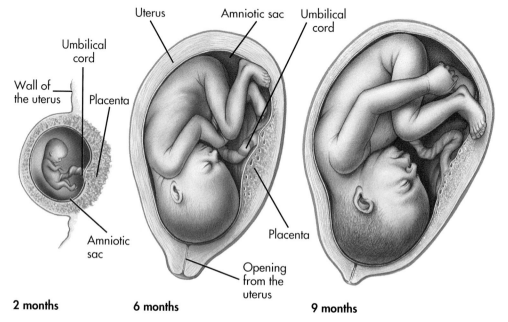

2 months   **6 months**   **9 months**

A baby begins to develop attached to the wall of the uterus and protected by layers of tissue, *left.* By the end of the sixth month, *center,* the baby fills the expanding uterus. It is fully developed by the end of the ninth month, *right.*

The skin

The skin, which is the largest organ, protects the body against disease, injury, and water loss. It also helps control body temperature, excretes some wastes, and serves as a major sensory organ. Skin includes membranes that coat the inside of organs such as the mouth and nose. The skin has three layers—the epidermis, the dermis, and the subcutaneous tissues.

THE EPIDERMIS forms the outermost layer of the skin and serves as a barrier between the outside world and the body's inner tissues. The outer portion of the epidermis consists of tough, dead cells that prevent bacteria, chemicals, and other harmful substances from entering the body. It also protects the body's inner tissues from the harsh ultraviolet rays of the sun and prevents

Skin is made up of three layers—the epidermis, dermis, and subcutaneous tissues—as well as hair follicles, sweat glands, oil glands, blood vessels, and nerve endings.

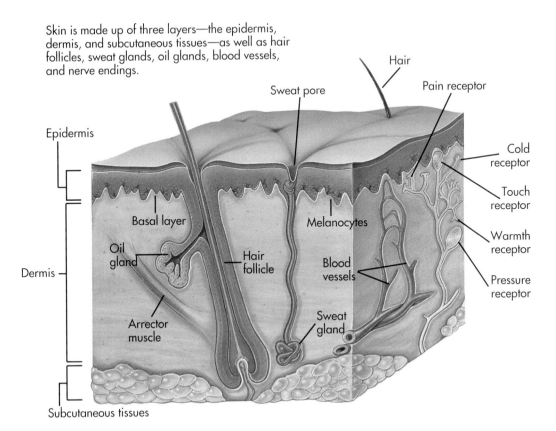

the loss of water from these tissues. Hair, nails, and glands in the skin are called *epidermal appendages*. They are formed from the basal cells of the epidermis.

THE DERMIS, or middle layer of the skin, helps keep the temperature of the body within its normal range. The body produces tremendous amounts of heat as it breaks down food. Some of this heat escapes from the body through the blood vessels in the dermis. When the body needs to retain heat, these blood vessels narrow and thus limit heat loss. When the body needs to give off heat, the blood vessels expand and thus increase heat loss. The sweat glands, which are part of the dermis, also help control body temperature. These glands produce sweat, which is released through pores on the surface of the epidermis. As the sweat evaporates, it cools the body.

The dermis also serves as an important sense organ. Nerve endings within the dermis respond to cold, heat, pain, pressure, and touch.

SUBCUTANEOUS TISSUES, sometimes called the *hypodermis*, form the innermost layer of the skin. This layer provides the body with extra fuel, which is stored in fat cells. It also helps retain body heat and cushions the inner tissues against blows to the body.

A*IDS*

The human body is constantly exposed to invaders known as *pathogens*—disease-causing microorganisms such as bacteria and viruses. If the immune system needs help, medical technology may be able to intervene and help in the fight. But recently, a dreadful new pathogen has emerged. It is so cunning and so elusive that it leaves the body defenseless, and medical researchers have not yet found a way to overcome it. That pathogen is HIV, the virus that most researchers believe causes AIDS.

A closer look at the immune system

Immunity is the body's ability to resist certain harmful substances, such as pathogens. When a harmful substance—called an *antigen*—enters the body, specialized cells react. Some cells manufacture proteins called *antibodies* that are released into the blood. These antibodies neutralize or destroy the antigen. Other cells attack the antigen without producing antibodies.

White blood cells play a major role in immune responses. As we know, these cells circulate in the blood and lymph. There are two kinds of white blood cells—T cells and B cells—and both types have the ability to recognize antigens. B cells produce antibodies; T cells help regulate the production of antibodies by the B cells. Another group of cells, called *macrophages*, also play a part in the immune response by surrounding harmful invaders and digesting them.

When a B cell identifies an antigen—a virus, for example—it produces antibodies against the antigen. These antibodies paralyze the virus so that it cannot invade new cells. The B cell then starts to multiply so that many more antibodies can be made to fight the virus. T cells—called *helper cells* and *suppressor cells*—regulate the production of antibodies.

What is AIDS?

AIDS—*a*cquired *i*mmuno*d*eficiency *s*yndrome—is an extremely serious disease that results from severe damage to the body's immune system, and it often leads to death. Most medical researchers believe that AIDS

In a healthy immune system, *left,* two kinds of white blood cells, T and B cells, destroy harmful antigens. HIV invades the immune system, *right,* by infecting certain white blood cells, taking over a cell's reproductive system, and using it to reproduce itself. Killing the white blood cell, HIV spreads.

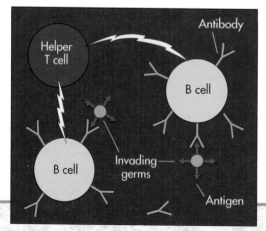
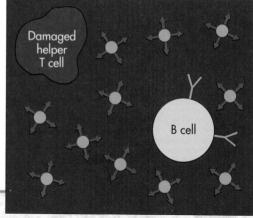

is caused by two viruses known as HIV-1 and HIV-2 that belong to a group called *retroviruses*. The AIDS virus primarily infects certain white blood cells, including T-helper cells and macrophages. When an AIDS virus enters one of these cells, the virus takes over the cell's reproductive system and uses it to reproduce itself. This effectively kills the white blood cell and spreads the AIDS virus to other white blood cells, where the process is repeated.

The symptoms

It is believed that HIV can be present in the body for 10 years or longer without producing any outward signs of illness. People infected with HIV eventually develop symptoms that also may be caused by other, less serious conditions. With HIV infection, however, these symptoms are prolonged and often more severe. They include enlarged lymph glands, tiredness, fever, loss of appetite and weight, diarrhea, yeast infections of the mouth and vagina, and night sweats.

HIV also commonly causes a severe "wasting syndrome," resulting in substantial weight loss, a general decline in health, and in some cases, death. In many patients, the virus infects the brain and nervous system. There, HIV may cause *AIDS dementia,* a condition characterized by sensory, thinking, or memory disorders. HIV infection of the brain also may cause movement or coordination problems.

Many people who are infected with HIV develop AIDS. After a while, the weakened immune system breaks down. Too many T cells have died and there are too many viruses in the body. The immune system can no longer protect the body. At this point, pathogens that would be harmless to a healthy person move in. The infections they

cause are called *opportunistic diseases.* With the onset of an opportunistic disease or one of several other severe illnesses, an HIV-infected person is considered to have AIDS.

Some people who have been infected with HIV for more than 10 years have not developed any symptoms or suffer only minor symptoms. Others have symptoms of HIV infection but none of the opportunistic illnesses. An HIV-infected person may develop AIDS from 2 to 12 or more years after becoming infected.

How AIDS is spread

Researchers have identified three ways in which HIV is transmitted: intimate sexual contact, direct contact with infected blood, or transmission from an infected woman to her unborn fetus. Intimate sexual contact with an HIV-infected person is the most common way of becoming infected because it can lead to the exchange of certain infected bodily fluids, such as semen. HIV also afflicts drug users who become exposed to infected blood by sharing hypodermic needles and syringes. Transfusion and transplant recipients and people with hemophilia may contract the virus from the blood, blood components, tissues, or organs of infected donors. However, this hazard can be eliminated by screening and testing donated blood and potential organ donors.

Since AIDS was first identified as a "new" disease in the early 1980's, scientists have been working to improve prevention and treatment of the opportunistic diseases suffered by AIDS patients. Scientists are attempting to develop vaccines that would prevent HIV infection or "boost" the immune systems of people already infected with the virus. However, a cure or vaccine for AIDS is unlikely to be found anytime soon.

Index